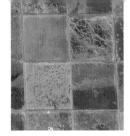

De Beers

guid... rocks and landforms

Geological Journeys

Nick Norman & Gavin Whitfield

The colourful sandstone cliffs of the Clarens Formation, made of fine-grained sandstone that was once wind-blown desert sand, are a characterisic feature of the eastern Free State landscape. This picture is of Mushroom Rock in the Golden Gate National Park.

Published by Struik Nature
(an imprint of Random House Struik (Pty) Ltd)
Reg. No. 1966/003153/07
80 McKenzie Street, Cape Town, 8001
PO Box 1144, Cape Town, 8000 South Africa

www.randomstruik.co.za

Images of Africa Photo Library
www.imagesofafrica.co.za

First published in 2006
10 9 8 7 6 5

Publishing manager: Pippa Parker
Managing editors: Lynda Ingham-Brown & Rod Baker
Editor: Helen de Villiers
Consultant: Marian Tredoux
Designer: Janice Evans
Cartographers: Elmi Dixon, Magda Roos &
Makhosazana Nkosi, Council for Geoscience
Illustrator: Ingrid Fineberg
Proofreader: Tessa Kennedy
Indexer: Cora Ovens
Reproduction by Hirt & Carter Cape (Pty) Ltd
Printed and bound by Tien Wah Press (Pte) Limited, Singapore

ISBN 978 1 77007 062 2

Picture credits

(CGS = Council for Geoscience of South
Africa; IOA = Images of Africa)

Photographs:
Nick Norman: pp. title (top), imprint, 4,
5 (top and centre), 9, 10 (courtesy of the
Athenaeum Trust, Newlands, Cape Town),
16, 30 (bottom), 32-3, 62, 63, 64, 65, 67,
68, 74-5, 75, 77, 79, 80, 81, 83, 84-5, 85,
87, 90, 91, 92, 93, 94, 96, 98, 99, 102,
104-5, 106-7, 107, 110, 113, 114, 118-9,
120, 123, 124, 126-7, 127, 128, 129,
130, 131, 132-3, 135, 137, 138, 139,
140-1, 142-3, 143, 144, 145, 147, 148,
149, 151, 152, 153, 154-5, 156, 159,
184-5, 189, 190, 191, 206, 207, 208,
211, 212, 213, 214, 215, 216, 218, 219,
220, 221, 222, 223, 237, 238, 244, 245,
246, 247, 248, 249, 250, 251, 271, 273,
300-1, 303, 304-5, 307, 308, 310, 311
Gavin Whitfield: pp. title (bottom), 5
(bottom), 12, 34-5, 35, 37, 41, 43, 46, 47,
48, 50, 51, 53, 54-5, 56, 57, 58, 59, 60,
61, 104, 162, 163, 165, 167, 168, 170,
172-3, 174, 175, 177, 178, 179, 181,
182, 183, 186, 187, 192-3, 193, 194,
195, 196, 198, 199, 200, 201, 202, 203,
204, 205, 224-5, 226-7, 228, 229, 230,
252, 253, 255, 256, 257, 259, 260, 261,
262, 263, 264, 265, 266, 267, 268, 269,
274, 274-5, 277, 278, 279 (top), 280,
282, 283, 284, 285, 286, 287 (top), 288,

289, 290, 290-1, 292, 294, 295, 296,
297 (bottom), 299
Andrew Bannister/IOA: p. 27
Anglo American: pp. 52, 185 (top), 197,
230, 233, 234-5, 239
Cape Argus/Trace Images: pp. 20, 134
Cedric Hunter, copyright Iziko Museum of
Cape Town: pp.71, 231
Colin MacRae: pp. 11, 30 (top), 116, 164
Colour Library/IOA: 287 (bottom)
De Beers Consolidated: 232, 240, 241
**De Beers Consolidated/Maggie
Newman**: p. 242
George Henry: p. 89
Koeberg Communication Department:
p. 69
Peter Steyn/Photo Access: 117
Photo Access: p. 73
Pietermaritzburg Archive Repository:
p. 22
Roger de la Harpe/IOA: pp. 160-1, 297
(middle), 298
SASOL Ltd: pp. 108-9
Serina Kaolin (Pty) Ltd: p. 66
Shaen Adey/IOA: pp. 78, 279 (bottom)
**South African National Roads
Association**: p. 33
Walter Knirr/IOA: pp. 26, 297 (top), 306
Graham Chamberlain: p. 272

Illustrations:
Fig 2, p. 18: modified from a CGS 'MiniMag'
publication, 2002; Fig 3, p. 19: modified

from Figure 4.14, 'Plate margins',
Geology Today, Second Edition, by Murck
and Skinner (Copyright John Wiley & Sons,
Inc. 2001); Fig 6, p. 28: modified from
illustration by Colin MacRae, 1999; Fig 7,
p. 29: modified from illustration by
RV Dingle et al, Mesozoic and Tertiary
Geology of Southern Africa, © Taylor &
Francis, 1983; Fig 8, p. 31: modified
from illustration by Colin MacRae, 1999;
Fig 9, p. 38: modified from a Walter Sisulu
National Botanical Garden JCI Geological
Trail pamphlet; Fig 11, p. 40: modified
from illustration in Guidebook to Sites
of Geological & Mining Interest on
the Central Witwatersrand, 1986, by
Geological Society of SA/SA Institute for
Mining & Metallurgy; Fig 12, p. 44: modified
from illustration by Chamber of Mines/
Geological Society of SA, 1986; Fig 13, p.
88: modified from illustration by Dr Hugh
Eales, 2001;
Fig 14, p. 101: Dr Guenther Brandl;
Fig 16, p. 146: modified from map by CGS;
Fig 18, p. 182: modified from illustration
by G Whitmore, R Uken & D Meth et al
of the School of Geological & Computer
Sciences, University of KwaZulu-Natal,
1999; Fig 19, p. 210: modified from
section by CGS; Fig 20, p. 244: modified
from illustration by BS Rubidge et al, 1995;
Fig 24, p. 304: APG Sohnge & IW Halbich
(eds), Geodynamics of the Cape Fold Belt,
© CGS, 1983

FRONT COVER: *About 700 m south of the Watervalkloof
rest and information spot in the Meiringspoort, hard,
nearly 500 million-year-old quartzites of the Cape
Supergroup have been folded as though made of
plasticine (see page 249).*

BACK COVER: *A rare sight in the Cape Peninsula, where
the sediments are almost entirely horizontal (as in Table
Mountain), steeply tiled beds of sandstone seen as you drop
down into Simon's Town on the M66 are a reminder of the
folding in the mountains north and east of Cape Town.*

Dedications

To God be the glory.
And to Sue, Sarah and Christopher, this book is dedicated in return for
the hours I should have given you, but gave to a more earthy passion.
NICK NORMAN

To the geoscientists of South Africa, both past and present, who have
contributed to the recognition and understanding of this country's
spectacular geology. Without their dedication over the years, these
geological journeys would remain little known and certainly untold.
GAVIN WHITFIELD

Council for Geoscience

All the maps in this book were
prepared and supplied
at no charge by the
Council for Geoscience.
Struik Publishers and
the authors thank them
for their generosity.

Chapman's Peak Drive in the Cape Peninsula
(prior to its upgrading to protect users from rockfalls)
follows very closely the contact zone between the Cape
Granite and the overlying Cape Supergroup sediments.

Contents

Acknowledgements 6

Preface 7

Foreword 9

Introduction 10

1 Greater Johannesburg and environs 34

2 Greater Cape Town and environs 62

3 Greater Durban and environs 74

4 N1: Johannesburg to Beitbridge 84

5 N1: Johannesburg to Cape Town 106

6 N2: Cape Town to Port Elizabeth 126

7 N2: Port Elizabeth to Durban 142

8 N2/N17: Durban to Johannesburg 160

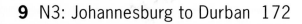

9 N3: Johannesburg to Durban 172

10 N4: Pretoria to Skilpadshek 184

11 N4: Pretoria to Komatipoort 192

12 N7: Cape Town to Vioolsdrif 206

13 N12: Johannesburg to Witbank 224

14 N12: Johannesburg to George 232

15 N14: Pretoria to Springbok 252

16 The Great Escarpment 274

17 KwaZulu-Natal Drakensberg 290

18 The Little Karoo 300

Glossary 312

Bibliography 316

Index 317

Acknowledgements

There are numerous Earth science colleagues and organizations that have contributed to the improvement of this book, all of whom deserve our gratitude. Some special words of appreciation and thanks are due.

First and foremost, without the generous sponsorship from De Beers Consolidated Mines, the preparation of the book could not have gone ahead. And without the nod from Gary Ralfe, then-CEO of De Beers, as well as that from Bill McKechnie, director and group manager of Exploration, that sponsorship might never have materialized; we owe them both a big debt of gratitude. We thank Dr Craig Smith and Dr Erika Barton at De Beers Consolidated Mines, Johannesburg, for reviewing the manuscript, for their many constructive suggestions and for their help on the topic of uranium dating; and Dr Jock Robey at De Beers, Kimberley, for information and digital images of kimberlites, and Marlaine Botha at the Anglo American and De Beers image library for willingly providing many digital images for possible use.

At the Council for Geoscience (CGS), Dr Robbie Kleywegt – in 2002, when the project started, still deputy director – gave it his full support and arranged for the loan of numerous geological maps. Thanks are due to him, as well as to Thibedi Ramontja, the current CEO of the Council, who has supported the work unreservedly; and to Dr Cornelius 'Nols' van Vuuren, recently retired from the CGS, who dedicated immediate and abundant time to an initial and very thorough technical proofreading of the manuscript, including many hours of valuable comments and discussion. The Spatial Data Management team at the CGS, led by Ken Wilkinson, readily came on board – thanks to Ken, and special thanks to Elmi Dixon and Magda Roos for the fine geological maps they have prepared, which required substantial time and effort on their part; and thanks to Dr Dave Roberts from the Bellville office of the CGS for providing greater insight into the discovery of the 'footsteps of Eve' found on the West Coast.

Various university professors made significant input, for which we thank them. Among them are Prof. Jay Barton at the University of Johannesburg for reviewing sections of the final text and for constructive criticism of the illustrations; Prof. Reiner Klemd at the University of Würzburg for his valuable suggestion on the Sand River gneisses; Prof. Bruce Rubidge, director of the Bernard Price Institute for Palaeontological Research at the University of the Witwatersrand, for permission to photograph an original watercolour by William Stanford painted in 1966; Prof. JS 'Goonie' Marsh at Rhodes University for information on the Drakensberg lavas, supplied while on a field trip in Lesotho; and to the Geology Department of the University of Stellenbosch, especially librarian Loxie Conradie, for allowing unrestricted access to their library and for general support.

We thank Colin McRae for allowing the reproduction of several illustrations from *Life etched in Stone* and the Geological Society of South Africa for allowing illustrations from that and several other of their publications to be reproduced. We owe gratitude, too, to John McCarthy, Lesley Turner and Prof. Izaak Rust for considerable time willingly given to clarify aspects of geology. Thanks to Dr Guenther Brandl for kindly providing an accurate geological cross-section of the Soutpansberg Range, north of Makado.

In the pre-dawn of the project, Colleen Goossen, Brian Marsh and Nik Wullschleger believed in it enough to help Nick Norman create the 'mock-up' that sold the concept to Struik and De Beers.

Our illustrator, Ingrid Fineberg, has gone the extra mile to provide the excellent graphics that bring life to our dry and dusty text: her patience and understanding are deserving of greater thanks than words can express.

Three people at Struik deserve special mention for their endless patience and untiring co-operation and encouragement in a project that far exceeded anyone's expectations of the work involved and the time it would take. They are the publishing manager of Natural History, Pippa Parker, editor Helen de Villiers, and designer Janice Evans. We cannot thank you enough.

And last, but by no means least, both authors owe a huge debt of thanks to their wives for unflagging support and understanding during the years it took to put the book together.

NICK NORMAN & GAVIN WHITFIELD

Preface

I was initially inspired to write this book by the curiosity of non-geological friends and family. On returning from holidays in the country, someone would always lament, 'We wish you had been with us! We saw the most amazing rock structures and we would have given anything to know what they meant!' It is a cry every geologist hears often.

So this book was written primarily to bring an understanding of geology to travellers on our roads, along routes they would travel in any case. The intention is not particularly to encourage detours to view structures of interest, however world-famous the geological occurrences might be – although this always remains an option. You don't have to venture off your own particular journey to see miracles in the rocks; they're to be seen wherever you go, be it every day or once a year – you just have to know what to look for and where and how to look.

A book that could be stored in a pocket in your car was never going to cover every byway, or even every highway. So I chose a spider's web of the main national roads that covered the country. I also singled out the three main metropolitan centres. Then, there were the places not necessarily en route from A to B, but which people choose for their sheer beauty and 'African-ness'. And that, in a nutshell, is what we have covered and described in terms, we hope, that will be easily understood.

To understand what we are viewing, it is important to establish the geological scene over time. We have tried to keep the explanations of geological processes and principles in the introductory chapter short and sweet, the idea being to flesh them out more fully at the appropriate points in the journey. We hope they will make more sense this way, when you can relate the phenomenon described in the book to what you see in front of you, in the relevant panorama or road cutting. Some basic technical background is indispensable, though; it is the balance between science and wonder that we have striven for.

More than just explaining the origins of what you see in the road cuttings and the mountains and valleys, I hope that this book awakens in readers a sense of the beauty in the rocks and landforms they pass, and an understanding of their elemental role in our lives on this beautiful planet Earth.

I could never have done it on my own. Circumstances at an early stage dictated that I bring in a co-author, and Gavin Whitfield – a complete stranger two years ago, now a good friend – was that author. He has been a blessing in every way, and has shouldered more than his half of what turned out to be a mammoth load, and I am eternally grateful to him.

We hope the book works for you.

NICK NORMAN

In reading the geological maps accompanying each section of the journey,
it is essential to refer to the key on the inside back cover flap for
an understanding of the geological units shown.

Folded Table Mountain sandstone makes spectacular scenery in Seweweekspoort.
This package makes up the range that separates the Karoo from the south coast and, where
cut by ancient rivers, exposes the same sediments as are seen on Table Mountain – where they
lie horizontally, as they were deposited around 500 million years ago.

Foreword

How many times have we driven the highways of South Africa and wondered about the geology and rock exposures seen along the way? Those who are trained geologists invariably lament having forgotten to pack the geological map of the country as an important reference. Those who are interested amateur geologists or who simply have the occasional interest in the natural environment that surrounds us have traditionally had no access to usable or understandable geological information.

A large part of South Africa represents one of the world's oldest continental fragments, and other parts of the country record continent-continent collisions through billions of years of earth history, a fundamental consequence of continental drift and plate tectonics. A major part of the country is covered by sediments and lavas of the Karoo system of rocks, deposited when the ancestors of the dinosaurs first emerged on land. Major volcanic events have affected our continent in the distant past, leaving a record of the deep earth processes that occurred then. The 'rock record' in South Africa ranges from the present day right back to 3.5 billion years ago. In our country we really can get a glimpse into 'deep time' that may be difficult or impossible to see in other parts of the world.

South Africa's unique geology and its associated mineral riches have had a fundamental impact on the country's economic development since the late 1800s, when the first diamonds were discovered around Kimberley and gold was found in the Witwatersrand. The prospecting rushes triggered by these events led in time to the establishment and development firstly of the modern South African mining industry and secondly the diversified South African economy that we all enjoy today.

This book is intended to provide general geological information to both the interested lay person and the professional specialist. It will help you to better see and understand South Africa's geological history. It is designed as a road log covering the major highway routes of the country, some of which have spectacular geology (once you know what you are seeing on the roadside landscape). General geological principles are also illustrated with the examples chosen.

De Beers is proud to be a sponsor of this book, as part of our close involvement with many aspects of the geology of South Africa. One of the world's most famous geologists, Alex du Toit (1878–1948), was consulting geologist to De Beers Consolidated Mines from 1927 to 1941. His life's work and his time with De Beers were not just focused on the commercial aspects of diamond mining and exploration, but also on the science behind our broad geological heritage. Du Toit published widely, and is perhaps most famous for his book Our Wandering Continents, concerning the then unproven hypothesis of continental drift. This set the stage for the later revolutionary developments in our understanding of the geology of the Earth dating from the 1960s. His work was based on fundamental geological observation (the kind that this book will assist you with) combined with a keen interest in understanding and communicating what he saw. Were he alive today, he would surely approve of the effort to make the country's geology more accessible to the broad public.

We at De Beers welcome the publication of a guidebook such as this, which will add a new dimension to your travels. Have a happy and safe motorcar journey, keep a copy of this book in the car and learn some new things along the way.

The geology of South Africa is a magnificent story, a journey through geological time going back almost four billion years. Enjoy the ride.

NICKY OPPENHEIMER
Chairman, De Beers Consolidated Mines
Johannesburg

Introduction

OUR UNIQUE HERITAGE

'South Africa: the world in one country' promise the posters. The waves of two oceans break on our beaches, towering mountains loom and wide plains abound; there are vineyards and indigenous forests and rolling fields of sugar-cane, and a network of roads second to none in Africa. In the bushveld, a herd of elephants ambles past a solitary, slumbering lion while, a thousand kilometres away, whales calve and great white sharks lurk. But if South Africa encapsulates the globe for the tourist, it does so just as richly from a geological standpoint. Our relatively small country boasts the world's biggest single deposits of its two most precious metals, gold and platinum. It has produced the bulk of the world's gem diamonds. It has vast coal fields and is a treasure house of other metals and minerals.

In addition, South Africa has produced an eminent geologist, Alexander Logie du Toit, who is recognised internationally for his role in shaping the seminal twentieth century theory of Continental Drift. Alex du Toit was employed by De Beers Consolidated Mines from 1927 to 1941 as a consulting geologist. His treatise on the theory, *Our Wandering Continents*, was published in 1937, the culmination of extensive travels throughout the Southern Hemisphere. It was decades ahead of its time and was received by a disbelieving world, as sceptical as that which confronted Charles Darwin. However, the wealth of hard fact he presented put beyond any doubt his argument: that our continent is a remnant of the ancient southern supercontinent, Gondwana, from which most of the other continents have drifted away.

LEFT: *Alexander Logie du Toit, field geologist of colossal achievement and theoretician decades ahead of his time, was the first to accumulate a mass of hard data sufficient to put the hypothesis of Continental Drift beyond reasonable doubt.*

OPPOSITE: *Fossilised leaves of* Glossopteris *flora, which is thought to have been the major contributor to the coal beds of the Ecca. Fossils of* Glossopteris *flora are found in Karoo-age rocks across Africa, South America, Antarctica, Australia and India. This was one of the early clues to the theory of a former unified Gondwana landmass.*

This view of the 'roof of Africa', showing the Drakensberg escarpment, illustrates the unusual phenomenon of undisturbed horizontal strata 3 000 m above sea level. These closely pre-date the break-up of Gondwana, as does the plateau-like erosion surface.

Think of Africa's tranquil antiquity: our continent, alone among all the world's major landmasses – taking Eurasia and Australasia as the geological wholes they are – is almost undisturbed by violent earthquakes. The Americas, Eurasia and Australasia all creep into the Pacific, their margins shuddering violently as they do so. Not Africa, though: it is primeval, stable. Should you visit the southern African subcontinent's highest points, in the Drakensberg, note that the strata are horizontal; this flatness is another symbol of stability. Ponder that not very far below those pinnacles, and thousands of metres above today's sea level, are sedimentary rocks, deposited eons ago in a huge inland sea. Visualise the whole African landmass floating ever higher on Earth's denser mantle, first as Gondwana slowly fragmented, then as millions of tons of soil were – and continue to be – stripped off every year, and carried offshore by rivers big and small into the ocean basins. A further legacy, established through the painstaking chipping of bones, skulls and teeth from the protecting rock, is that Africa, and South Africa in particular, is widely regarded as the 'cradle of humankind'. First there were the 'ape-men', *Australopithecus*, then *Homo habilis*, the first tool-makers; later came *Homo erectus*, hunters and fire-users, and finally *Homo sapiens*, our own ancestral beginnings – all creatures of the African savannah. It is not just for its 'big five' and its breathtaking scenery that South Africa is special, for those are creations of today; its legacy goes back into the mists of a geological time-scale measured in millions, even billions (thousand million), of years.

Structure of the Earth

It is now accepted that planet Earth formed around 4 500 million years ago by the consolidation of cosmic debris. From evidence of global seismic research, the Earth is known to be roughly concentrically layered, like an onion. It has four basic layers, namely the outer 'skin' or crust, the mantle, the outer core and the inner core (see fig. 1, below). The cold and relatively thin crust consists of a number of immense, but distinct crustal plates that float on the hotter plastic mantle, and which are in constant jostling motion. Beneath the continents, the crust is thicker and composed predominantly of granitic and sedimentary rock, while the much thinner oceanic crust, composed of basalt, occurs beneath the oceans. The crust beneath Africa is very stable and is particularly thick. The ultrahot core generates, within the overlying mantle, large-scale convection currents, which are the engines of plate movement in the surface crust. The mantle is made of dense silicate rock, samples of which have been brought to the surface by kimberlite, a magma of extremely deep (about 200 km) origin. The outer core is made of liquid iron-nickel, and flow within this zone generates the Earth's magnetic field, while the inner core consists of solid iron-nickel.

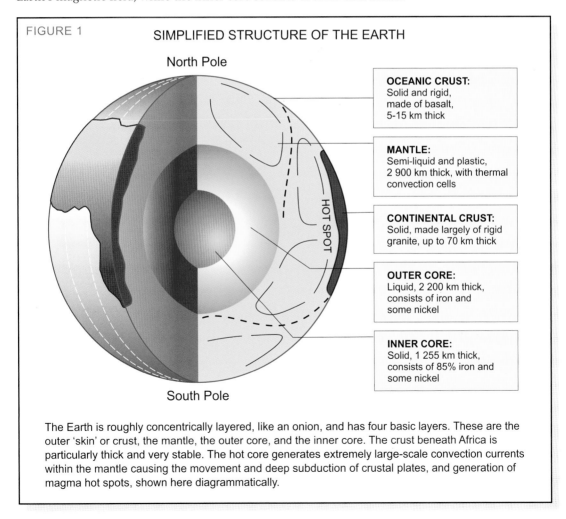

FIGURE 1 — SIMPLIFIED STRUCTURE OF THE EARTH

North Pole

OCEANIC CRUST:
Solid and rigid,
made of basalt,
5-15 km thick

MANTLE:
Semi-liquid and plastic,
2 900 km thick, with thermal
convection cells

CONTINENTAL CRUST:
Solid, made largely of rigid
granite, up to 70 km thick

OUTER CORE:
Liquid, 2 200 km thick,
consists of iron and
some nickel

INNER CORE:
Solid, 1 255 km thick,
consists of 85% iron and
some nickel

HOT SPOT

South Pole

The Earth is roughly concentrically layered, like an onion, and has four basic layers. These are the outer 'skin' or crust, the mantle, the outer core, and the inner core. The crust beneath Africa is particularly thick and very stable. The hot core generates extremely large-scale convection currents within the mantle causing the movement and deep subduction of crustal plates, and generation of magma hot spots, shown here diagrammatically.

Basic rock categories

All rocks are divided into three types: igneous, sedimentary and metamorphic.

Igneous rocks derive from deep within the Earth's crust or upper mantle, where they arise as molten magma. This either reaches the surface as volcanic eruptions, producing extrusive lava which cools very quickly or, alternatively, settles at a level just below the surface. If the molten magma reaches a level close to the surface, it cools relatively quickly, particularly if it intrudes as a thin body, resulting in an intrusive rock nearly as fine-grained as surface lava. If, on the other hand, a large volume of magma intrudes at depth where it is insulated from the atmospheric chill, it has time to grow easily discernible crystals of the rock-forming minerals, and becomes coarser grained.

The most conspicuous examples of fine-grained intrusive rocks in South Africa are vertical – or nearly vertical – dykes and horizontal sills of Karoo dolerite. The main 'igneous event' in South Africa's more recent geological history was an outpouring of thick basalt that still caps the Drakensberg mountains of KwaZulu-Natal and which forms the high plateau of Lesotho. We know that this lava field was, at one time, considerably more extensive, but that erosion over millions of years has stripped much of it away, to be carried by rivers to the distant oceans. The most widespread slow-cooling igneous rocks

TABLE 1

CLASSIFICATION OF COMMON IGNEOUS ROCKS					
Consisting mostly of silicate minerals, igneous rocks form when molten magma, generated deep within the Earth's crust, rises to shallower levels, crystallising as it cools. Volcanic rocks erupt, from volcanoes or fissures, at the surface or underwater. They cool and crystallise fast, so are fine-grained. Those that don't quite make it to the surface, called hypabyssal rocks, crystallise more slowly and are moderately fine-grained, while plutonic rocks, which intrude at deep levels in the crust, cool even more slowly and may be very coarse-grained.					
		SILICA CONTENT			
GRAIN SIZE	FORMED AS	HIGH SILICA	< INCREASING	DECREASING >	LOW SILICA
		FELSIC generally light-coloured, contains both feldspar and quartz	INTERMEDIATE intermediate colour, contains feldspar and dark minerals but very little or no quartz	MAFIC dark coloured, contains abundant dark minerals plus feldspar	ULTRAMAFIC dark coloured, contains predominantly dark minerals or carbonate
Coarse-grained	Deep intrusives (Plutonic)	Granite, Granodiorite, Tonalite, Pegmatite	Diorite, Syenite	Gabbro, Norite	Pyroxenite, Peridotite, Dunite
Medium-grained	Shallow intrusives (Hypabyssal)	Quartz Porphyry, Granophyre	Trachyte	Dolerite, Diabase	Kimberlite, Carbonatite
Fine-grained to glassy	Eruptives (Volcanic)	Rhyolite, Dacite, Felsite	Andesite	Basalt	Komatiite

are the granite family, found from the beaches of the Cape Peninsula to the far northern corners of the country. That these coarsely crystalline rocks are now seen at the surface is testimony to the removal by erosion of billions of tons of enclosing rocks that once lay above and around them.

It is this erosion and river transport of the clay, sand and gravel produced as rocks decompose that gives rise to most sedimentary rocks, such as sandstone, mudstone, shale and conglomerate. These are almost always water-laid, forming along rivers, in lakes, estuaries and deltas, along beaches and in ocean basins. Such rock formation is a process that generally takes millions of years, during

TABLE 2

CLASSIFICATION OF COMMON SEDIMENTARY ROCKS

Sedimentary rocks include clastic rocks, made from mineral grains and rock fragments derived from pre-existing rock, and chemical and organic sediments. Sediment is deposited as layers or strata, in oceans and along their beaches, in lakes, river systems and in wind-blown dune fields. Over time the sediment becomes cemented, or lithified, to form hard rocks.

SEDIMENT TYPE	FRAGMENT OR GRAIN SIZE	MADE FROM	ROCK NAME	DESCRIPTION
Clastic rocks	Very coarse > 2.5 mm	Boulders, cobbles, pebbbles & grit	Conglomerate	Very coarse-grained, mostly with rounded clasts cemented to form a concrete-like mixture. Where the clasts are angular the rock is called a breccia. Glaciers and ice sheets produce tillite, where large clasts 'float' in a clay matrix.
	Coarse to medium 0.05 mm to 2.5 mm	Sand	Sandstone	Most sandstones consist of quartz grains, but they may, in addition, contain feldspar, mica, carbonate and heavy minerals.
	Fine 0.005 mm to 0.05 mm	Silt	Siltstone	Commonly quite quartz-rich like sandstone, and noticeably coarser-grained and paler than shale, forming a transition between the two.
	Very fine < 0.005 mm	Mud and clay	Mudstone and shale	The finest-grained clastic sediment: mudstone is mostly devoid of bedding, while shale shows conspicuous bedding laminations along which it usually splits.
	From coarse to very fine	Volcanic debris	Agglomerate and tuff	These volcaniclastic rocks form from volcanic material, varying from coarse fragments to fine ash, explosively ejected into the atmosphere. Deposition may be on land or under water.
Chemical sediments	Fine	Carbonate mud or minute debris	Limestone and dolomite	Deposits of organically derived carbonate shells, particles or precipitate. Dolomite is magnesium-rich limestone formed from algal beds and stromatolites.
	Extremely fine	Silica deposit	Chert	Dense, cryptocrystalline deposits of silica, commonly associated with banded ironstone and dolomite. Usually grey or white, and, being extremely hard, chert resists weathering and erosion. Varieties include jasper and chalcedony.
	Very fine to extremely fine	Thin layers of iron oxides and silica	Banded ironstone	Alternating bands of iron oxides (magnetite or haematite) and chert or jasper, the bands usually only a few millimetres thick.
	Fine	Carbonate or silica surface deposit	Calcrete and silcrete	Generally 'young' deposits formed during long periods of crustal stability by the accumulation of calcium carbonate or silica near the surface of the soil, commonly forming a hard capping.
Organic sediments	Fine	Carbonised plant material	Coal	An accumulation of fossilised plant-derived carbon, with minor impurities, formed in an oxygen-deprived environment. Peat is an intermediate stage of the process of carbonisation.

ABOVE LEFT: *Two igneous rocks: the younger, dark, fine-grained dolerite cutting coarse-grained Cape Granite.*

ABOVE CENTRE: *Alternating hard and soft sedimentary rocks – the paler sandstone and dark shale – upended during Cape folding.*

ABOVE RIGHT: *This well-developed mineral banding typifies the metamorphic gneisses ubiquitous in Namaqualand.*

which time sediment becomes compacted by the weight of younger sediment deposited over it. In exceptional circumstances this process may be more rapid, especially when there is much lime in the system. The grain size of sediment is a function of the energy of the water flow that deposited it, so that coarse gravel is deposited by fast-flowing streams or rivers in flood, either along their courses or where they debouch into the sea. Sand does not drift very far out to sea, as opposed to clay, which continues to be moved by ocean currents into the deep ocean basins hundreds of kilometres offshore. Chemical sediments like limestone may form far offshore, in very deep, lime-laden water, or close inshore, where decomposing shells and coral reefs supply calcium carbonate to the marine environment, or even onshore where chemically charged water evaporates, leaving a crystalline residue. Wind-formed sedimentary rocks called aeolianite, deposited as sand dunes of various shapes and sizes, are found in desert climates or in belts of high wind regime along the coast.

Metamorphic rocks are those that have changed, sometimes drastically, from their original identity. The agencies for this are extreme heat and pressure, generated either by the intrusion of rising magma or from the processes of deep burial and folding within the crust. Heat bakes the rock, sometimes to the point of almost melting it, and if folding has been in response to major earth movements, the large-scale intrusion of granites will often have been an accompanying process, so there is a twofold thermal input. The clay minerals making up shales will, given enough heat and pressure, reorganise themselves into new minerals long before temperatures are high enough for them to melt. They will form hornfels, slate and phyllite, then schist and, finally, as melting points are reached and recrystallisation starts, gneiss. At these temperatures, limestones will recrystallise to marble, and sandstones will become so well cemented by their own silica that the resulting quartzite will lose many original sedimentary features.

TABLE 3

CLASSIFICATION OF COMMON METAMORPHIC ROCKS

Metamorphic rocks result when intense heat and/or pressure change pre-existing rocks, with usually minor changes to the bulk chemical composition of the original rock. New minerals and textures form, the change in appearance being slight during low-grade metamorphism, extreme when it is high-grade. These rocks (except for migmatite) do not reach the stage of melting.

METAMORPHIC ROCK NAME	PARENT ROCK	TEXTURE	GRAIN SIZE	DESCRIPTION
Gneiss	Granitic rock or coarse clastic sediment	Streched-out and/or deformed	Coarse-grained	Formed during regional deformation and high-grade metamorphism of rocks of felsic composition, resulting in a swirling banded or gneissic texture. The main minerals are quartz, feldspar and mica, with rarer dark minerals.
Migmatite	Gneiss	Gneissic to recrystallised	Coarse-grained	Very high-grade metamorphic rock, where partial melting has taken place and the molten component has been injected into the unmelted rock. The final stage before complete remelting.
Schist, Phyllite	Fine clastic sediment or volcanic	Well-foliated, platey minerals predominate	Coarse- to medium-grained	Low-grade metamorphic rock comprising mostly flattened, flaky minerals like micas, chlorite and talc, formed by directional stress during folding.
Amphibolite	Mafic volcanic or intrusive	Usually well-foliated to gneissic	Medium-grained	Dark rocks comprising mainly amphibole, commonly with minor feldspar. Formed from mafic igneous rocks like dolerite, as well as from high-grade metamorphism of sediments rich in calcium, magnesium and iron.
Quartzite	Sandstone	Granular and often showing bedding	Medium-grained	Recrystallised sandstone with the fusion of sedimentary quartz grains into larger interlocking crystals.
Hornfels	Mudstone or shale	Textureless and hard	Fine- to very fine-grained	Shale or mudstone 'baked' by the intrusion into it of hot magma. The resulting rock is hard and brittle and contains metamorphic minerals like andalusite and cordierite.
Slate	Shale	A platey structure is the defining feature	Very fine-grained	Formed from shale that has undergone strong folding and low-grade metamorphism. The foliation developed during folding, called slaty cleavage, is often, though not always, parallel to the bedding planes of the shale.
Marble	Limestone	Granular but showing recrystallisation	Medium- to coarse-grained	Metamorphosed limestone, with any impurities forming minerals other than calcite, and leading to banding and the characteristic patterns.

The story of plate tectonics

The cast for the drama of plate tectonics (a term familiar to most of us) comprises a complex family of crustal fragments of differing rock formations. We know that the currently well-defined rigid plates of which the Earth's crust is composed (see fig. 2, below) may, over geological time, change their size as well as their movement in relation to each other. Of continental scale, the crustal plates may behave in a number of dramatic and Earth-changing ways, as illustrated on the page opposite. They may:

- *break apart, as along the Great Rift Valley of Africa;*
- *grow with the outpouring of new lava along their edges, as seen along mid-oceanic ridges;*
- *collide, as has the Indian plate into its Eurasian neighbour, forcing up the Himalayas;*
- *disappear, as plates of the Pacific Ocean floor do as they are forced back into the mantle, a process known as subduction;*
- *grind past each other while moving at different speeds, as along the San Andreas fault in California.*

Earthquakes and associated tsunamis (also called tidal waves) provide dramatic evidence of plate movement, with their epicentres invariably located on the boundaries of moving plates.

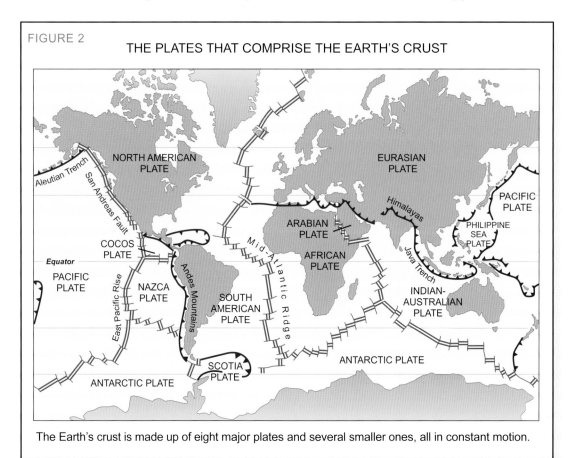

FIGURE 2

THE PLATES THAT COMPRISE THE EARTH'S CRUST

The Earth's crust is made up of eight major plates and several smaller ones, all in constant motion.

The ordered plate movement observed today is probably different from that which shaped the Earth over three billion years ago. But whatever the exact *modus operandi*, and whenever it happened, crustal disturbances have, from a very early stage, caused folding and faulting. The prevailing rock environment, including temperature, directed stress, load pressure, rate and direction of movement, as well as the nature of the rocks themselves, has determined whether strata are deformed without rupture, by folding – much like the pages of a magazine in the hands of a child – or whether they are faulted, with one block of rock moving against another along a well-defined break that may be millimetres or metres thick (see fig. 3, below).

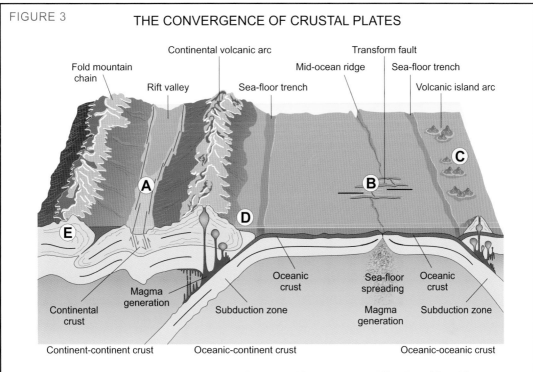

FIGURE 3 — THE CONVERGENCE OF CRUSTAL PLATES

A. On **continental crusts**, spreading margins create rift valleys. In the Rift Valley of East Africa there is substantial crustal thinning, not shown above, accompanied by the well-known volcanism

B. By the process of sea-floor spreading, **thin oceanic crust** moves apart creating new crust and forming mid-ocean ridges, cut by numerous transform or cross-faults, such as seen along the Mid-Atlantic Ridge

C. **Oceanic to oceanic:** converging margins create subduction zones as one crustal plate is forced beneath the other, forming volcanoes, deep ocean trenches, earthquake zones and strings of volcanic islands, such as the Indonesian archipelago

D. **Oceanic to continental:** converging margins also create subduction zones and form continental volcanic arcs, such as the Andes of South America

E. **Continental to continental:** converging margins are marked by the formation of fold mountain ranges like the Himalayas or, closer to home, the Cape Fold Mountains, themselves probably of Himalayan proportions when first formed

Collapse of an old wall in Tulbagh during the earthquake of 1969 is a reminder that even ancient faults may still move.

We all know about the effects of faulting and earthquakes. Most years, and a safe distance from home, we read of hundreds, sometimes thousands, of people killed in the devastation of earthquakes. So what happens deep below the surface in places like Turkey, India, Peru or Japan when villages and towns are flattened? As crustal plates – or even parts of plates – strain to move past each other, the accumulated stress reaches the point where something has to give. Deep in the lower crust and below that, in the more malleable mantle, the stress is constantly being accommodated. But the Earth's cooler, more brittle upper crust can only react to those forces by breaking. At this point, faulting and earthquakes happen. The only time in living memory that South Africa has experienced a quake with a high rating on the Richter scale was in September 1969, when some of the older buildings in Tulbagh and Ceres in the Western Cape were damaged, some severely. This unusual event was related to reactivation of movement along an ancient fault, resulting in a release of built-up stress.

The major mountain peaks, those towering, icy, awe-inspiring heights that pose the ultimate challenge to mountaineers, lie on the boundaries of colliding plates. Which mountaineer standing on Mount Everest's summit gives a thought to the fact that the mountain at their feet was built by the collision of two crustal plates? Volcanoes, built by ascending magma, add to the construction of these colliding-plate ranges.

Geological timescales

Perhaps the most challenging aspect of geology is the scale of geological time, which covers more than four billion years. We cannot comprehend life without communication as we know it, let alone our planet without life, and without an oxygen-rich atmosphere. In the vast time that has elapsed since the formation of our planet, massive mountains have been built up and torn down – again and again. We must see the displacement of a railway line across the San Andreas fault in California for what it is: a single, momentary move in a gigantic game that will have taken place over tens of millions of years by the time it is played out, eons hence. We must make the connection between the pulse beats and the lifetime; between what we can personally observe – the bending of the track by a few centimetres – and the end result: a fault line that may show a displacement measurable in kilometres. Geologists have devised a formal timescale to put geological events into perspective, and to interpret the history of the Earth. This scheme divides geological time into eons, eras and periods, as shown in the table opposite, together with important events that happened in South Africa's geological past.

TABLE 4

GEOLOGICAL TIMESCALE AND MAJOR EVENTS
IN SOUTH AFRICA'S PAST

Ma*	EON	ERA	MAJOR EVENTS IN SOUTH AFRICA'S GEOLOGICAL HISTORY
65	PHANEROZOIC	CENOZOIC	3 Ma - Development of hominids and early humans 65 Ma - Extinction of the dinosaurs
250	PHANEROZOIC	MESOZOIC	183 Ma - Karoo dolerites intruded and Drakensberg basalts erupted 250 Ma - Permian-Triassic extinction event in the Karoo
545	PHANEROZOIC	PALAEO-ZOIC	320-270 Ma - Great Ice Age of the Permo-Carboniferous 400-300 Ma - Plant life and amphibians move onto land 540-506 Ma - Intrusion of the Cape granites
900	PROTEROZOIC	LATE	545 Ma - The Precambrian Period ends 740-570 Ma - Pan-African mountain building
1600	PROTEROZOIC	MIDDLE	1 000-1 100 Ma - Namaqua-Natal mountain building 1 400-1 200 Ma - Intrusion of numerous alkaline igneous complexes e.g. Pilanesberg
2 500	PROTEROZOIC	EARLY	1 900-1 799 Ma - Deposition of first Waterberg and Olifantshoek 'red-beds' indicating free oxygen in atmosphere 2 023 Ma - Vredefort meteorite impact event 2 061-2 054 Ma - Intrusion of the Bushveld Complex 2 200 Ma - Transvaal iron formations deposited 2 600-2 400 Ma - Transvaal stromatolitic dolomites formed and free oxygen generated
3 000	ARCHAEAN	LATE	2 714 Ma - Extrusion of Ventersdorp flood lavas 2 900-2 800 Ma - Formation of Witwatersrand gold-bearing conglomerate reefs
3 400	ARCHAEAN	MIDDLE	3 300-3 000 Ma - Intrusion of post-greenstone granites
4 500	ARCHAEAN	EARLY	3 500-3 300 Ma - Barberton and other greenstone belts form from early crust; evidence of single-cell life found in chert 3 600-3 400 Ma - Intrusion of first granites, oldest dated at 3 644 Ma 4 500 Ma - Creation of the Earth

NOT TO SCALE

* Ma = millions of years ago; for example, 65 Ma indicates about 65 000 000 years ago

The South African landscape

Most South African mountains are different from those formed elsewhere, just as the African plate is different from the other major crustal plates. Elevations of 3 000 metres and more in the Drakensberg result not from folding and plate collision, but from uplift and erosion. These are residual mountains – what is left of a high-standing continental plateau when everything around it has been stripped away by the irresistible forces of erosion and river transport. Their formation is much slower and less dramatic than mountains built by plate collision or repeated volcanic eruptions, but the end result is practically the same, as attested to by our spectacular Drakensberg range. Ultimately, residual mountains may become striking 'inselbergs' (literally 'island mountains') that rise from a flat plain or pediment. Table Mountain in Cape Town is a fine example of an inselberg. This is illustrated on the page opposite.

The aftermath of flooding in KwaZulu-Natal dramatically illustrates how material is transported from the hinterland down to the sea. Muddy rivers in the eastern part of the country are testimony to this ongoing process.

FIGURE 4

THE CREATION OF LANDSCAPE

(Note: The vertical scale is exaggerated for greater clarity)

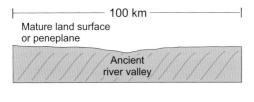

Mature land surface or peneplane
Ancient river valley

a. At the end of a long cycle of erosion

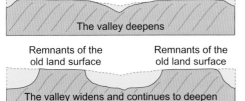

The valley deepens

b. After an Ice Age has lowered global sea level, and rivers start to cut down as they reach for the new level

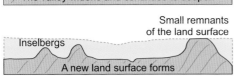

Remnants of the old land surface   Remnants of the old land surface

The valley widens and continues to deepen

c. The rivers have still not reached the new base level and are still actively cutting down

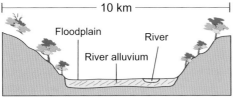

Small remnants of the land surface

Inselbergs

A new land surface forms

d. The new base level has been reached and the land surface is gradually being brought down to the new level

A. The evolution of new land surfaces, the preservation of the old surfaces and their eventual destruction to form inselbergs

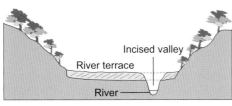

Floodplain   River
River alluvium

a. At an advanced stage of valley formation

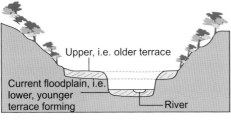

Incised valley
River terrace
River

b. The river incises deeper as a new cycle of erosion commences and new, lower base levels are set

Upper, i.e. older terrace

Current floodplain, i.e. lower, younger terrace forming

River

c. As the new valley matures, the river cuts – and fills – a new floodplain

B. The formation of terraces at different elevations above the current river

The evidence of how residual mountains form lies in our rivers. The Vaal, Orange, Thukela and Mgeni are all quite big rivers and, during seasonal floods, their waters are murky brown with suspended silt and clay. In this way, hundreds of tons of topsoil reach the coast every day. Of the quantities of soil constantly being formed from rocks decomposing under the agencies of rain, frost and baking heat, a high proportion is carried off as surface run-off feeds the streams and, in turn, the rivers that eventually reach the sea.

Over time, rivers cut down and cut back. They will continue to do both until they have reached equilibrium with their environment. Their carrying capacity depends on their energy and on their gradients. As their courses level off, much of their load will settle, only to be dislodged by the next flood. And in the headwaters, steep slopes are being cut back. Not much comes off the top, but the scarps retreat steadily until the last pinnacle has been destroyed. Once that has happened, the top is lowered quite quickly. What were once scarp-edged plateaus now become rounded hills and, over time, flat plains (see A in fig. 4, p. 23).

Meanwhile, the plains along the coast with a very low gradient towards sea level are widening. Stable base levels are being formed upstream, with valleys widening and level sections stretching outwards. Everything is tending towards equilibrium. Given an infinite period of stability, the land would evolve to a barely convex landscape with no mountains or noticeable hills even, but with vast coastal plains, swamps and sluggish, meandering rivers. But stability is never very long-lived; as the shift of the Earth's rotational axis changes, so does global climate, causing polar icecaps to grow and sea levels to drop: and a new set of base levels is formed. That is how terraces form, both river terraces and marine terraces. When the sea level rises again in response to global warming and the shrinkage of polar icecaps, the low-lying land is flooded and sedimentation begins in the shallow seas on the continental shelf (see B in fig. 4, p. 23).

A geological incident

The agencies that shape our world are not always as undramatic as the sketch (A, fig. 4, p. 23) might suggest, even in peaceful realms far from earthquake belts and volcanoes. The night of 7 May 2002 was wind-free and the autumn sky over our house in Franschhoek a mass of stars. Quickly the roaring that started as if it might have been an aeroplane became too loud, unless it was going to crash into the mountains behind us. It wasn't thunder and it wasn't a freak wind. For a few seconds the sound grew and grew. Abruptly, it stopped; there was some crashing, and then silence.

The next morning, the cause of the disturbance was evident. At the foot of a nearby rocky slope, a new run of white rocks in the 'V' of a valley pointed upwards to bleached scars on the grey rock face, topped by the rust-red stained underface of an overhang that had not been there before. Tons – perhaps a hundred – of rock had fallen hundreds of metres and lay strewn about, leaving a trail of rubble. Huge trees had been smashed and lay, stripped and splintered, within the mass of rock, the biggest blocks of which must have reached 20 tons.

Even in the tranquil geological regime of South Africa, geological destruction may be close at hand. This incident gives a vivid example of the time perspective of geological processes. In my 20 years in Franschhoek, a single piece of the mountain, so small as to be insignificant, almost unnoticeable, had fallen some hundred metres. How many years will it take to flatten the mountain? What is remarkable is not that it happened at all; it's that it happens so seldom. (NN)

The framework of southern African geology

While this book aims to unfold theory only in relation to a range of hills or mountains ahead of you, or a valley as you look out across it, or an outcrop you can touch, it is important to establish the geological scene over time. The fundamental structure of the southern African crust, shown in the illustration below, provides the basis for this.

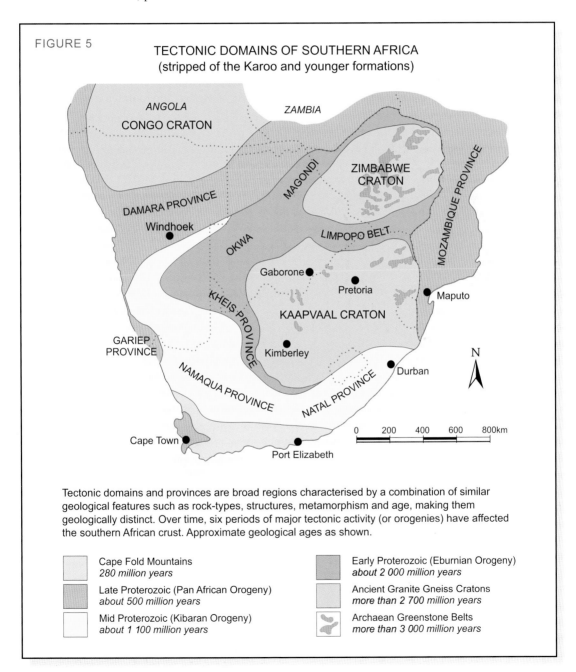

FIGURE 5

TECTONIC DOMAINS OF SOUTHERN AFRICA
(stripped of the Karoo and younger formations)

Tectonic domains and provinces are broad regions characterised by a combination of similar geological features such as rock-types, structures, metamorphism and age, making them geologically distinct. Over time, six periods of major tectonic activity (or orogenies) have affected the southern African crust. Approximate geological ages as shown.

Cape Fold Mountains
280 million years

Early Proterozoic (Eburnian Orogeny)
about 2 000 million years

Late Proterozoic (Pan African Orogeny)
about 500 million years

Ancient Granite Gneiss Cratons
more than 2 700 million years

Mid Proterozoic (Kibaran Orogeny)
about 1 100 million years

Archaean Greenstone Belts
more than 3 000 million years

A BRIEF GEOLOGICAL HISTORY OF SOUTHERN AFRICA

- In the beginning, around 4 500 million years ago, as planet Earth settled into its orbit around its own particular star (we call it 'Sun'), its composition was essentially homogeneous. It was hot: 500°C at the surface and perhaps 2 500°C at the centre. Radioactive elements – uranium, thorium and potassium – decayed, giving off heat as they did so. The iron melted and, being particularly dense, was pulled by gravitational forces towards the centre; and still temperatures rose. Materials of different density separated out into concentric shells around the iron centre, with a thin crust forming on the surface, and a heavier, thick mantle between it and the core.

- By 3 800 million years ago, the first identifiable rocks had started to form within the crust and a prolonged period of cooling began. Massive volcanic outpourings were accompanied by billowing water vapour and gases such as carbon dioxide and methane, with steam condensing as cooling continued, and ultralight hydrogen escaping out of the early atmosphere. The first seas were formed as clouds condensed and rain fell and, within these seas, the first sedimentary rocks started to form.

- Well into the Archaean Eon by now, microscopic single-cell blue-green algae made their appearance around 3 500 million years ago. Thus began the conversion, by photosynthesis, of enormous volumes of carbon dioxide into oxygen, with carbon being used in the building of living tissue. The oxygen production line was slowly gathering momentum. Primitive continental nuclei started to form as early granites were evolved from the upper mantle, intruding and thickening the thin crust.

- Temperatures were still much higher than today and the crust thinner, with much igneous activity – volcanic outpourings and granitic intrusions – accompanied by intense folding. Nuclei became welded together to form cratons, large islands of relatively stable, thicker crust, rooted deep in the upper mantle. The Kaapvaal Craton underlay the whole of the northeastern part of South Africa. It was later to be welded to the Zimbabwe Craton to the north, generating the Limpopo Belt. We see this as a wide orogenic zone of more active geology, showing intense deformation, high-grade metamorphism and granitic intrusions.

- By 3 100 million years ago, the Kaapvaal Craton was consolidated and stable. Shallow ocean basins accumulated sediment from surrounding Archaean mountains. The formation of large sedimentary basins on the Kaapvaal Craton was to be a recurring theme of South African geology through time, and reflects the relative geological stability of the crust of southern Africa.

- Among the first of these was the celebrated Witwatersrand Basin, with sediments deposited in an environment that was still strongly oxygen deficient, and which resulted in the formation of its fabulous gold-rich conglomerate reefs. Then, around 2 700 million years ago, flow after flow of basaltic lava in the Ventersdorp Basin covered the western half of the Kaapvaal Craton. Periods of sedimentation between the eruptions caused a pile of mixed lava and sediment to build up, nearly 8 km at its thickest, spreading over a quarter of South Africa.

- By 2 500 million years ago, as the Proterozoic Eon began, the accumulation of billions of tons of dolomitic limestone in the Transvaal-Griqualand West Basin had started. Calcium in sea water combined with carbon dioxide, and vast limestone layers were precipitated by algae in the warm, shallow sea. This brought down the level of carbon dioxide in the atmosphere drastically, and released life-giving oxygen on a grand scale by algal-generated photosynthesis. When calcium combined with carbon dioxide, vast limestone layers precipitated in the warm, shallow sea. Sedimentary shales and sandstones continued to accumulate in the Transvaal Basins, and the production of early oxygen in sea water resulted in the formation of immense iron oxide deposits (banded iron formations).

- Around 2 000 million years ago, the Kheis Metamorphic Province in the west and northwest, and the complex Limpopo Belt in the north, had already become part of the growing craton.

- By 1 900 million years ago, after a short but critically important break, the widespread 'red-bed' sediments (caused by the formation of red iron oxide) of the Waterberg Group, the Soutpansberg Group and the Olifantshoek Supergroup were deposited, revealing that, by now, oxygen (without which oxides cannot form) was freely available in the atmosphere. The period between the end of the Transvaal sedimentation and the beginning of that of the Waterberg is of special interest, because it was during this period that the extraordinary intrusion of the Bushveld Complex took place, the largest layered igneous intrusion exposed at the surface of the Earth.

- In the oceans off the Kaapvaal Craton, other deposition was also taking place, as thick sequences of sediments and lavas accumulated in linear belts that were to become major fold mountain chains. These rocks and the pre-existing underlying crustal formations became intensely deformed, heated and contorted to the point of being welded – or accreted – onto the craton margin. In this way, the 1 100 million-year-old Namaqua and Natal Metamorphic Provinces were formed in the west and south respectively.

- Off the craton, both further to the west and the south, it was still unstable. Elongated, fast-sinking basins and continental shelves continued to accumulate sediments shed from mountain chains now long gone. Examples of these accreted belts are the 700 million-year-old Gariep Supergroup, the similar-aged Malmesbury and Kango Groups, and the 600 million-year-old Nama and Vanrhynsdorp Groups. Metamorphosed to a varying degree, they were intruded by the Cape Granites some 540 million years ago, close to the start of the Phanerozoic Eon when Gondwana was being formed.

- Later, around 400 million years ago, the sediments forming the Cape Supergroup, well known to anyone who has had their first awed look at Table Mountain and the Cape Fold Mountains, were deposited in an elongated southern ocean. Folding and uplifting of the Cape Supergroup formations took place much later, around 250 million years ago, during early Karoo times.

- Around this time, a glacial event lasting 50 million years and on a grand scale had got under way. Across Gondwana, which was then sprawled over the southern polar region, vast ice sheets ground over India, nearly all of Africa south of the equator, southeastern South America, Antarctica and southern Australia, leaving, as evidence, a thick layer of glacial sediments (known in South Africa as the Dwyka Group) as they melted (see fig. 6, p. 28).

- Slowly Gondwana drifted northwards, away from the South Pole, and sedimentation proceeded in the full range of conceivable environments: in deep freshwater lakes; in marine and coastal areas; along rivers and deltas; and across windswept desert and volcanic flood lavas. Thus the expansive main Karoo Basin accumulated over 10 000 metres of sediments and lavas during its 130 million-year life span. Today, Karoo rocks cover some 60 per cent of South Africa's surface.

- But, in the mantle, preparations were under way to disrupt the peace that had reigned for so long in the Southern Hemisphere. Around 180 million years ago deep cracks started to form over most of Gondwana, through which basalt magma from the mantle welled up, and spread out widely across the landscape, giving birth to what we now refer to as the Drakensberg and Lebombo lavas. Later, some of the cracks widened and rift valleys formed, breaching the Gondwana coastline to let the sea in. Inlets became seas; seas became oceans. New coastlines were formed and, at the leading edge of receding continents, new mountains were built from the collision of crustal plates. The final sculpting of South Africa as we know it had started (see fig. 7, p. 29).

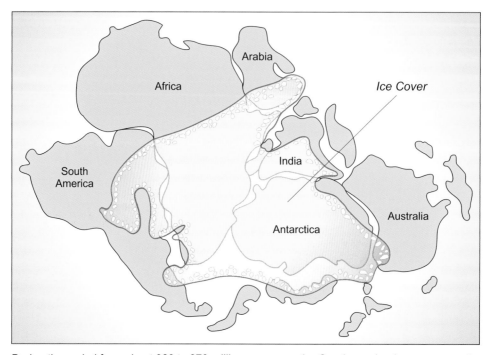

FIGURE 6

THE EXTENT OF ICE COVER OVER GONDWANA
DURING THE GREAT ICE AGE

During the period from about 320 to 270 million years ago the Gondwana landmass was partly covered by ice as the supercontinent migrated over the South Pole. The extent of the vast ice is known from the presence of widespread deposits of similar-aged glacial sediment. Known as the Dwyka tillite in South Africa, this sediment was derived from melting glaciers and ice sheets. It was deposited into a large inland sea, forming the unusual tillite we see today at the base of the Karoo sequence.

The age of rocks

In the early days, geologists established the relative age of sedimentary strata from the fundamental 'Law of Superposition', which simply states that younger rocks lie above older rocks; and from fossils. The same fossils occurring in strata at widely separated localities were interpreted – correctly – to mean that those beds were the same age. It also seemed logical that simpler forms of life were older than more sophisticated forms. As far as the igneous rocks were concerned, the contact relationships between them and the sedimentary rocks found next to them could be interpreted, and their age relative to those sedimentary rocks established. Gradually, a relative ordering and correlation of rocks evolved.

Progress was made towards determining the absolute age of rocks when it was discovered that a number of common chemical elements in nature exist in slightly different forms, called isotopes, some of which are stable, others not. Unstable isotopes decay to stable forms at a rate that could be

THE BREAK-UP OF GONDWANA AND THE EFFECT OF CONTINENTAL DRIFT OVER TIME

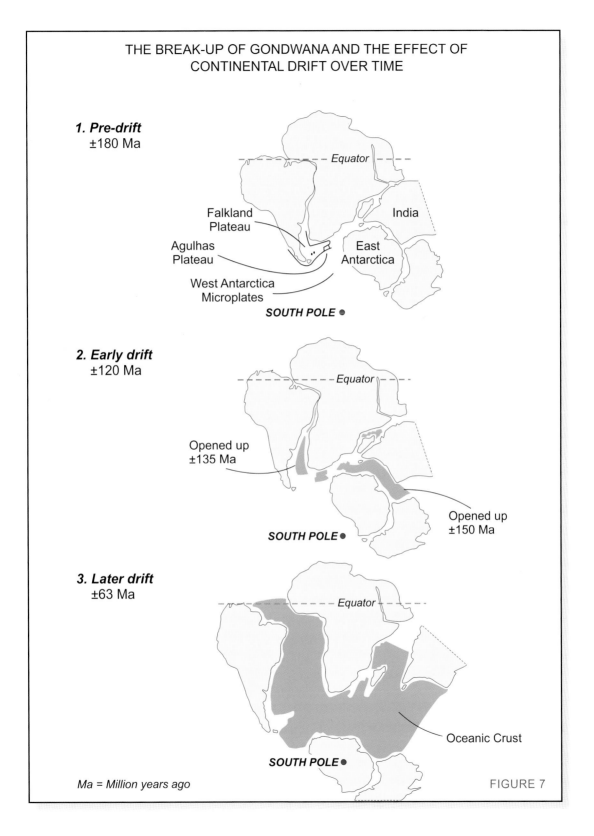

1. Pre-drift
±180 Ma

Equator

Falkland Plateau

India

Agulhas Plateau

East Antarctica

West Antarctica Microplates

SOUTH POLE ●

2. Early drift
±120 Ma

Equator

Opened up ±135 Ma

Opened up ±150 Ma

SOUTH POLE ●

3. Later drift
±63 Ma

Equator

Oceanic Crust

SOUTH POLE ●

Ma = Million years ago

FIGURE 7

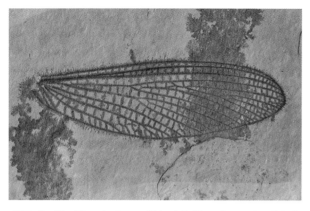

This fossilised insect wing could be dated by reference to related igneous events and could be used wherever it is found to assign an age to the sediment that contains it.

determined. Once the 'half-life' (the time it takes for half of the original material to decay or transmute into something else) of an isotope was established, and by measuring the ratio of 'mother-to-daughter' elements, it could be established how much time had elapsed. Using the analogy of sand flowing through an hour-glass, where the relative amount of sand in each cone of the hour-glass tells exactly when it was upended, the ratio of 'mother-to-daughter' isotope tells when the mineral carrying that element crystallised from magma, or recrystallised during metamorphism.

With sedimentary rocks, dating is indirect. For example, sandstones commonly contain grains of the mineral zircon, derived from original granite source rocks and, invariably, zircon contains traces of radioactive isotopes. The zircon grains can thus be dated, given that the sandstone containing them is younger than those grains, which are themselves as old as the granite in which they crystallised. At the other end of the spectrum, the sandstone is older than any datable igneous intrusive rock that cuts across it. Add to this any contribution in the sedimentary package from the fossil record and we have taken another leap forward, bearing in mind that similar fossils can, in a general sense, realistically be correlated around the globe in terms of their age, which must be established by accurate dating from interlayered igneous rocks.

On the lower right of this picture, taken in the Eastern Cape, an inclined dolerite sheet is seen cutting Beaufort sediments. We can date the dolerite quite accurately: from this age we can determine the minimum age of the sediments cut by it.

Uranium-lead age dating

Perhaps the best-known example of a chemical isotope system that's useful in age determination is the carbon-dating technique, based on the relative abundance of carbon isotopes of mass 12 and 14. The two isotopes differ slightly in mass because of different numbers of neutrons in the atomic nucleii. However, this 'chronometer' can only 'see back' around 50 000 years, far too short to measure geological time in millions or billions of years. In order to measure this 'deep time', several isotope-based geochronometers are available. Of these, one is based on the natural radioactive decay of the isotopes of uranium 238, the parent element, to lead 206, the daughter element, with a half-life of 4.5 billion years, approximately the age of the Earth. This means that, for a given number of uranium 238 atoms, half will convert to lead 206 in 4.5 billion years, and a further half will convert during the next 4.5 billion years, leaving a quarter of the original uranium. This process is depicted in the graph (see fig. 8, below). By carefully measuring the present-day ratio of the uranium 238 and lead 206 in a mineral, and knowing the constant half-life that governs the steady rate of radioactive decay, a reliable age can, under ideal geological circumstances, be calculated.

An entire branch of research geology is focused on what is called geochronology, which utilises a number of isotopic geochronometers. South African geochemists played a major role in establishing this branch of science worldwide during the 1950s and 1960s. This field of study has allowed geologists to build a better and much more accurate picture of Earth history, based on absolute rather than relative ages. Very few aspects of geology today are independent of the reliable dating of geological events.

FIGURE 8

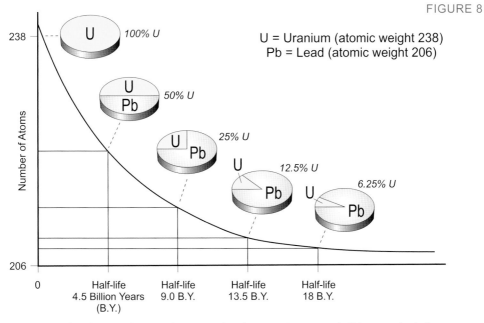

The decay of radioactive isotopes is a natural and constant process. In this example during one half-life period, half of the original (parent) uranium 238 breaks down into (daughter) lead 206. During the next half-life period, half of the remaining uranium 238 breaks down to lead 206, and so on. By very accurately determining the proportion of parent uranium 238 to daughter lead 206 in a rock, and knowing the constant half-life of uranium 238, scientists can calculate the age of the rock.

How rock units and geological formations are named

A number of supergroups and groups have already been introduced; in the pages that follow, a host of other new names make their appearance. It is important to start with a basic idea of how the groupings of rocks interrelate, a branch of geology called stratigraphy, which is the descriptive science of rock strata.

Although all parts of a continuum in space and time, geological processes leave a record that is far from continuous. Consecutive sedimentary rock units, one laid down above another, may be separated by millions of years in the geological timescale. It may be that there was no sedimentation during the intervening time, or that sediments were deposited and then stripped off without trace. Similar rocks laid down during one general depositional event are grouped together as a formation, the fundamental unit of stratigraphic classification. Think of this as a chapter in a book, with special pages within the chapter being called members or beds. Different sedimentary formations, formed in the same basin but in different depositional environments, form what is called a group, analogous to a 'book' or 'chapters' of the same book if it is thick. And, in cases where more than one group is deposited in the same general basin and in a more or less continuous but long-lived process, they belong to a single supergroup, like a book of several parts, or like books in a series. The time interval and environmental difference between the deposition of consecutive formations is less than between the various groups in a supergroup. It is common practice to use geographic place names to identify the various rankings of the hierarchy, based on a designated standard type locality where the strata are well exposed.

The Cape Supergroup, for instance, is made of three groups: Table Mountain, Bokkeveld and Witteberg Groups. Each group is made of several formations; for example, the Table Mountain Group is made of the Piekenierskloof, Graafwater, Peninsula, Pakhuis, Cedarberg and Nardouw Formations (from bottom to top), and so on for the other groups.

Each supergroup is formed in unique circumstances, quite distinct from those above and below it. A group or supergroup of rocks commonly undergoes deformation – in other words tilting, folding and faulting. This is followed by a break in sedimentation and planation by erosion and river action, before deposition of the next unit begins. In such cases the older and younger groups of rocks are said to be separated by an unconformity.

Volcanic rocks that conform to the general stratigraphy or layering are regarded as part of the sedimentary sequence. Cross-cutting igneous rocks and high-grade metamorphic rocks are referred to as a suite, or a complex if consisting of a complexity of rock types and structures. Large-scale regions of metamorphic and structural similarity are referred to as a province.

In the foreground, the shaly Bokkeveld Group sediments have been easily weathered into rolling 'ruens' around Bredasdorp. The much harder Table Mountain Group sandstones make the high-standing ranges that form the skyline and tower over the downs.

On the road: understanding geology

Geology, including geomorphology – the study and configuration and evolution of landforms – is the main, but not the only discipline covered in this book. The route-by-route treatment also lends itself to brief descriptions of the vegetation you will see and, where applicable, agriculture and even history. As you drive the national highways or explore urban or tourist areas, you will be introduced to geological maps and cross-sections. Geological maps, constructed from detailed mapping of rock outcrops, show an interpretation of the underlying geological formations as if all soil and overburden had been removed. Generally, the maps in this book show geological formations at the 'group' level to avoid unduly complicated images. Geological cross-sections are idealised pictures of what the underlying rock formations would look like if you could see them side-on, and this adds the third dimension to the geological picture. A selection (but by no means all) of places or sites of geological importance or interest, called 'geosites' ❷, are also shown on the maps and referred to in the relevant text, and are often accompanied by a photograph.

Along nearly all national roads, blue kilometre marker boards or beacons, located every 200 m, have been put in place by the National Roads Agency (SANRAL). They are clearly visible and comprise valuable markers to pinpoint sites referred to in the text. In some cases, for example the N14 in the Northern Cape, SANRAL has taken over management of national roads from the provincial administration and the old white bollards, spaced at one-kilometre intervals, are in the process of being replaced by the new boards.

The richness of our geological heritage is all around us: as we travel together across the length and breadth of South Africa, you will be reminded time and time again of the mining heritage of our country, its gold and platinum, its granite and sandstone. And as you wander off the beaten track to corners beyond the reach of these pages, you will delight in knowing, from afar, that the knoll where the leopard lies up is of granite; that the flat-topped silhouette on the skyline tells of stability over the eons; that the landscape, the kranses and the cuttings hold no mysteries you cannot start to unravel. You will exult in the meaning of landscape and the intricate patterns in the passes and road cuttings, in the changes, some subtle, some dramatic, as you journey. For you, too, every journey will be one of discovery.

Blue kilometre marker boards, or beacons, have been put in place by the National Roads Agency every 200 m along nearly all national roads.

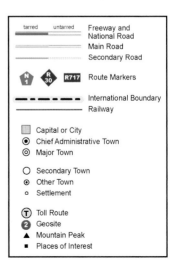

1 Greater Johannesburg and environs

GEOLOGICAL OVERVIEW

This chapter covers a series of geological superlatives; Johannesburg is the financial centre of the world's greatest gold field, with some of the deepest mines on Earth; not far north of Pretoria lies the Bushveld Complex, where most of the world's platinum is mined; and less than an hour away is Cullinan Mine, where the fist-sized Cullinan diamond was found, by far the biggest gem ever discovered. West of Johannesburg, at the Cradle of Humankind, one of eight (at time of publication) World Heritage Sites in South Africa, are the Sterkfontein and other caves with their incomparable collection of clues to man's beginnings. The Tswaing meteorite crater just north of Pretoria is richly deserving of a visit, as is the Vredefort Dome, an ancient, 300 km-wide meteorite impact structure southwest of Johannesburg.

This is an area of great antiquity, with good exposures of Archaean granite – and the older greenstone remnants caught up in it – to be seen in the northern suburbs of Johannesburg. While all of original Johannesburg is built on the south-dipping sedimentary rocks of the Witwatersrand Supergroup, Alberton and other southernmost parts, including Soweto, lie largely on Ventersdorp Supergroup lavas that cover Witwatersrand sediments. As you head southwards, you will cross the thin Black Reef Formation before moving onto the Malmani dolomite of the Transvaal Supergroup.

Caves in this dolomite provided a refuge for man's distant ancestors in the Cradle of Humankind, while around Pretoria the landscape is made up of north-dipping quartzites and shales of the Pretoria Group that overlie the dolomite. The granitic Johannesburg Dome, centred on Midrand, has acted as a resistant, slowly rising feature throughout geological time; the younger formations referred to above can be thought of as being draped over it, and dipping away from it.

After the impact of the giant meteorite in the Vredefort-Parys area, 1 700 million years were to pass before the next event left a geological record. Massive ice sheets spread out from the polar mountains when the Gondwana supercontinent straddled the South Pole 300 million years ago. There's abundant evidence that these sheets passed over the area before thick sequences of Karoo shale and sandstone were laid down. After the break-up of Gondwana, these were almost entirely stripped off, exposing the pre-glacial landscape, which has essentially been the same since then.

MAIN PICTURE: At the confluence of the Braamfontein and Montgomery Spruits in Victory Park, there are excellent outcrops of fresh, pinkish granite that has been dated around 3 200 million years old. This rock type makes up most of the underlying geology of Johannesburg's northern suburbs.

INSET: In Montgomery Spruit look for the small outcrop of a darker gneissic rock, one of the earliest granitic rocks forming the Earth's crust, around 3 500 million years old. This rock type is older than the granites but younger than the greenstones.

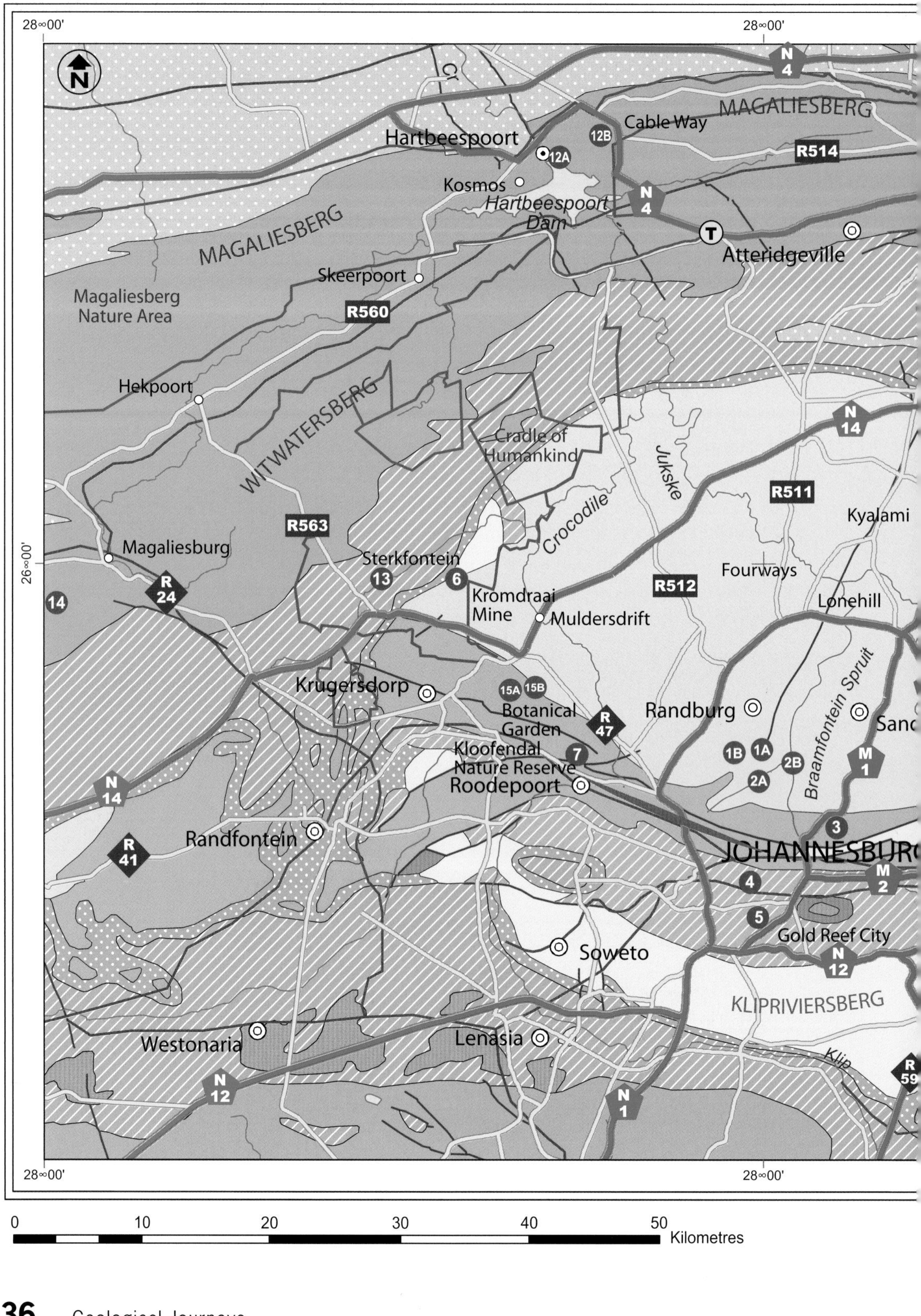

MAP 1

28∞00'

28∞00'

N
4

MAGALIESBERG

Cable Way

12B

R514

Hartbeespoort

12A

Kosmos

*Hartbeespoort
Dam*

N
4

T

Atteridgeville

MAGALIESBERG

Skeerpoort

R560

Magaliesberg
Nature Area

Hekpoort

WITWATERSBERG

Cradle of
Humankind

Jukske

N
14

R511

Kyalami

26∞00'

R563

Magaliesburg

Sterkfontein

13

6

Crocodile

R512

Fourways

Lonehill

14

R
24

Kromdraai
Mine

Muldersdrift

Braamfontein Spruit

Krugersdorp

15A 15B

Botanical
Garden

R
47

Randburg

Sand

M
1

1B 1A

Kloofendal
Nature Reserve

7

2B

2A

N
14

Roodepoort

3

JOHANNESBURG

R
41

Randfontein

4

M
2

5

Gold Reef City

N
12

Soweto

KLIPRIVIERSBERG

Westonaria

Lenasia

Klip

R
59

N
12

N
1

28∞00'

28∞00'

0	10	20	30	40	50

Kilometres

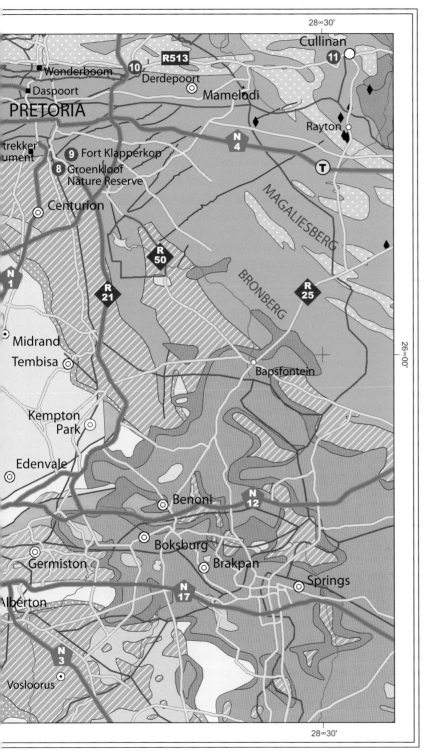

Cullinan

11

R513

10 Derdepoort

Wonderboom

Daspoort

Mamelodi

PRETORIA

Rayton

N4

trekker
ument

9 Fort Klapperkop

T

8 Groenkloof
Nature Reserve

MAGALIESBERG

Centurion

R50

BRONBERG

N1

R21

R25

Midrand

Tembisa

Bapsfontein

Kempton
Park

Edenvale

Benoni

N12

Boksburg

Brakpan

Germiston

Springs

N17

Alberton

N3

Vosloorus

28°30'

26°00'

28°30'

TOP: *An entrance to the old Blaauwberg mine, where thin quartz veins are the source of gold discovered near Magaliesburg village in 1874. Now a tourist attraction, the mine still produces gold on a small scale.*

ABOVE: *In 1885 the Struben brothers discovered the Confidence Reef, a shear zone hosting high-grade gold mineralisation. The site, commemorated by a National Monuments plaque, is located within the Kloofendal Nature Reserve, Roodepoort.*

THE WITWATERSRAND SUPERGROUP – A UNIQUE GEOLOGICAL PHENOMENON

The name 'Witwatersrand' or 'ridge of white waters', because of the many waterfalls that once cascaded off the scarps, was coined by the Boers for a series of prominent, roughly east-west stony ridges, extending from Krugersdorp in the west to Bedfordview in the east. Part of the main continental watershed, it has streams draining to the north and south, eventually feeding the Indian and Atlantic oceans respectively. When gold was discovered here in 1886, the name became associated with the new gold field, soon to become known as 'the Rand'. When in 1888 the sequence of sedimentary rocks that hosts the gold was recognised as a series, it was called the Witwatersrand Series (later System, now Supergroup). But the most far-reaching reminder of its iconic status is the use of its name for our currency.

The gold fields in Gauteng, North West and Free State provinces lie along the margin of the roughly oval-shaped, sedimentary Witwatersrand Basin (see p. 42), extending about 300 km on its long axis, which runs from northeast to southwest. The gold 'reefs', actually thin layers of conglomerate, are minimally exposed at the surface, with the Evander, Welkom and Carletonville gold fields being entirely blanketed by younger formations. The five lying between them, the South Rand, East Rand, Central Rand, West Rand and Klerksdorp gold fields, show themselves, to a greater or lesser degree, in outcrop.

FIGURE 9

CROSS-SECTION OF THE JOHANNESBURG DOME

(Note: The vertical scale is exaggerated for greater clarity)

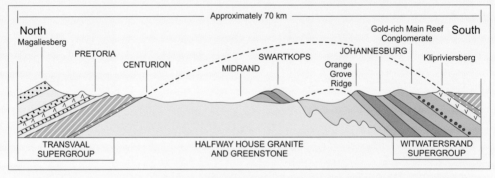

This idealised cross-section of the Johannesburg Dome, between Johannesburg and Tshwane, covers a distance of about 70 km and is centred on an inlier of Archaean granite-gneiss and greenstone. On this ancient basement to the south, the Witwatersrand Supergroup was deposited and now dips southwards at about 30°, while to the north the somewhat younger Transvaal Supergroup dips northwards at around 20°. On the western side of the dome, is Swartkops, a small, isolated outlier of Witwatersrand rocks emplaced by thrusting from the south.

- Greenstone
- Basement granite-gneiss
- Witwatersrand shales
- Witwatersrand quartzites
- Ventersdorp lava
- Black Reef Formation
- Malmani dolomite
- Hekpoort lava
- Pretoria shales
- Pretoria quartzites

FIGURE 10

STRATIGRAPHIC COLUMN OF THE WITWATERSRAND BASIN

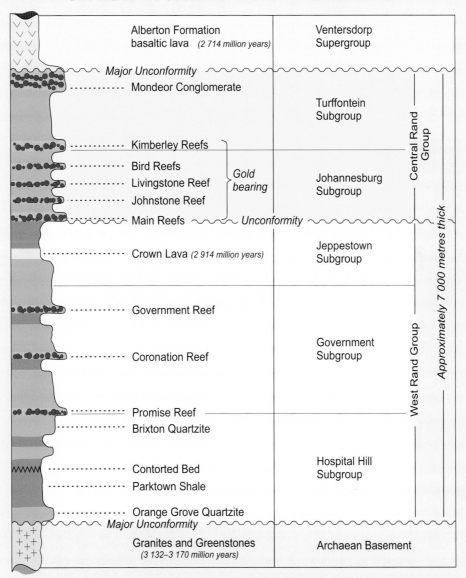

Alberton Formation basaltic lava (2 714 million years)	Ventersdorp Supergroup	
Major Unconformity		
Mondeor Conglomerate	Turffontein Subgroup	Central Rand Group
Kimberley Reefs		
Bird Reefs	Johannesburg Subgroup	
Livingstone Reef (Gold bearing)		
Johnstone Reef		
Main Reefs — Unconformity		
Crown Lava (2 914 million years)	Jeppestown Subgroup	
Government Reef	Government Subgroup	West Rand Group
Coronation Reef		
Promise Reef		
Brixton Quartzite		
Contorted Bed	Hospital Hill Subgroup	
Parktown Shale		
Orange Grove Quartzite		
Major Unconformity		
Granites and Greenstones (3 132–3 170 million years)	Archaean Basement	

Approximately 7 000 metres thick

This rock column illustrates schematically the full 7 000 m sequence of Witwatersrand geology from the Archaean granitic Basement to the overlying Ventersdorp lavas.

The Witwatersrand Supergroup is divided into two groups based on differing types and proportions of sedimentary strata. The lower West Rand Group, 4 300 m thick, contains roughly equal amounts of shale, sandstone and minor conglomerate layers. The upper Central Rand Group, 2 500 m thick, contains far more quartzite than shale, as well as most of the gold-rich 'reefs', which are generally only about one metre or less thick, and in this section have been exaggerated relative to other rock formations.

Johannesburg is the world's greatest mining metropolis. Since they were first mined in 1887, the Witwatersrand gold reefs have produced over 50 000 tons of gold, perhaps half of all gold mined on Earth to date. In recent years many 'Wits' mines have closed, and those remaining have been forced deeper, into areas containing less gold, while elsewhere in the world many new mines have come into production. South African gold production in 2002 amounted to 398 tons, but the Wits contribution to total world gold production had dropped to 15 per cent, and this will continue to decline. The Witwatersrand Basin still contains over 40 per cent of all identified world gold resources, although only a small part of that is commercially workable at current prices. For a single sedimentary basin this is a statistic that's unlikely to be repeated.

SECTION THROUGH THE WITWATERSRAND BASIN IN JOHANNESBURG

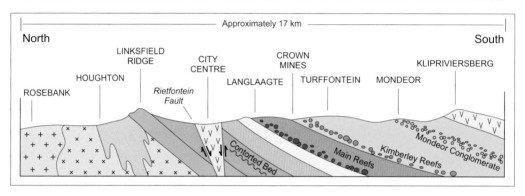

The important gold-bearing Main Reef conglomerate horizons in the upper part of the sequence were mined by operations such as Crown Mines, Robinson Deep and City Deep. In the city centre, the Rietfontein Fault system allowed younger Ventersdorp lava to be down-faulted into a graben-like structure

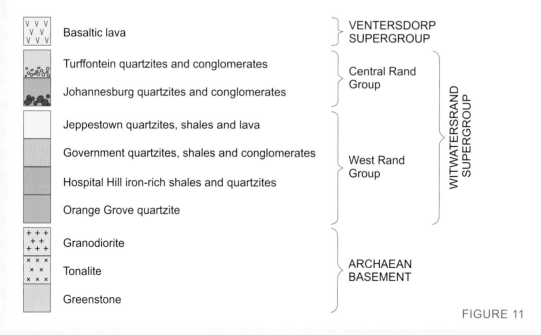

FIGURE 11

Ancient greenstone remnants – Emma Park and Darrenwood Dam

On the northern side of the Witwatersrand ridge, several 'koppie-sized' bodies of dark greenstone of varying types can be seen. In 5th Avenue, Linden, a small koppie at Emma Park (with a Voortrekker *Eeufees* monument at its crest) is composed of magnesium-rich komatiitic basalt **(geosite 1A, map 1)**. In nearby Darrenwood **(geosite 1B, map 1)**, another small, bush-covered hill consists of serpentinite also showing thin asbestos veinlets, well exposed in the Republic Road cutting nearby. Wander around these small hills, still covered by natural vegetation, and you will be walking on some of the oldest formations in South Africa, dated around 3 500 million years old. These rocks originated from very early intrusives and lavas, and formed part of the Earth's earliest ocean floor, which was primitive crust before the first appearance of any granite.

Several koppies in northwest Johannesburg are made of what is generally called greenstone, varieties of dark rocks that are older than the enclosing granite. This koppie in Linden is typical, showing roughly weathered brown outcrops of serpentinite, a typical ultramafic rock.

A note on sedimentary basins

With geologists using the term as regularly as they do, it's necessary to explain what we mean when we talk about 'basins'. Reduced to simple terms, a basin is a depression in the Earth's crust, usually filled with water in the middle for all or most of its lifetime. In most cases the part under water will comprise most of the basin, and in the middle it may be tens, even hundreds of metres deep. Unless the basin is connected to the sea, the water will be fresh, which is generally the case.

A basin will almost invariably be rimmed by mountains, from which will drain streams and rivers feeding into it. The flat, low-lying section between the shore of the basin and the mountainous hinterland may be narrow, but will widen with time.

Basins commonly form because forces below the Earth's surface cause the crust to be depressed over an area which may be as small as tens of kilometres across or as big as a few thousand, but is commonly measured in hundreds of kilometres. The forces dragging that part of the crust down generally persist for many millions of years, so that, although a considerable amount of sediment may be deposited into the basin, it does not fill up, but maintains approximately the same depth of water, or may even deepen. Similarly, the mountains shedding sediment into the basin may not become worn down to level flats, because the subsurface forces that pushed them up in the first place continue to do so.

Inevitably, though, the point is reached where those forces are spent, the high ground has been levelled and the basin filled. It may not be the end of the history of the basin, though. After a break, the restlessness may be revived and the whole process may start again, perhaps with a slight shift of the centre of the basin to one side or the other. Very often there are faults between the rising ground and the sinking basin, along which is shed very coarse conglomeratic material.

As a final point, it needs to be noted that most of the sediments preserved in basins are not formed in their permanently submerged parts, but in the low-lying coastal flats. Remember that the size of material that rivers carry – whether boulders, pebbles, sand or clay – depends on the gradient of the river. Steep, high-energy rivers carry coarse material, while those that wind lazily across coastal flats do not, except in times of flood. By the time mature rivers reach basin coastlines, they will often carry nothing coarser than clay. Sediments formed on land may be submerged if the basin sinks faster than it is accumulating material, and they will then be reworked by wave and current action. South Africa is noted for a number of large sedimentary basins, namely the Witwatersrand Basin, the Ventersdorp Basin, the Transvaal Basin, the Waterberg Basin and the Karoo Basin – all of which are traversed in the routes that follow.

Basement granites – Montgomery and Braamfontein Spruits

Near Fourways, look for Lonehill or Norscot Koppie, both urban nature reserves showing small, reddish-weathering granite tors reminiscent of those in Mpumalanga or in Zimbabwe. For a closer look, there are several streambed exposures; at the Montgomery Spruit in Emmarentia (**geosite 2A, map 1**), opposite the kink in Hofmeyer Road, find the little waterfall and you will see dark, coarsely banded or foliated granite-gneiss. This rock is the result of partial melting of the primitive greenstones forced by Earth movements into deeper, hotter levels of the crust. As a result of the surrounding high pressure, the newly mobile, melted portion was forced up and intruded into the cooler, solid greenstones above it, where, under lower pressure, it cooled and solidified.

The first granitic intrusions were formed around 3 200 million years ago and, with them, the thicker continental crust started to develop. At the rock exposures in Victory Park, along the Braamfontein Spruit (**geosite 2B, map 1**) off Rustenburg Road, there is none of the banding or foliation evident at the Hofmeyer Road outcrop and the granitic rock is lighter coloured and more massive (meaning, in a geological sense, unbanded). This suggests it is slightly younger than the foliated granite-gneiss mentioned above, which was squeezed in while the rocks were still in motion, the banding reflecting the motion frozen in time. The massive rocks, on the other hand, were intruded once all movement had ceased, and solidified just as they were. The granite here contains glassy quartz, white plagioclase, pink microcline and less shiny black biotite mica. Also revealed in this excellent exposure are coarse-grained pegmatite veins cutting through the granite. These represent the last part of the magma to crystallise, very slowly, giving the minerals time to grow larger.

The 'Contorted Bed' – Braamfontein Ridge

One of South Africa's few geological national monuments, the 'Contorted Bed', runs along the crest of the Braamfontein ridge (**geosite 3, map 1**), and is best seen in the cutting on Jan Smuts Avenue, opposite the University of the Witwatersrand, and on nearby Melle Street. A feature of the bed is the unique small-scale folding (the 'contortions'), as well as its remarkable, basin-wide extent. The latter makes it one of the most important marker beds of the West Rand Group, occurring consistently about 750 m above granitic Basement, towards the top of the Parktown Shale Formation. The rock is banded ironstone, consisting of thin bands of black magnetite, red jaspilite, grey chert and iron-rich shale layers. Its usefulness also lies in its strongly magnetic character, which allowed the West Rand Group to be traced geophysically under a thick cover of younger formations, leading to the discovery of the Carletonville and Welkom (Free State) gold fields.

Lonehill Koppie, north of Johannesburg, is a typical example of a tor. Their formation is the result of weathering of rectangular blocks of granite showing conspicuous jointing. Now surrounded by urban development, this hill is also an Early Stone Age site.

FORMATION OF THE WITWATERSRAND GOLD REEFS

Two aspects of sedimentology are important to our understanding of the Witwatersrand gold deposits. First, over geological time the shoreline moves: seawards as the hinterland is uplifted and the sedimentary basin sinks; and landwards as the hinterland is levelled by erosion, which, as it slows, results in the basin receiving little new sediment, causing it to stop sinking until faulting along the coastline sets the process in motion again. And second, vigorous rivers and longshore currents move coarse sediment, cobbles, pebbles and sand, while dwindling, low-energy currents carry finer sediment such as silt and clay particles great distances; hence the endless cycles, from coarse sediments (conglomerates) through medium (sandstone) to fine (shale), and back again, as nature constantly works to maintain the balance. In very simple terms, this is how the 7 000 m-thick Witwatersrand sedimentary 'package' and the pebbly conglomerate reefs containing the gold were formed.

The idealised and simplified block diagram (fig. 12, below) illustrates the main geological features of the Witwatersrand Supergroup, shown here at the end of sedimentation and eruption of the first Ventersdorp lavas. The rock formations making up the Witwatersrand were deposited over a time span of more than 250 million years. Numbers shown on the illustration are referred to in the text opposite.

RECONSTRUCTION OF WITWATERSRAND SEDIMENTATION

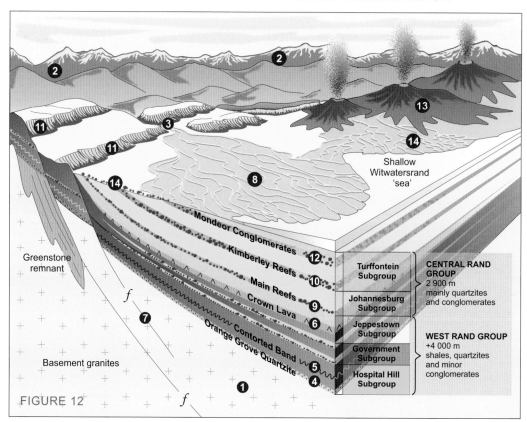

An artist's impression of the formation of Witwatersrand Supergroup at the end of sedimentation

KEY TO FIGURE 12

1. Around 3 000 million years ago, part of the granitic crust began to sag, creating a large inland Witwatersrand 'sea' into which sediment was deposited on older Basement granites and greenstones.
2. Distant mountains to the north and west of the basin, made of granite and greenstone, and containing mineral deposits, provided the vast volume sediment that was ultimately deposited into the Witwatersrand sea.
3. Sediment, ranging from fine silt to coarse pebbles, was brought down by major river systems that eventually entered the sea. The rivers also brought in heavy minerals like magnetite, pyrite, uranium oxides and probably much of the gold.
4. The basal unit of the sequence, the Orange Grove Quartzite, formed in shallow water and today forms the prominent northernmost ridge of the Witwatersrand. This marks the start of the West Rand Group.
5. Both deep and shallow water marine sedimentation followed, including the deposition of iron-rich shales, notably the Contorted Bed, a strongly magnetic layer of deformed banded ironstone.
6. Higher up in the sedimentary sequence is the Crown Lava, a thin, discontinuous volcanic formation of andesite that has been dated at 2 914 million years, the oldest measured age of the Witwatersrand sequence.
7. Basin margin faulting accompanied the on-going sedimentation and basin development. Over time, the nature of the basin changed, and sand and pebbles from rivers became the more dominant sediment.
8. The rivers had to cross wide plains on which large alluvial fans and braided river channels were formed, and on which the sediments were reworked and sorted over many millions of years, gravitationally concentrating the gold, uranium and pyrite.
9. Close to the base of the Central Rand Group a number of very extensive layers of pebbles were formed, also containing fine-grained pyrite and gold. These pebble beds became the gold-rich Main Reef conglomerates.
10. Higher up in the sequence, several other gold-bearing conglomerate reefs were formed, notably the thick Kimberley Reef conglomerates, mined in gold fields away from the Central Rand field.
11. During the development of the basin, fault-controlled scarps resulted in earlier-formed West Rand Group formations being exposed and eroded into the basin, adding to the filling of the basin by reworked sediment.
12. Changing conditions within the Earth's crust eventually resulted in the shallowing of the sea and the basin filling with coarse sand and thick quartz layers of pebbles, shown by the gold-poor Mondeor Conglomerates.
13. Around 2 714 million years ago, the first continental-scale outpourings of basaltic lava of the Ventersdorp Supergroup took place (here shown diagrammatically), which eventually covered the entire Witwatersrand Basin.
14. But in places, before it was covered by lava, a coarse residual quartz pebble conglomerate developed on the palaeo-surface, within which much gold was concentrated, forming the extremely rich Ventersdorp Contact Reef.

It is notable that there is still the question of the enigmatic origin of the Witwatersrand gold; with nearly 50 000 tons already recovered, this has not been completely answered, despite over a 100 years of detailed observation, research and debate. Competing placer (alluvial), modified placer and hydrothermal theories have been proposed, all with compelling scientific evidence.

Most people accept the 'placer theory', in terms of which minute gold particles, far denser than other sediment carried by the rivers, stayed with the pebbles in the alluvial fans and along the beaches rather than being washed out into the deeper sea with material of equivalent particle size but lower density. A second school of thought says that the gold was introduced into the conglomerates much later by hot fluids that permeated the Witwatersrand strata; this is known as the 'hydrothermal theory'. The jury is still out on this matter.

In terms of the 'placer theory', it is argued that some rivers drained areas with no gold, or had insufficient energy to transport it. So there were gold-bearing systems and barren systems, gold-bearing times and barren times. Each of the eight gold fields was formed by a major river system in a setting of coalescing alluvial fans along the coastal plain before leading into the shallow sea. This is shown diagramatically in the composite block diagram (see fig. 12, p. 44).

During countless cycles of reworking, the selective winnowing out of lighter material was constantly in progress, concentrating the pebbles and denser particles such as gold, pyrite and uranium. It was a slow but steady process of upgrading, leading eventually to the compact, well-sorted, gold-rich pebble reefs we see today.

Exposures of the famous Main Reef at George Harrison Park, only a few kilometres west of Johannesburg's city centre, commemorate the discovery site of these pyritic, gold-bearing conglomerates, which started theWitwatersrand gold-rush in 1886.

Main Reef discovery site – George Harrison Park, Langlaagte

A must-see for those interested in the geology of the Witwatersrand, the history of gold mining, even the history of South Africa, is at George Harrison Park (another national monument) near Langlaagte Station, about 5 km west of the city centre (**geosite 4, map 1**). The park abuts the west-bound lane of busy Main Reef Road, immediately west of Nasrec Road, and is best visited over a weekend when the traffic is lighter. The park is on a portion of the original 'Zoekers' Claim No. 19, awarded to George Harrison. Here, in February 1886, history was made when Harrison, probably with George Walker, serendipitously discovered the fabulous Main Reef conglomerates. Old workings show excellent exposures of thick, south-dipping Main Reef conglomerate and thin, overlying Main Reef Leader conglomerate, opened up by early mining. Informative illustrative plaques outlining the early history of the gold field are on display, produced by the Geological Society of South Africa. Despite the roar of traffic and the high-rise buildings and towers on the skyline, there is a palpable sense of history here, of where Johannesburg really began and South Africa's gold-mining history was made.

Once the world's greatest gold mine, only the headgear over No. 14 Shaft, sunk in 1916, remains operational. Tourists can venture underground here at Gold Reef City's authentic mining museum.

Gold Reef City and the Mining Museum

With all the razzmatazz of a full-blown theme park surrounding you, it's difficult to transport yourself back in time at Gold Reef City (**geosite 5, map 1**), a short distance away from George Harrison Park, but it's worth the effort. Here, still operational, is No. 14 Shaft of world-renowned Crown Mines, one of the richest gold mines the world has ever known. Down the shaft and in a tunnel 220 m underground, with the only illumination coming from your headlamp, the mining experience becomes a powerful reality as you walk through authentic underground workings and see the gold-bearing Kimberley Reef, as it was mined. Although Harrison's claim was where it all began, the period of surface working was short-lived compared to the hundred or so years of underground mining that were to follow.

The Gold Reef City Mine Museum, located near the steel headgear over the shaft, exhibits evocative historical documents and geological maps and cross-sections. Also on display are 3-D geological models of how the Witwatersrand Basin is thought to have evolved, based on critical scrutiny by geologists of many kilometres of underground workings and diamond drill core. For this lesson in geology and mining, a visit to Crown Mines is strongly recommended.

Revisiting the hills of gold

They're not really hills, they're mine dumps, and they're fast disappearing. But, even as old dumps are re-landscaped or torn down and relocated further away, they continue to carry gold – less with every refashioning of the topography, certainly, but even the slimes issuing from the reprocessing contain a small amount of gold. The grades are almost certainly too low by now ever to warrant another circuit through the plant, but it would be a bold man to put that on paper and sign it.

Two types of tailings deposits are seen on the Rand: the early, more or less conical sand dumps, and the later, rectangular, terraced and flat-topped slimes dams. In general, these reflect evolving gold recovery processes, the earlier sand dumps being the residue after relatively coarse crushing by stamp mills, and the later slimes dams resulting from the much finer tube milling and cyanidation process. The early recovery process was comparatively inefficient, leaving up to one gram of gold in every ton of sand sent to the dumps. This makes them attractive reprocessing targets and, over the years, many have disappeared. In general, only the older slimes dams contain enough gold to make further recovery profitable.

More than 30 years ago, technological improvements in metallurgy changed the extraction of millions of ounces of gold known to be held in existing mine dumps from an idle dream to feasibility. New age carbon-in-leach or carbon-in-pulp plants were built, initially ERGO (for East Rand Gold Operations) by Anglo American, and later plants by Crown Gold Recoveries. Where underground gold mines traditionally declared handsome dividends with grades of 10 grams of gold per ton of rock, studies showed that new plants would be profitable, even operating at a recovery of 0.4 g per ton, given that 'mining' of dumps is an ultra low-cost operation compared to breaking narrow reefs of hard rock deep underground.

Liquidising the sand or slimes takes place on site, for the slurry to be pumped – sometimes many kilometres – to a central plant for processing and extraction of the gold. The rub is this: although there may be a gram of gold, or more, in that ton of mine dump sand, recovery of the last 0.1 to 0.2 g becomes prohibitively costly, and is left – perhaps for the next quantum leap in technology?

Many of the older Witwatersrand mine dumps, made from the finely crushed and milled residue of gold-bearing reefs, have been reprocessed for the gold they still contain. **ABOVE LEFT:** *This is one of the earlier conical sand dumps at the old West Rand Consolidated Mine near Krugersdorp that is slowly being removed for reprocessing.* **ABOVE RIGHT:** *Larger rectangular 'slimes' dams were constructed later, like this one in Johannesburg's southern suburbs. Generally, these do not contain recoverable gold.*

EARLY GOLD MINING ON THE WITWATERSRAND

1874: Australian prospector Henry Lewis discovered alluvial gold at Blaauwbank (**geosite 6, map 1**), west of Krugersdorp, near today's Magaliesburg village. Later mining of mineralised quartz reefs in Timeball Hill shales proved disappointing (see p. 57-8).

1881: Stephanus Minnaar found gold at Kromdraai (**geosite 6, map 1**), 10 km north of Krugersdorp, now part of the Cradle of Humankind. Proclaimed a public digging in 1885, the farm was subsequently taken over by Jan Gerritse Bantjes, with much underground mining later done on the Black Reef.

1884: On Wilgespruit, now part of the Kloofendal Nature Reserve, north of Roodepoort, brothers Fred and Harry Struben found high-grade, gold-bearing quartz veins, the first in Witwatersrand rocks. Called the 'Confidence Reef' (**geosite 7, map 1**), this was an unfortunately inappropriate name.

1885: The Strubens erected a 5-stamp mill, the first on the Witwatersrand, with the help of George Walker. They started crushing conglomerate bands from Roodepoort, without reported success.

February 1886: One Sunday morning George Harrison, while working on the farm Langlaagte, and probably accompanied by George Walker, discovered the Main Reef outcrop (**geosite 4, map 1**) on Langlaagte. In July Harrison formally reported a payable 'gold field' and the Witwatersrand gold rush was on.

July 1886: Mining magnates from wealthy Kimberley, like JB Robinson, Dr Hans Sauer, Cecil John Rhodes and Charles Rudd, arrived at the new gold field and started taking up prospective ground. Prospectors and entrepreneurs started flocking into the new Rand gold field.

September 1886: President Paul Kruger of the Zuid-Afrikaansche Republiek issued a proclamation, declaring nine Witwatersrand farms public diggings, starting on 20 September 1886. This event signalled the official founding of the Witwatersrand gold field.

November 1886: To establish a mining village, the government surveyed over 100, 50-foot-square stands on a nearby triangle of vacant land called Randjeslaagte. In December, these plots were sold, thereby establishing the township soon to be known as Johannesburg. This area is marked by Commissioner Street in the south, Diagonal Street to the west and End Street to the east.

1887: Cecil Rhodes sent Charles Rudd to London to register 'The Gold Fields of South Africa', South Africa's first mining house, with capital of £250 000, and his brother Thomas as the first chairman. More stamp mills were erected, soon giving an indication of the unprecedented richness of the Rand.

1888: From mostly small surface workings, recorded production reached over 120 000 ounces (nearly 4 tons) of gold. Alfred Beit, Hermann Eckstein and Lionel Phillips laid the foundations of what became Rand Mines Limited: the era of the Randlords had begun.

1889: The mines started running into hard, unweathered conglomerate at around 30 m. This pyritic reef was harder and costlier to mine, gold grades were declining, and the fresh ore did not easily release gold in the extraction process being used. Banks called in loans and the Stock Exchange slumped. The Barnato brothers arrived and set up the Johannesburg Consolidated Investment Company (JCI).

1890: In a historic technology breakthrough, gold was extracted from fresh ore using the new McArthur-Forrest cyanidation process, with much higher recovery than before. The gold industry was saved. Geologist Joseph Curtis drilled the first core borehole to the south of Johannesburg and found the gold-bearing South Reef and Main Reef Leader conglomerates at over 500 feet (152 m) from the surface.

1899: The Anglo-Boer War started, affecting every corner of the country. Gold mines closed down. Had the discoveries of the previous decade and the prospect of fabulous wealth not raised the stakes to feverish levels, South Africa might have been spared this cruel war.

Beyond Greater Johannesburg

Pretoria

The area now known as Tshwane, around Pretoria, was occupied variously by migrant tribes; by colonial hunters, who used it as a remote trading post; and, in 1837, by Boer pioneers who settled along the Apies River valley before the area was declared the new central capital town of the *Zuid-Afrikaansche Republiek* in 1853. Strong springs emanating from the Malmani dolomite to the south in the Groenkloof provided abundant water, while the fertile valleys were protected by prominent east-west-trending quartzite ridges **(geosite 8, map 1)**. This terrain, characterised by shallow dip slopes and stepped, resistant scarps, is known as bankenveld.

Some 15 km to the southwest of central Pretoria lies the 3 200 million-year-old Johannesburg Granite Dome, from which all the Transvaal Supergroup formations dip shallowly to the north and northeast. Malmani dolomite, underlain by thin Black Reef Formation, forms a belt up to some 10 km wide around the Dome, and provides the flattish terrain of Irene, Lyttleton and Thaba Tshwane (formerly Voortrekkerhoogte). Within Pretoria, a series of three parallel, arcuate quartzite ridges, in places repeated by faulting, form the hilly expression of the city, and extend far to the west and southeast. These north-dipping ridges have given name to three associated geological formations, from oldest to youngest, the Timeball Hill, Daspoort and Magaliesburg formations. The intervening valleys are filled by more easily weathered shales and lavas. Numerous sills of dark-coloured igneous rock, called diabase, have intruded the sediments, and faulting, particularly of the Timeball Hill Formation, is evident. Collectively the whole package is called the Pretoria Group of the Transvaal Supergroup.

Known as Wonderboompoort, this gorge north of central Pretoria is one of the few road and rail access routes through the Magaliesburg Range. Here you can see the full sequence of the north-dipping Magaliesburg Quartzite Formation that forms the extensive east-west-trending Magaliesburg.

TOP: *This hard, well-bedded, north-dipping quartzite formation, midway within the Pretoria Group, creates a prominent ridge. It has been tunnelled through for easier road access in the city, and the same quartzite has been tunnelled on the N4 at Waterval-Boven in Mpumalanga.*

ABOVE LEFT: *Klapperkop, one of the hills south of central Pretoria, provides a panoramic view of the city. On the road to Fort Klapperkop look out for the thick, north-dipping bed of Timeball Hill magnetic ironstone, that further west from here provided iron ore for South Africa's first blast furnace in 1918.*

ABOVE RIGHT: *Close to where the N1 highway cuts through the Magaliesburg at Derdepoort, this unusual carbonatite breccia can be seen in the resort area. A small kimberlite intrusion also occurs here.*

This sequence was deposited within the very large inland body of water referred to as the 'Transvaal Sea' on the Kaapvaal Craton around 2 200 million years ago. To the north of Pretoria, around Onderstepoort and Wonderboom, the 2 050 million-year-old Bushveld Complex makes its appearance, usually beneath thick black soil, characteristic of the Mafic Phase. Sites of geological interest around Pretoria include Malmani dolomite in Groenkloof Nature Reserve, shales and ironstone at Fort Klapperkop **(geosite 9, map 1)**, the Daspoort Tunnel quartzite, the thick Magaliesburg quartzite at Wonderboompoort, and the carbonatite breccia at the Derdepoort Resort **(geosite 10, map 1)**.

Cullinan Mine and village

Cullinan is best accessed on the N4, taking the Rayton off-ramp some 25 km east of Pretoria. For a hands-on experience of a working diamond mine, the Cullinan (formerly Premier) Mine **(geosite 11, map 1)**, in the quaint historic village of the same name, is a must. No name resonates through

This immense excavation at Cullinan, at least four times the size of Kimberley's 'Big Hole', is about 1 000 m long, 500 m wide and over 200 m deep. The diamond recovery plant is in the foreground. Mining now takes place underground.

the world of diamonds like Cullinan, calling to mind the fist-sized stone opportunistically picked out of the sidewall of the open working, 9 m (30 feet) below the surface, in January 1905. In an act of colonial generosity it was given by the Transvaal government to King Edward VII, and found its way into the Crown Jewels where, cut into nine large, perfect gemstones (and 96 smaller ones), it can be seen by millions of TV viewers every time a British state occasion is broadcast.

It all started in 1898 when Thomas Cullinan, later Sir Thomas, a successful businessman and part-time prospector from Johannesburg, heard that diamond digger Percival White Tracey had found a beautiful three-carat, blue-white diamond not far east of Pretoria. The Anglo-Boer War was imminent, though, and it was not until 1902 that Cullinan could buy the farm, opening the mine the following year. Since its discovery in 1905 by Frederick Wells, the Cullinan diamond, at 3 106 carats, has never looked like being toppled from its pinnacle as the biggest gem diamond ever found. The mine has also produced a large number of other diamonds above 500 carats. Some of the celebrated diamonds mined here are the Niarchos, cut from a 426 carat rough; the flawless 137-carat Premier Rose, cut from a 353.9 carat rough, which was saved from the crusher; the 599.1-carat De Beers Centenary that was recovered from the mine in 1986; and the 545-carat Golden Jubilee, the biggest cut diamond in the world, today owned by the King of Thailand.

There is a delightful irony in the geographic sandwiching of the mine that produces more big gemstones than any other in the world between the globally pre-eminent Witwatersrand gold reefs just to the south and the Bushveld platinum reefs only a little further north. At surface, the kidney-shaped Cullinan kimberlite pipe originally covered 32 hectares, or about 64 rugby fields. Before mining it was 900 m long and 450 m at its widest, making it by far the biggest pipe in South Africa – though, like all kimberlite pipes, it tapers, carrot-like, downwards. The other characteristic is that it is not alone – there are another 10 pipes and dykes in the vicinity.

With its centenary well behind it and, potentially, years of life ahead, this is a mine of rare longevity, mining a deposit of unique antiquity; for, at 1 200 million years old, Cullinan is the oldest kimberlite being mined in the world.

Tswaing Meteorite Crater

To get to Tswaing, go north from Pretoria to Onderstepoort and, with Bon Accord Dam on your right, take the M35 to Shoshanguve. Another 25 km will take you to the Soutpan Store with the Tswaing entrance gate on the left; the area is now a nature reserve.

Man has always marvelled at stars that appeared to fall from their ordained place, pulling a dazzling but momentary tail behind them before disappearing forever. But who would dream that these 'stars' might leave their celestial realm to enter ours?

Viewed westwards across the 1 000 m-wide crater, this is one of the best preserved and most accessible small meteorite impact sites in the world. Tswaing Crater was formed only some 200 000 years ago. Today it is a nature reserve.

Certainly Stone Age and Iron Age man knew of the strange circular basin, and collected crusty accumulations of salt there. The remains of rock tools and earthenware pots at Tswaing are testimony to that. And 'Tswaing', meaning 'place of salt' in Setswana, was the name in use for the crater long before the arrival of European settlers. Geologists in the early 1900s knew of the crater and sought to take it out of the realm of fable into science. Some considered there to be enough evidence to prove it was an old volcano. Careful geological study found no meteoritic remnants on the surface. What they did find was shattering of the coarse-grained Bushveld granite making up the surrounding ridge, as well as huge fragments that appeared to have been blasted out of the crater – but that was by no means conclusive proof of an impact origin.

In 1990, with the application of high-power microscopes, the experts found what they were looking for: evidence of the extraordinary temperatures and pressures of shock metamorphism. Minute spherical particles of glass, formed at the time of impact, were found in rock core drilled from the sandy fragmental breccia. Core from deeper in the borehole showed equally diagnostic microscopic deformation features. Thanks to the expertise of impact specialist Professor Uwe Reimold, the mystery had been solved, and the crater identified as that caused by a meteorite. Fission-track age dating showed the glass is some 220 000 years old, thus giving us the estimated date of the impact.

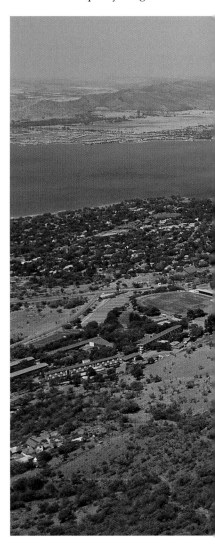

The diameter of the crater, about 1 100 m, tells us something about the meteorite's probable size: between 30 m and 50 m in diameter, bigger than the average house. Because of the meteorite's immense speed, it would probably have taken no more than 10 seconds to slam into the ground after entering the atmosphere, releasing the energy of about 100 Hiroshima atom bombs. All life in the vicinity would have been vaporised, with anything surviving the air blast buried by the ejecta up to 1.5 km from the point of impact. Winds of up to 1 000 km per hour would have been felt many kilometres away, with all vegetation flattened within a radius of 40 km. The only near-impact whose effects were recorded photographically happened in 1908 in the Tunguska region in Siberia, and showed total devastation.

Salt (sodium chloride) and trona (sodium carbonate) were formerly extracted on an industrial scale from below the floor of the crater lake, which fills only the flat 'pan' at the bottom of the crater. Tiny amounts of these salts from surrounding rocks are washed into the lake during summer rains. Concentrations of such salts are common in 'blind' pans and lakes that have no through-flow, and where the only loss of water is by evaporation.

At Hartbeespoort Dam a cable-car ride to the top of the range provides a magnificent all-round panorama. Viewed westwards, the mountains are topped by a thick, north-dipping layer of resistant Magaliesburg quartzite. Look out for the coarsely recrystallised quartz grains in the outcrops.

Hartbeespoort Dam and Magaliesburg

From Pretoria, there are several ways to get to Hartbeespoort but it's probably best to take the N4 westwards. From Johannesburg, the most scenic route is via Fourways and the R511. From here you will cross the ancient Basement granites of the Johannesburg Dome, and the Black Reef Formation near the Hartbeespoort Dam turn-off. The hilly terrain composed of the Malmani dolomites follows, and is best seen around Hennops River.

As you near Hartbeespoort Dam, you will see three prominent ridges formed by resistant quartzites and broad intervening valleys filled by shales, all of the Pretoria Group, named after their type locations in Pretoria. At Hartbeespoort, the very resistant, north-dipping Magaliesburg quartzite, coarsely recrystallised by the heat from the nearby Bushveld Complex, builds the crest of the imposing mountain range that extends from east of Pretoria to west of Rustenburg. The ridge here **(geosite 12A, map 1)** is crossed by a north-trending fault zone that resulted in the gorge (or *poort*) formed by the Crocodile River, which was dammed in 1923 for downstream irrigation purposes.

It is worthwhile taking a trip to the top of the 1 600 m-high range by cablecar for a panorama of the whole region. At the top **(geosite 12B, map 1)**, have a good look at the excellent regional geological model prepared by the Geological Society of South Africa. To the north you will see the flat country of the Bushveld Complex, but there is very little outcrop, as almost the entire area is covered by black soil. To the south you will see Pelindaba and, on a clear day, the Johannesburg skyline.

Sterkfontein Caves – Cradle of Humankind

Palaeoanthropologists come from far and wide to visit Sterkfontein and other sites nearby, to study evidence of prehistoric man, his close relatives, and the environment existing at the birth of mankind. It would be a pity to be in Johannesburg or Pretoria, even for only a few days, and not to see Sterkfontein **(geosite 13, map 1)**. The area has revealed a greater wealth of human prehistory than any other on Earth, and contains at least 12 major fossil sites. It is the main *raison d'être* of the 470 sq km Cradle of Humankind World Heritage Site – now one of eight such sites in the country – and only an hour from Johannesburg. Nearby is the historic Kromdraai gold mine **(geosite 6, map 1)**.

Dipping shallowly to the northwest off the Johannesburg Dome is the 1 500 m-thick Malmani dolomite sequence, a magnesium-rich limestone deposited in a shallow, tropical sea some 2 500 million years ago. Algae in this primitive sea were involved in the precipitation of carbonate sediment resulting in the build-up of the dolomite. These algae are thought to have introduced oxygen to the atmosphere; by prolonged photosynthesis, they added enough oxygen to screen out harmful ultraviolet rays and to sustain more complex life.

ABOVE: *While lime quarrying continued into the 1950s, it was at this excavation in 1947 that the almost perfectly preserved skull of Mrs Ples was discovered. A small plaque on the wall marks the site of this discovery.* **INSET:** *The bust of Dr Robert Broom at the entrance to the Sterkfontein Caves.*

At Sterkfontein you are on hallowed ground. Site of the discovery of th
1947 and, more recently, of 4.1 million-year-old 'Little Foot', it was hailed ɑ
treasure house of the world' by Dr Robert Broom, one of the most respected ɪ
of all time, not only in South Africa but internationally.

The Sterkfontein Caves facilities have been considerably upgraded. A guidɩ
of part of the cave system, together with an account of how the fossils were foυ
sense of prehistorical perspective. Take a look into the fenced-off open workiɪ   , ɑɪᴜ you
will see the exact place where 'Mrs Ples' was discovered in 1947. Nearby, at Mohale's Gate, the
Cradle of Humankind management has developed an exciting new visitors' centre called Maropeng
(a Setswana word meaning 'returning to place of origin') of international calibre. This centre offers
a 'journey of discovery', including a display of the original fossils on loan from various scientific
institutions, together with state-of-the-art exhibitions and recreational facilities.

Historic Blaauwbank Mine, near Magaliesburg village

To see the oldest producing gold mine in Gauteng, take the R24 or R47 northwest of Krugersdorp and,
after driving over both Witwatersrand and basement rocks, you will cross the Black Reef Formation
near Oaktree. After passing Tarlton, continue across flattish farmland underlain by Malmani dolomite.
Close to Magaliesburg, and about 25 km from Krugersdorp, you will notice brownish, well-bedded,
northwesterly-dipping shales of the Pretoria Group, giving rise to the attractive hilly countryside of
these parts. Pass through the village and head off to the left, past the old railway station; from there,
the Blaauwbank Mine **(geosite 14, map 1)** is signposted and can be seen near the top of the hill to
the south. For the more adventurous, there's a steam train that travels out here on certain Sundays.

*Gold ore is still being mined on a small scale at Blaauwbank Mine near Magaliesburg, and is recovered
using primitive but effective machinery. Visitors can also pan their own gold on site.*

al gold was discovered here by Australian prospector Henry Lewis in 1874, and soon traced ucropping quartz reefs on the north-sloping hillside. The old mine is a safe walk-in tourist raction, and provides a fascinating guided underground trip. Thin quartz veins, interbedded and cross-cutting within Timeball Hill shales, were mined, partially at the surface, but mainly underground, from 1875 to 1879. The recovery plant is still in place, illustrating how gold was, and still is, recovered. With luck, your guide will show you fine-grained gold being hand-panned from the crushed ore. This mine started a minor gold rush, and was the first gold-mining company to be established in today's Gauteng. But the results were disappointing and the mine was never a successful gold producer despite many trials over the years. Today, however, it is once more producing gold, albeit on a small scale.

Geological Trail and Rock Garden – Walter Sisulu National Botanical Garden

The Walter Sisulu (formerly Witwatersrand) National Botanical Garden is reached by heading northwest out of Johannesburg on Hendrik Potgieter Avenue or the R47 towards Muldersdrift. At Doreen Road turn south towards the Witwatersrand ridge and, at the far end of Malcolm Road, you will find the garden within a picturesque poort.

The backdrop is the Witpoortjie Waterfall, where the headwaters of the Crocodile River cascade 70 m over a cliff of Orange Grove quartzite and shale. There are two geological interests here: the 3.5 km JCI Geological Trail and the Geological Rock Garden.

At the start of the Crocodile River, the 'ridge of white waters' is well illustrated as
Witpoortjie Waterfall plunges over ledges of south-dipping Orange Grove Formation quartzite
and shale, which in turn overlies much older greenstone.

From the base of the waterfall at the Walter Sisulu National Botanical Garden, a walking trail designed by the Geological Society of South Africa winds its way over the ridge. This shows the sequence of quartzite and shale, cut by later faulting.

JCI Geological Trail

This well-marked walking trail **(geosite 15A, map 1)** is a gem of Witwatersrand geology. Starting at the base of the waterfall, the trail follows a roughly circular route that takes in major geological features and marker beds of the south-dipping, lowermost formations of the West Rand Group (see p. 44), including the Orange Grove quartzite and Parktown shales, and returns via outcrops of 3 500 million-year-old talc schist of the underlying greenstone formation. There are panoramic views of the entire northern side of the Witwatersrand, as far as the Magaliesburg, and across the Johannesburg Dome.

Geological Rock Garden

Some 20 ultra-large rock specimens from all over the region have been brought to the Garden **(geosite 15B, map 1)** for display. These are laid out in a landscaped area of the Garden in order of geological time, starting with ancient Basement granites and greenstones, moving upwards through time to end with specimens from the Karoo, and even younger cave breccia from the nearby Cradle of Humankind. All specimens are well annotated on site and a more detailed booklet on the collection is available. This is an excellent geological learning experience.

Numerous large rock specimens from the region, laid out in order of geological age, are on display in the Walter Sisulu National Botanical Garden, and provide visitors with an excellent illustration of a variety of important rock types.

Vredefort Dome, around Parys

The Vredefort Dome marks one of the most celebrated meteorite impact sites in the world and has recently been declared a World Heritage Site. At 300 km across, it's one of the biggest impact sites in the world (orders of magnitude bigger than Tswaing), but because it is so big and so old, it has, to a large extent, been levelled off by erosion. It therefore does not have the obvious appearance of a crater, and was only recognised as such after considerable scientific investigation. To get there, take the N1 south of Johannesburg and head for Kroonstad; after about 90 km of typical Highveld country you cross the Vaal River and enter the Free State. On your right-hand side you will begin to see a range of hills in the distance. Exit the N1 at the next off-ramp and head west on the R59 to Parys. You are now driving on the Vredefort Dome, the oldest known meteorite impact structure on Earth.

It has the villages of Parys and Vredefort near its centre and, to the south, is covered by much younger, flat-lying Karoo sediments. But what you see today is only the central remnant of an originally much larger structure that has been eroded away over the last two billion years.

In simple terms, the Vredefort structure consists of a complex core zone of ancient granite, some 50 km across, that forms flattish, rolling country. On buildings around Parys you will see attractive polished blocks of this stone, and some of the quarries that have produced this material are still evident. If you proceed as far as Vredefort, just before the Viljoenskroon turn-off, look out on your right-hand side for a small, bald, reddish hill made up of colourful streaky granite, which is worth a walk around. Access needs to be gained from the local landowners

To have a look at the surrounding ring-like 'collar zone' made of steeply dipping sedimentary and volcanic formations of the Witwatersrand and Ventersdorp Supergroups, cross the Vaal River in Parys on the Potchefstroom road (R53) and then take the Venterskroon turn-off to the left. But before you

This bare, dome-shaped hill just north of Vredefort village provides a good look at the typical granite-gneiss of the Basement. From the top, fairly close to the original meteorite impact site, there are excellent views of the surrounding countryside.

ABOVE & INSET: *Leeuwkop Quarry northwest of Parys, located within the so-called Parys Granite, shows magnificent exposures of these enigmatic rocks (the darker rocks containing large rounded clasts), the result of the catastrophic impact of the immense meteorite two billion years ago.*

go on, it is worth trying to get access (with the permission of the landowners) to a large quarry located on an isolated hill called Leeuwkop; here you will see remarkable, gigantic granite breccias and an unusual dark, glassy rock called pseudotachylite filling the space between the blocks. The latter was formed by the almost instantaneous melting of the granite with the impact of the meteorite.

Towards Venterskroon, the rugged, bush-covered hills through which you drive are made of the same Witwatersrand shales and quartzites seen in Johannesburg, more than 100 km away. This tells you two things: firstly, that the Witwatersrand Formations extend far beyond the basin edge at Johannesburg or Klerksdorp; and secondly, that an extraordinarily powerful geological event must have brought the sediments of the Witwatersrand Basin up to the surface – they should lie some kilometres below the surface, buried by younger formations.

It is now accepted that, around 2 020 million years ago, an extremely large meteorite, probably 10 to 15 km across, impacted into the Earth near today's Vredefort village. The force of this impact penetrated deep into the Earth's crust, tens of kilometres, completely destroying the original meteorite, and causing strong rebound of the deeper portion of the crust. Only the central, now uplifted portion of the structure is exposed at the surface today. The Vredefort structure, recently declared a World Heritage Site, contains numerous sites showing evidence of enormous deformation and melting of the rock, providing unequivocal evidence of its unique and catastrophic extraterrestrial origin.

2 Greater Cape Town and environs

GEOLOGICAL OVERVIEW

Most of the lower slopes around the Cape Peninsula are shaped from either granite of the Cape Suite or the formations the granite magma was intruded into, which are folded and metamorphosed sedimentary rocks of the Malmesbury Group. These are the most ancient rocks you'll see here, and form the basement of this region. For about 20 million years after the granite intrusion (some 540 million years ago), the high 'Malmesbury' mountains and granites were gradually reduced by erosion to an almost flat surface, before the next cycle of sedimentation began. Then, slowly, meandering rivers dropped their load of sand in deltas and along the beaches of a shoreline very different from what we see today.

The formation of the Cape Supergroup had begun. For the most part subsidence of the basin kept pace with the supply of sediment and the environment was one of long-lived stability. Around 250 million years ago – and about 50 million years after the Cape sedimentation had ended – great welts of crust were seized by convulsions as the Cape Fold Belt was born. But like the peaceful eye in the hurricane, a small area around Cape Town was spared and the magnificent folds seen north and east of the Peninsula are missing in the centre. The new generation of fold mountains shed their detritus into the Karoo basin to the north for 70 million years, until crustal stretching began and vast tracts of Gondwana were covered by the floods of Drakensberg basalt that surged up the tensional fissures. On went the stretching, and Gondwana fragmented, as first the proto-Indian Ocean opened up and then the proto-Atlantic Ocean, 125 million years ago. New rivers joined primeval ancestors to breach coastlines never seen before; new base levels were formed, and a landscape that would be moulded to the shapes we know.

OPPOSITE: *The clearly bedded Table Mountain sandstone in the slopes above Simon's Town forms a remarkable contrast with the massive granite on the beach at Froggy Pond.*
LEFT: *At the same locality, a fine-grained dolerite dyke – even younger than the sandstone – cuts the granite.*

Places of geological interest within the Cape Peninsula

The best way to see the rich panorama of geology that Cape Town offers is by making a tour of the Peninsula. We suggest you follow a clockwise route, approaching Muizenberg from the north, and from there heading towards Cape Point. But first you need to visit Table Mountain, the iconic symbol of Cape Town, arguably South Africa's most visited geological site, and a declared World Heritage Site. (The mountain's geological evolution is summarised on the opposite page.)

In Muizenberg, where the road gets down close to the beach, here and there you will see scattered outcrops breaking through the beach sand; this is the same Peninsula Formation sandstone that makes up the bastion of Table Mountain (**geosite 1, map 2**). It persists until near Simon's Town, where you might notice that the beach rock is reminiscent of the beach outcrops at Clifton or Sea

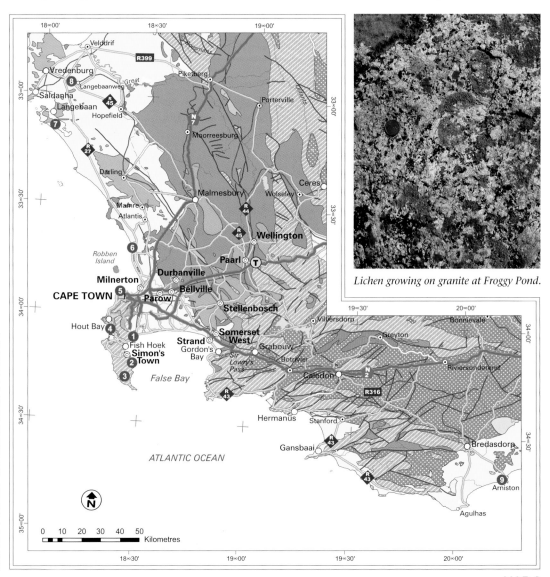

Lichen growing on granite at Froggy Pond.

SEE KEY FOR MAP ON INSIDE BACK COVER FLAP

MAP 2

How Table Mountain came to be

Table Mountain and its attendant range form an excellent example of a residual mountain. Four major formations are involved: the earliest are steeply dipping dark grey slate and sandstone of the Malmesbury Group that underlie much of Cape Town's city centre. Coarse-grained Cape Granite that intruded these rocks around 540 million years ago is seen as bare, rounded outcrops below Lion's Head and on many beaches. The horizontal overlying Table Mountain Group consists of about 50 m of reddish sandstone and shale of the Graafwater Formation, followed by a 500 m-thick sequence of light grey sandstone of the Peninsula Formation, which make up the higher mountains and major cliff faces of Table Mountain and extend as far south as Cape Point. Now connected to the mainland, 25 million years ago these mountains existed as an island.

Unlike the flat-lying sediments on Table Mountain, 'massive', crystalline rocks such as the Cape Granite require long-term planation to be flattened. The flat rock surface seen on the skyline above was bevelled by wave action during a prolonged period of sea-level stillstand in the geological past, and marks that level.

Point (see p. 67–8). These outcrops are all granite of the Cape Suite which, to a large extent, makes up the floor on which the sandstone rests. What has happened is that tectonism over the geological history of the Peninsula – both faults and some folding – has disturbed the base of the sedimentary package so that in the St James stretch of the coast it is below sea level, at Simon's Town, above.

Froggy Pond, just south of Simon's Town, is a good place to stop and look at the granite **(geosite 2, map 2)**. Look for the line of loose blocks of rock perched on the rounded slabs. To the south of this, towards Cape Point, the granite is crowded with xenoliths, inclusions of material that are clearly not granite. They consist of the sedimentary Malmesbury Group into which the molten granite magma was intruded as it surged upwards from the high-pressure, deep zone of the crust where granite is generated. Note the twinned crystals of feldspar, some centimetres across. These were the first crystals to form in the cooling magma and, because the granite intruded at depth and cooled very slowly, they had time to grow and grow. If you walk about, you'll find dolerite dykes cutting through the granite, also intrusive, but very different from granite. The difference is two-fold: (a) the dolerite is dark mainly because it is mafic, whereas granite is acid, and (b) the dolerite is fine-grained, mainly because the dyke is so thin (see p. 14).

As you leave Simon's Town you will notice granite boulders or rounded blocks quite high up the slope; and as you leave the coast and climb towards the crest of the Peninsula, you will see weathered granite in road cuttings. Further on towards Cape Point, stop where the road leaves the coast to cut westwards, about a kilometre before you reach the entrance gate of the Cape Point Reserve **(geosite 3, map 2)**. Look down to the beach, where you will see, nestled in the cove, a cluster of houses and boats at Smitswinkelbaai. You will also see that on the south side of the cove, the rocks are sandstone again, as they were at Muizenberg. Between the granite you have been crossing as you climb above sea level and the sandstone, there is a sedimentary contact, which is visible in the cutting north of the road as it swings inland. It is weathered and not as clear as the sharp contact you can see on Chapman's Peak Drive, but there's no doubt it is the contact. Standing at that cutting, you're 100 m above sea level, with the basal sandstone at eye level; yet way down on the other side of Smitswinkelbaai cove are sandstones with waves crashing onto them, their basal contact with the granite somewhere below the water. That is because between where you are and the other side of the cove is a fault, with the downthrown side to the south. And if you were to clamber down to Smitswinkelbaai and walk along the beach, you would walk over the faulted contact between granite and sediment.

The deep weathering of the granite you see in road cuttings as you climb this slope is not characteristic of the present climate. Such intense kaolinisation of granite confirms a period of intense weathering towards the end of the Cretaceous Period, when the climate here was 'humid-tropical'; more like, say, Rio de Janeiro today. Much later, within the last two million years, massive icing over of the poles during glacial periods lowered sea levels by as much as 140 m. Not only was the whole planet colder, but the Cape coastline – like all coastlines – was far seaward from its present position. This meant the moderating effect of the sea on atmospheric temperature was lost and mechanical weathering was assisted by frost action to promote pronounced break-up of the sheer quartzite slopes above the granite. Rockfalls then would have been a regular occurrence, not the rare and noteworthy phenomena they are today, and most of the blocks of quartzite strewn over the slopes, some enormous, would have crashed down the mountains during those times.

The Serina kaolin deposit exemplifies the deep weathering that characterised more humid conditions in the geological past.

The next recommended geological stop is just north of Witsand Bay on the west coast of the Peninsula, where there are fine exposures of cross-bedded Peninsula Formation quartzite, which tell of their deposition in a periodically ocean-flooded deltaic environment, rather than offshore, as was previously thought.

Before the relatively recent urban development of Hout Bay beach, sand was blown high up – and over – the hills behind the bay by the prevailing south to south-easterly wind.

Carrying on through Kommetjie towards the low neck across the Peninsula brings you to the intersection of Kommetjie Road with Ou Kaapseweg, where you are close to the original Serina Kaolin Mine. The original working is closed down; kaolin is still processed and packed on the property, but it is now piped from a newer mine (see p. 66) towards the southern end of Chapman's Peak Drive. The product is high-quality white kaolin, resulting from deeply weathered granite and is used in the making of crockery and in the manufacture of glossy paper.

The route northwards along the western side of the Peninsula takes you through Noordhoek and onto the recently reconstructed Chapman's Peak Drive toll road. There can be few other routes in South Africa where you drive so close to a major unconformity for several kilometres as you do here (see picture, p. 3). The Cape Granite is, for the most part, below the road; above it are the cross-bedded pale quartzites and thinly bedded maroon and red-brown mudstones of the basal member of the Table Mountain Group, called the Graafwater Formation. These sediments are interpreted to have been deposited in a fluvial environment, at the point where a river must have splayed out into a delta just before entering the sea. Several deep gorges cutting back into the near-vertical coastal slope mark faults, which also show themselves in displacing the line of the granite-sediment contact quite noticeably.

Hout Bay was once known for its manganese mine, which closed in 1911. Manganese oxides occur as thin, vein-like deposits in zones of fracturing in Table Mountain sandstone. Ore was exported by sea from a local jetty, the concrete pillars of which still exist near the Flora Bay Resort. Another feature of geological interest in Hout Bay is the sand blown off the wide beaches **(geosite 4, map 2)**. The old dunes can still be seen on the slopes northwest of the bay, but short-sighted human intervention has stopped the natural movement of sand from the bay, over the neck and on-to beaches to the north, as far, possibly, as Clifton. Unless remedial action is taken, and their supply of essential sand restored, these beaches face the prospect of becoming rockier and rockier.

The last stop on this lightning tour is at Sea Point, where a celebrated geological contact can be seen **(geosite 5, map 2)**. Stop at the parking area off Beach Road south of the President Hotel and get down onto the beach (see text box, p. 68). Two very drastically different rock types are present at this locality – the dark, banded Malmesbury sediments and coarsely crystalline, pink Cape Granite, which intruded them. The relationship between the two rock types illustrates the process of slow granite intrusion into preheated sediments deep in the Earth's crust.

Darwin's genius, or was it Captain Basil Hall's?

Historically, geologists questioned the origin of granite: did it come up from the depths or was it formed in situ as a precipitate from sea water? The debate was raging at the time Charles Darwin was on his travels, and he decided to visit an outcrop at the Cape of Good Hope that might help resolve it.

The outcrop was brought to his attention by comments in a paper read to the Royal Society in 1813, based on observations made by Royal Navy captain Basil Hall. After calling at the Cape, Hall had written: 'I came, after a short ascent, to a space where many yards of the rock were laid perfectly bare, and I found myself walking on vertical Schistus, or on what might be called Killas.

This rock was in beds highly inclined, and stretching from east to west, which is nearly the direction of the mountain ... On looking forward a little higher up I saw another portion of rock that was also laid bare, and which appeared to be Granite. I had now no doubt of reaching in a few minutes the precise junction of the two rocks, and I ventured to predict ... that we should immediately see veins from the main body of the granite, penetrating into the rock on which we were now standing. In this I was not deceived; the contact was the finest thing of the kind I ever saw ...'

A fragment of metamorphosed Malmesbury sediment within coarsely crystalline Cape Granite at the Sea Point contact.

More than 30 years later, Darwin walked over the same contact. After careful scrutiny, he found himself in agreement with Hall's interpretation of granite intruded into the fragmenting 'roof' of schist, with fragments and slivers of the latter ripped off, and 'floating' in the granite. To Darwin, this interpretation was infinitely more plausible than the alternative – then still popular – notion of the granite formed by conversion of the schist. Look at the evidence and see what you think.

Beyond the Cape Peninsula

Like the Peninsula itself, the geosites beyond the fringes of Greater Cape Town lend themselves to being viewed by pursuing continuous routes. Again, these happen to stick close to the coast: in this case we've chosen to detail the West Coast first.

North of Cape Town

The R27 takes you through Milnerton, Bloubergstrand and Melkbosstrand, and then into the open countryside. Mostly you will be within 10 km of the beach, with farms to the east of you and the mountain ranges more and more distant as you travel northwards.

You drive past a complex of isolated buildings and low cooling towers soon after leaving Cape Town, the convergence of power lines leaving no doubt as to the nature of the industry **(geosite 6, map 2)**. This is Koeberg, South Africa's only nuclear power station. The facility is not generally open to the public, but their Visitors' Centre, open during normal office hours, is worth a visit. In addition to the 3 000-ha nature reserve, with marked hikes across it, and where several species of antelope and small predators may be seen, sterling work is being done in rehabilitating strandveld and dune veld.

The nuclear industry in SA

Koeberg is the most overt reminder of South Africa's status as a global player in nuclear technology. South Africa's role in the industry was sparked by the 'Manhattan Project', the development of the nuclear bomb during the course of the 2nd World War. All potential sources of the critical raw material, uranium, were investigated by the Allies, and with South Africa's Jan Smuts a key figure in the war arena, and several known occurrences of uranium in South Africa, eyes turned to this country, and old geology reports were dusted off.

Amherst University's Professor George Bain visited the Witwatersrand gold mines in 1941 and collected, among many others, a sample of the so-called Kimberley Reef, which was shipped to the USA for metallurgical testwork, and yielded positive results. The Witwatersrand mines had, for decades, been mining uranium as well as gold.

After the war, nuclear power became an attractive option for the industrialised nations, and nuclear fuel was needed. Pilot plants extracting uranium from gold ore were soon in place on a number of Witwatersrand mines. In September 1952 West Rand Consolidated Mine at Krugersdorp opened the world's first plant to produce uranium commercially. Others followed, and for a time South Africa became a leading global uranium producer.

With vast reserves of high-grade coal on the Highveld, close to the mining and industrial hub of the country, and coal-burning power stations a familiar part of the landscape, there was no urgency for nuclear power generation in South Africa. Nevertheless, a strategic nuclear research facility was established at Pelindaba, close to Pretoria, to investigate the feasibility of nuclear power as a clean, long-term alternative to coal. Bearing in mind the distance to the power-generating regions, a decision followed to build Koeberg Nuclear Power Station in the Western Cape, and this became operational in 1975. From its clandestine beginnings during the dark years of war, nuclear technology had come of age in South Africa.

A view of the Koeberg Power Station on the West Coast, looking south towards iconic Table Mountain.

In very general terms, the countryside you find yourself in once you've left Cape Town is low and rolling, with hilly farmlands to the east of the road and renosterveld-covered sand to the west. The sand flats extend east of the road around the Mamre-Atlantis turn-off, with an uncovered dune field catching your eye near Mamre. This is wind-blown sand from the Atlantic beaches, mostly quite recently stabilised by vegetation.

Outcrops of rock are rare, though granite can be seen in road cuttings and in the typical low, rounded outcrops on both sides of the road north of the Yzerfontein turn-off as you approach Langebaan. There are also pronounced hills on the spit of land between the Langebaan lagoon and the ocean, which are visible from the road.

South of Saldanha Bay, in the Postberg Nature Reserve at Kraalbaai, a stop to see the 'Preekstoel' or Pulpit Rock is worthwhile (geosite 7, map 2). Park your car at the well-marked spot and walk down to the beach and along it for 100 m. You will find the Preekstoel, a 4-m-high outcrop that has become separated by wave erosion from the main line of the broken rock wall that forms the beachhead. Together with other parts of the rocky beachhead behind it, this is as fine an example as you will find of dune cross-bedding. The soft sandstone that makes up these exposures is very young, wind-deposited dune rock or aeolianite, consisting predominantly of shell fragments, with some quartz sand. It was consolidated, or lithified, probably about 100 000 years ago from sand blown in during the last glacial lowering of the sea level, when vast tracts of unvegetated sand lay exposed on the emerging sea floor. The steeper-lying beds, formed on the lee side of the dune, show that the wind was southerly at that time. Thirty kilometres north of here, at Langebaanweg, lies a spot more visited by palaeontologists – scientists who study fossils generally and the story they tell, as opposed to palaeoanthropologists, whose interest is in the bones of earliest man and his forebears – than any other in South Africa (geosite 8, map 2). And were it not for the fact that the sands in this locality

The footprints of Eve

Not far from the Preekstoel and in dune rocks identical in age and genesis, two footprints were found by Dave Roberts of the Council for Geoscience in 1995. Immortalised in stone, these footprints quickly found their way into the pages of National Geographic. Tracks in rock are rare enough: what made this one unique was that it was of Homo sapiens; not its antiquity, but its youth.

The rock bearing the prints – thought to be a woman's because of their small size – was dated at 117 000 years old, corresponding with the Last Interglacial Period. It is accepted by palaeoanthropologists that, by this time, hominid evolution had reached the point where emerging man was anatomically modern, and perhaps only slightly less sophisticated than he is today. He was probably capable of strategic thinking; of rationalising, recalling specific memories and planning. In this he was what might seem like a small step – but was in fact a giant leap – ahead of his predecessors, whose behaviour was more animal than human.

It was concluded that the Langebaan footsteps were made by a small female, crossing diagonally over a wet dune. According to the widely accepted 'out of Africa' theory, modern humans evolved in Africa and then colonised Eurasia – the reason the track-maker was whimsically nicknamed 'Eve'. As the footprints were threatened by both natural forces of rapid erosion, and by immediate destruction by humans, it was reluctantly decided to remove part of the sandstone block containing the footprints in late 1999. They are now archived in the Iziko Museum, Cape Town. A perfect replica is on view at the historic farmhouse at Geelbek, West Coast National Park.

The huge wealth of fossil bones has enabled palaeontologists to reconstruct the environment at Langebaanweg as it must have been around five million years ago.

are rich enough in phosphate to have been profitably worked, the fossils might have lain buried to this day. In 1958, soon after small-scale mining had started here, a mine employee, Mr Brown, showed some fossils he had collected in the shallow pit, including an elephant's tooth and the ankle bone of a short-necked giraffe, to three visiting palaeontologists. There was a problem, though: the discoveries were from within the area being mined, and the scientists had to wait patiently. It was only in 1965, when the scale of mining was drastically increased, that the first hint was given of the richness of the treasure being opened up. A joint venture was constituted between mine owners, CHEMFOS, and the South African Museum in Cape Town, to develop this priceless resource sensitively.

Forty years later, the phosphate is mined out and palaeontologists rule. Mine offices have been converted to a display centre and the fossil-rich parts of the pits cordoned off and marked. A visit to the West Coast Fossil Park at Langebaanweg (tel. 022 766-1606) is an unforgettable experience. There are regular tours by a leading palaeontologist from the South African Museum: whether you go on one of these or visit the display centre on your own, it's well worth the trip from Cape Town.

Allow yourself to be transported back five million years. In this spot you might have seen lion-sized sabre-tooth cats, elephants, rhinoceros, any of three types of giraffids or hyaenas. The 'big six' would have included bears weighing three-quarters of a ton, wolverines and musk oxen, and you would have seen a host of smaller mammals too. Tall savannah and riverine forest would have provided shelter and herbivore food for this richly diverse collection. On the beaches two kinds of penguins jostled between the seals; ostriches roamed the plains, and flocks of parrots shrieked through the woodland canopy.

Langebaanweg is described as 'one of the most prolific sources of late Tertiary vertebrate fossils in the world'. Geological investigation on a wider scale has provided details on sea-level movements over the past 24 million years, which has enabled us to understand how it was all possible, and fit Langebaanweg into its true context.

A key event in the story of a changing environment was the separation – about 15 million years ago, in the Miocene – of Antarctica from the rest of Gondwana. It headed towards the South Pole, leaving behind the warm ocean currents of the tropics and the warm winds. For the first time, Antarctica felt the full effects of being a polar continent, and a massive icing-up began. Around the world, sea levels and temperatures dropped as the icecap grew. The Mediterranean became a closed inland sea and extensive salt deposits formed as evaporation shrank the water surface. Because low sea levels lead to accelerated erosion, the continental environment is one of non-deposition and very little record is left of events.

As the Antarctic ice began to melt, around five million years ago, sea levels rose, to peak at Langebaan at just over 60 m above present sea level. Subsequent regressions, or lowering of sea levels, have seen erosion remove most of what was deposited, but luckily some pockets have survived. And it is those remains that have given us the West Coast phosphate deposits and fossil beds.

As we now know, sea levels are in a constant state of long-term flux. But not once since those steamy days five million years ago have there been beaches higher than 20 m above present sea level, and the oscillations seem to get smaller and smaller. It will be a long time before a range of large and ferocious creatures will again be seen in their natural environment a few hours from Cape Town.

East of Cape Town

Along the coast east of Cape Town lie resorts that grow steadily in number and in popularity, and residents of – as well as visitors to – Cape Town will probably visit Arniston sooner or later. The way most people get there is along the N2 to Caledon, and then along the R316, via Bredasdorp. But a very scenic coastal alternative does exist via the R44, in part known as Clarence Drive, from Gordon's Bay to Betty's Bay and Hermanus. This route via the Kogelberg Biosphere Reserve reveals spectacular exposures of the folded Table Mountain Group. It will also take you past impressive, almost overhanging sandstone peaks called Klein Hangklip and Hangklip.

The beautiful exposures of folded Bokkeveld shales with Liesegang banding that this formation shows in the southern Cape are described, with an illustration, in the section on the N2 (see p. 130). And practically anywhere along the Arniston beaches you are within sight of examples of Tertiary dune rock as good as you'll see anywhere.

Arniston is also known as Waenhuiskrans **(geosite 9, map 2)**. The *waenhuis*, or wagon-house, refers to the big cave southwest of the village. With an oval-shaped entrance onto the sea and a small portal onto the beach to the northeast of the cave – just big enough to crawl through at low tide – the cave is carved from the limestone cliffs that form the rocky coast around here. These cross-bedded aeolianites are part of the Waenhuiskrans Formation of the Bredasdorp Group, formed from dunes blown into place during a glacial regression of sea level in the Late Pleistocene.

But the most exotic thing about Arniston – even if it is the dullest-looking – is the pumice you'll find on the beach if you look carefully. Now pumice, more usually seen in the bathroom, is nothing more than solidified volcanic froth. To track the history of these drab stones we need to travel 7 000 km east of Arniston, and more than 100 years back in history.

At 12 noon on 28 August 1883, a telegram reached Singapore from Batavia, the capital of the Dutch East Indies, that read as follows: 'Where once Mount Krakatoa stood the sea now plays.' Two-thirds of a volcanic cone measuring 9 km by 5 km at sea level had disappeared, collapsed into the caldera formed as the volcano blew its top. Rafts of floating pumice, some big enough to take the weight of a grown man, crossed the entire width of the Indian Ocean in 10 months. And so it was that chunks of volcanic pumice found their way onto beaches of east and southern Africa, select beaches – such as Arniston – favoured by the whims of giant ocean currents as they eddied around coastal irregularities.

We are reminded of the 1883 explosion of Mount Krakatoa (in Indonesia) by the small fragments of pumice on Arniston beach, products of that historical event.

With the explosion of Krakatoa on 27 August, ash fell on Singapore 840 km to the north and on Cocos Island 1 155 km to the southwest, and darkness covered the Sunda Straits, where Krakatoa had stood, from 10 o'clock that morning to dawn the next day. Waves 40 m high hurled ashore coral blocks weighing up to 600 tons and obliterated 165 coastal villages, claiming the lives of over 36 000 people. Fine ash and aerosol reached heights of 50 km into the stratosphere, circling the equator in 13 days. Global temperatures were lowered by as much as half a degree Celsius in the year after the eruption, with normal temperatures returning only five years later.

What causes lava to froth and explode out of its volcano, as it did at Krakatoa? All lava contains quantities of water vapour and other gases, all held in solution. Mostly it stays in solution, only bubbling out when the lava is extruded at the surface, when it forms the vesicles, or bubbles, that are quite common in volcanic rocks other than pumice.

But pumice is no ordinary volcanic rock, any more than champagne is an ordinary wine. It's a question of how much gas there is, and under what sort of pressure. Think of it: a bottle of champagne shows few bubbles until the cork is pulled. Similarly, when freakishly sudden changes in the pressure balance in the Earth's crust bring lava up to the surface much more quickly than usual, it froths, solidifying as pumice.

The instability of this part of the Earth's crust is highlighted by the fact that the 2004 tsunami was generated in the same subduction system as Krakatoa.

3 Greater Durban and environs

GEOLOGICAL OVERVIEW

The beaches of Durban offer incomparable examples of processes of coastal geology. The hard sandstone with shells of oysters indistinguishable from those found today is strongly reminiscent – if you take away the shells – of rocks half a billion years old just 20 km away, and tells of sedimentary processes as old as time and still active today. Up on the Berea, by contrast, dune sandstone that's older than the beach rocks has been broken down by the subtropical coastal climate to vivid red sand, which has lost all traces of its original identity. And, if sweltering summers seem to have been part of the Durban year for ever, have a look at a beautiful glaciated pavement in

Three 'sets' of cross-beds, inclined to the horizontal and truncated above and below, tell of discrete sedimentary events in the deposition of the Ecca sandstone, about 300 million years ago.
INSET: At least six sets of cross-beds tell a similar story, except that these ones formed only about 5 000 years ago.

Westville, where giant ice sheets ground the underlying rock surface smooth 280 million years ago, at a time when South Africa straddled the South Pole. High quarry faces of glacial Dwyka tillite can be seen across Durban, a sedimentary rock profoundly different from sandstones both older and younger. Durban is a geological experience of contrasts.

The route we take you on through Greater Durban starts at the beginning (inland), in the oldest rocks, and works progressively upwards to very young sediments.

The Basement: granites and gneisses

If you've ever run – or even watched – a Comrades Marathon (along the R103, which in the built-up area is called the M13), you have seen, if not noticed, the oldest rocks in these parts. They are the Basement gneisses and granites, known here as the Natal Metamorphic Province. There are a couple of good outcrops of relatively fresh, megacrystic biotite granite in road cuttings as you approach the village of Drummond, set in more weathered rock that clearly shows its coarse crystallinity despite its high degree of decomposition (**geosite 1, map 3**). The outcrops are of biotite granite, with a striking preponderance of pale grey plagioclase feldspar, with crystals up to 5 cm across, minor quartz and some black biotite. Even in the well-weathered exposures in the road cuttings, the coarse granularity of this granite is a striking feature.

These are the floor rocks across which – 490 million years ago – the rivers flowed that accumulated the pebbles, sand, and (less commonly) the mud that would make the Natal Group. The process continued until, at its maximum development, several hundred metres of sandstone and interbedded mudstone had built up.

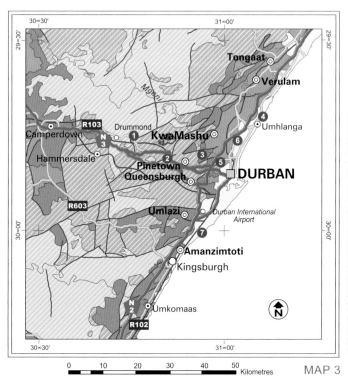

SEE KEY FOR MAP ON INSIDE BACK COVER FLAP

MAP 3

The sandstones of the Natal Group

Heading back to Durban, stay on the Old Main Road (the M13), and you'll find yourself going down Field's Hill immediately after leaving Kloof. As you wind down the slope, you'll see the high, vertical cuttings to your right, which halfway down have generous showings of bare rock (**geosite 2, map 3**). There's a place to pull your car off the road if you should want a more leisurely look than driving in traffic allows, and you can see one particularly fine example of cross-bedding, as well as the range of pinks and mauves and pale greys the sandstones come in. Interestingly, these sandstones are of similar age to the Table Mountain sandstones of the Cape Supergroup, but were deposited on a stable shelf.

A range of palaeo-environments: the Karoo Supergroup

When the deposition of sediments in the Natal Basin had finally run its course, a period of erosion followed. At the same time, Gondwana was inching southwards into icy polar climes, and continental-scale glaciation followed. As they ground over the slopes, the vast sheets of ice ripped material off the floor beneath them, from fine clay to big blocks. The fine material at the base of the ice sheet polished the surface it moved over, and the coarser, harder fragments scoured into it. Find your way to the Westville Campus of the University of KwaZulu-Natal, as you approach Durban, and ask at the Information Centre where the glaciated pavement is **(geosite 3, map 3)**. Recognised for its geological significance, this natural pavement, which was exposed during excavation of the site at an early stage of construction, has been preserved, and a plaque erected that briefly describes what is to be seen. The tillite itself, moraine left behind as the ice at the base of the massive glaciers melted, can be seen in a big quarry just outside the university gates, to your right as you leave, where the mixture of shapes, sizes and rock types can be seen. By far the bulk of material is the fine 'glacial flour'; but the coarser fragments caught up in it catch your eye, and are what give the rock's glacial origins away. Equally characteristic is the lack of any sorting according to size. (We call an unlayered rock like this 'massive', whether there's a huge bulk of it or not.) The direction of scratch marks, as well as the identity of the fragments lifted off the surface in one part of the topography and dropped in another, tell the direction of travel of the glaciers and where they had picked up their load. Alex du Toit and his co-workers used this information as one of the key arguments in putting the case for Continental Drift.

After many millions of years at the pole, Gondwana moved northwards again; the glacial times were forgotten, and the fresh-water Karoo sea formed in central-west Gondwana. Rivers flowed into the basin from all directions, transporting their sediment. In the north, before it got to the sea, the sand and mud settled out in huge deltas criss-crossed by networks of rivers. The deltas were covered with dense stands of temperate forests. If you travel to Salt Rock you can see thin coal seams in the Karoo sandstone down at the beach. But you don't have to go that far to see the sandstone formed in these times in the middle part of the Ecca Group. If you find your way to the beach

Formed more than 400 million years ago, these Natal Group sandstones seen in the cutting on
Field's Hill show the oldest – but not the only – cross-bedding to be seen around Durban.

The Valley of a Thousand Hills: a legacy of instability

The R103 around Drummond takes you along the edge of one of the country's major landscape divides. Up here you are on the edge of the gently rolling hills of the old Natal; to the north, in old KwaZulu, and stretching away into the hazy horizon from the sandstone cliffs close by, is the deeply incised Valley of a Thousand Hills, cut by the Mgeni River and its tributaries. The geology of these parts has shaped not only its geography, but its history too.

The landscape to the south of the scarp invites development, with its easy access and mild slopes: reminiscent of the soft, well-watered downs they had come from, it beckoned to the settlers of earlier centuries. The edging sandstone cliffs formed a barrier to the warlike Zulus, denizens of the aloe-studded, steep, dry, granite-gneiss slopes below, a world mysterious and reachable by only a select handful of colonials on a mission.

Beyond the Mgeni River basin are the Mvoti and the Thukela valley systems, the last being the biggest of all the KwaZulu-Natal basins. These river systems cut deep into the roots of ancient granite-gneiss of the Natal Metamorphic Province, and the country is wild, its inhabitant clans traditionally bellicose, divided as much by topography as by historical differences, or by the quest for land.

The granites and gneisses of the Valley of a Thousand Hills were formed around 1 000 million years ago during subduction (see fig. 3, p. 19) and collision along the southern edge of the Kaapvaal Craton far to the north. No sooner had the mountain chain – thousands of kilometres long, extending as far as today's Namaqualand – been formed, than its erosion began. On and on this went until the metamorphic belt had been eroded down to its deep roots, tightly folded in part. These are the gneisses and granites you will see wherever the cover has been stripped off in the KwaZulu-Natal coastal belt.

Half a billion years were to pass before the destructive forces gave way to a new phase of building. The Cambrian to Ordovician basin, formed over 450 million years ago, accumulated thick sediments that we see today in the Natal Group, those of coastal KwaZulu-Natal, mostly sandstones, forming along wide coastal plains criss-crossed by meandering rivers that drain highlands to the northeast.

Comprising mostly quartz sand, the sediments compacted and consolidated, and were bound together by silica cement. Quartz-rich sandstones were formed, almost impervious to the forces of weathering and erosion. They survived the landscape denudation that followed until the onset of the deposition of Karoo sediments. Then, for many tens of millions of years, they were shielded from erosion by the Karoo sediments that had been draped over them. The great Karoo event of sedimentation and volcanism came to an end, and continental drifting got under way. New rivers formed and the Karoo cover was stripped off, exposing the Natal Group sandstones once again. Slowly the Mgeni and other rivers, all of great antiquity, made inroads into the resistant sandstones. Once through this capping, the regular summer rainstorms that have battered the eastern part of the country for millions of years quickly cut down into the Precambrian basement, producing the scenery we see today. With time the valleys will deepen and, at their edge, the tendrils of the streams will continue to eat their inexorable way to the south, pushing the kranses back. In your life, though, and your great-grandchildren's, the change will be imperceptible.

just below the lighthouse at Umhlanga Rocks, you'll see excellent examples of conspicuously cross-bedded middle Ecca sandstone, varying from quite gritty to fine-grained, but still sandy **(geosite 4, map 3)**. Cross-bedding is again manifest, as in the Field's Hill sandstones, but here it formed 150 million years later.

The break-up of Gondwana

En route from Westville to Umhlanga Rocks, if you follow the N3 and then the N2 northwards, you'll cross over the Mgeni River just inland – and west – of an excellent example of a fault scarp. Look towards the ocean just before you cross the river, or as you cross it, and, in the middle distance, you'll see a steep slope of pale grey rock between the bush-covered high ground and the floodplain of the river **(geosite 5, map 3)**. This is one of the many faults that your map shows criss-crossing Durban and, in fact, the whole of the Natal coastal region. It's called the Springfield Fault and has dropped soft Ecca sediments north of the fault against the much older Natal Group sandstones. The Ecca shales have been more susceptible to weathering and erosion so that, over the geosites, the fault scarp has grown to an impressive height.

The faulting was related to the break-up of Gondwana some time after 180 million years ago, when some uncommon things were happening in these parts. Earlier researchers made much of

The glacial striae – or scratches – across the Natal Group sandstone 'pavement' on the University of KwaZulu-Natal's Westville campus: this spot is easily accessible and well worth visiting.

what they called the Natal or Lebombo Monocline, the formation of which was seen as a unique event in the shaping of South Africa. They proposed that, not long after the last lava had been erupted and the great event of Karoo sedimentation and volcanism had been brought to a close, the eastern part of northern South Africa had been gently folded down. Recent research, however, has shown that the process was more one of down-faulting than of monoclinal folding. Detailed geological and geophysical surveys have clarified the picture considerably. During the fragmentation of Gondwana, a small crustal plate dislodged itself from the east coast of Africa and set off on a long journey, first southwards, and then westwards, to finish up close to the southern tip of South America. The westward drift of the Falkland Plate from its original position in eastern Gondwana has caused the branch-faulting within the zone where this wrenching was taking place along the coast of KwaZulu-Natal, as well as the curved, drift-related sedimentary basins along the Cape south coast.

In and around Durban we see cross-bedded beach- and dune-rocks at the coast where they were formed. It brings to life the sedimentary structures seen in rocks 490 million years old when we see

An exposure in Malacca Road, Durban, that's a classic sedimentary unconformity, with dark Ecca shale below and the Quaternary Berea Formation above. Note the beautifully rounded clasts in the basal conglomerate of the younger sediments, and the pale lowest metre of the overlying dune sand, leached by ground water held up by the impermeable shale.

closely analogous forms in beds capped by a layer of oyster shells essentially the same as those we might leave on our plates today. The geology of Durban is a valuable bridge between process and product.

The best place to see the youngest cross-bedded sandstones is in a beautiful exposure not far south of Durban International Airport. On the way there from Umhlanga Rocks, you should stop and see the contact between the older basement and the young sediments on which a lot of Durban, including the Berea and the Bluff, is built. Branch off the N2 as you head from Umhlanga Rocks towards the centre onto North Coast Road and look for Malacca Road, which soon branches off to the left. Keep an eye on the slope up to your left as you get onto Malacca Road and, within about 200 m, you'll see the outcrop of basal conglomerate on the black, west-dipping Ecca shale behind the buildings next to the road (**geosite 6, map 3**). It is a beach conglomerate just older than the red decalcified dune sand that makes up the Berea Formation (formerly called the Berea Red Sand). This is an unconformity of the sort that geologists delight in, because it gives us a datum level from which to work. For the most part we find ourselves looking at an outcrop of rock formed at some indeterminate stage during a particular event. Sedimentary unconformities, on the other hand, tell us clearly we are at the beginning of a particular geological sequence. We can say this with confidence if the rock sequence below the postulated unconformity is tilted with respect to the overlying sediment, as in the Malacca Road example.

Let's review what was happening as shown by the rocks here. Gondwana break-up was under way. A new coastline had formed and the young Indian Ocean was starting to shape our continent. Wave-cut platforms developed along the rifted slopes.

Along these, accumulated beds of boulders were carried to the shore by young rivers. The sea level dropped and the waves crashed on new beaches below boulder beds now left high and dry, and onshore winds blew sand off the beaches and onto the conglomerate.

The dunes thus formed were mostly of quartz, feldspar and sea-shell fragments made of calcium carbonate. A climate dry enough for dunes to form was also conducive to the calcification of the dunes. Very slightly acidic rainwater dissolved some of the calcium carbonate off the shell fragments and used it to cement the clastic fragments until it was no longer a dune but a dune-rock or aeolianite. In a much later, much wetter climatic regime, the calcium carbonate cement was redissolved and permanently flushed from the system: decalcification was under way. During this later process, iron was released from certain minerals, and was redistributed as iron oxide through the rock, hence the strongly red colour.

It was an age-old process happening at a location as young as the process was ancient, and it will continue to operate as long as we can imagine. The sea level falls, pulling the beach with it, and rises, pushing the beach ahead of it. Along the beach, rivers make deltas and lagoons, longshore currents move the river loads deposited, onshore winds blow sand inland, on and on. It's a three-dimensional process of which we see, for the most part, only a single surface at any time, with most of the evidence buried and obscured from view. And, of course, as the sea level falls and new streams and rivers carry away material off the slopes, evidence is removed. So it's a fragmentary picture, making the unravelling of the recent geological history as much of a detective game as any scientific investigation.

Cross-bedded beach sandstone south of Mbokodweni River mouth immortalises the effect of water currents flowing in different directions.

Pleistocene Ice Ages lowered the sea level globally by up to 120 metres, so that all rivers cut their valleys accordingly in reaching for coastlines far seaward of those we know along the edge of the continental shelf. As levels rose, these valleys became 'drowned' and sediment soon filled them. Or, if there was not sufficient sediment being brought in, they became only partially silted up. Wave and wind action was under way continuously, accumulating sand along and behind the beach; and elongate spits were formed, breached only at narrow river mouths. In the case of the Mhlatuzana River, the quantity of sand, silt and clay was less than was required to fill the lagoon it had formed, which remained deep enough to offer the safe haven of Port Natal to later sailors seeking shelter from the stormy blast. Thus was formed South Africa's biggest harbour. The Bluff, which forms the main barrier between Durban Bay and the crashing Indian Ocean, was formed during a regression of sea level several million years ago, while the Point, now home to Durban's new tourism focus, is a much younger feature, formed as the last Ice Age waned between 18 000 and 6 000 years ago and the sea level rose from its much lower levels.

After the last Ice Age: the more things change …

… the more they stay the same. Let us show you what we mean by that, in this context. Find your way to the beach immediately south of the Mbokodweni River. To do this you'll have to go past the international airport and find Golf Course Road off Kingsway (the R102) at the northern end of Amanzimtoti. Follow Golf Course Road as far as you can, virtually onto the beach. A short walk southwards along the beach brings you to the outcrops, where you can see a truly wonderful example of a raised beach deposit (geosite 7, map 3).

As you look at it, cast your mind back to the sandstone in the cutting halfway down Field's Hill. Those sandstones were in the Natal Group, formed in the Ordovician nearly half a billion years ago. At a glance, this sandstone is not very different, is it?

How was the environment back in the Ordovician? There were shells in the tidal and sub-tidal sea water, and the first extremely primitive fishes had just made their appearance. On land there were neither plants nor animals of any kind. Imagine the desolation: not a speck of green, just rock, fresh and decomposing, grey and brown; away from the crashing surf, only the wind could break the silence. Compare it with the verdant bush covering the dune so close by now, teeming with insects, birds and small animals, and gulls shrieking as they wheel overhead. Through all the changes that evolution has wrought, the geological process has, to all intents and purposes, stayed the same. The cross-bedded sandstone in front of you is probably about 5 000 years old. Superficially it differs little from the Field's Hill beds that are not just 10 or 100 times older, but 100 000 times older. One formed before life had emerged from the sea, the other after the last Ice Age. Have a good look at those in front of you.

See the calcium carbonate-cemented beach sands, beautifully cross-bedded, the fossil crab burrows and beds of oyster shells. Note, as you look at the most inland part of the outcrop, the black layers of iron-rich heavy minerals: if you walk to the dune immediately north of the river, you'll see modern wind-blown sand conspicuously enriched in the same heavy minerals, in an area known as Umbogintwini. For a brief period in the 1950s, these sands were commercially exploited further south at Umgababa for their high titanium and zircon content, just as Richards Bay's dunes are mined today. Imagine: with a few extra metres of height and breadth added to the dunes, and a kilometre or two to their length, what might the southern gateway to Durban look like today? As it is, it's a monument to the immutability of geological process.

The black ilmenite in these sands south of the Mbokodweni River mouth might bring to mind the fact that, some 50 years ago, similar sediments south of Durban were seriously considered as a source of titanium.

4 N1: Johannesburg to Beitbridge

GEOLOGICAL OVERVIEW

Like the N1 route from Johannesburg to Cape Town, this route starts and ends in Precambrian Basement. That, though, is where the similarity ends. More than half the highway to Cape Town crosses a single geological unit, the Beaufort Group of the Karoo Supergroup. The northern N1, by contrast, crosses two Precambrian basins, the mighty Bushveld Complex and – lest we forget how widespread they are – outlying strata of the Karoo Basin, before getting back to Basement rocks south of Musina (formerly Messina).

You cross some of the flattest terrain in the country as you skirt the Springbok Flats; you encounter a range so rugged that men had to tunnel through it. You see granite and greenstone of the Kaapvaal Craton, metamorphic rocks of the Limpopo Mobile Belt and, at Mokopane (formerly Potgietersrus), dolomite of the Transvaal Supergroup, with the Makapan's caves and the vivid story they tell of our earliest prehistory. First and foremost, this part of the N1 is a Precambrian experience.

LEFT & ABOVE: *These pictures, taken 13 km south of Musina, show the relative ages of intrusions. A steeply dipping diabase dyke (above and far right of main picture, its approximate contact marked by a dashed line) cuts off, and so is younger than, the white, nearly horizontal quartz vein. The vein itself cuts the ancient gneiss, which makes up most of the main picture.*

85

MAP 4

Geology of the route

Johannesburg to the Nyl Toll Plaza

We've dealt briefly with the rocks of the Transvaal Supergroup in Chapter 1, and it's probably as well to revisit that chapter as you retrace your steps now. Northeast of Pretoria, at Derdepoort, you emerge from a cutting through thick quartzites of the Magaliesberg Formation, and ahead and to the west of the road is a row of low, hummocky koppies in the middle distance. These are built of gabbro of the Main Zone of the Bushveld Complex. The line of hills reaches the road at the Pumulani Toll Plaza, about half a kilometre north of where the new N4 comes in from the west. And that is as much of the basic rocks of the fabulous Bushveld Complex – or the main part of it, anyway – as you'll see for quite some time.

Before long you're on the open road, the concrete and the traffic a fast-dimming memory. There is a very handsome rock next to the road just over half a kilometre north of the Bridge Restaurant (**geosite 1, map 4**). Once you've seen a lot of granite, you'll appreciate that this Nebo Granite – part of the Acid Phase of the Bushveld Complex – is redder and more fine-grained than average.

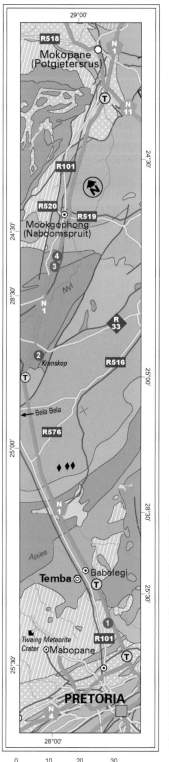

Acidity in rocks

*Igneous rocks with significant quartz in them are called **acid**; granite and felsite are good examples. Often, the word 'felsic' is used for these rocks. Those at the other end of the scale that are rich in iron and magnesium (and/or calcium) – like most of the rocks in the Bushveld Complex – such as norite and gabbro, are **mafic** and even **ultramafic**, such as pyroxenite. Speaking generally, those rocks that fall between these extremes are called **intermediate**, such as diorite and andesite, while – not nearly so common – those with no quartz but rich in sodium and potassium are said to be **alkaline**, for example syenite and trachyte. (For more on rock classification, see tables 1–3, pp. 14–17.)*

The outcrop runs on and there are others further on, but you might want to stop at the first cutting. To understand where this granite fits into the scheme of things, look at the text feature on the evolution of the Bushveld Complex (pp. 88, 89). As you go northwards, you'll notice the granite becomes more weathered, with occasional exposures showing a creamy colour, which is typical of well-weathered granite. Note that the countryside here is smoothly rolling, indicative of geomorphological maturity.

A few kilometres after the last granite outcrop, as you approach Hammanskraal and Temba, you might notice a dump and a couple of old smoke stacks off to the west side. This is an old refractory fire-clay working, long since abandoned. The published geological map shows several occurrences of fire clay here, formed from weathered shale of the Ecca Group of the Karoo Supergroup. So you have passed from Precambrian granite onto very much younger Karoo sediments. Regardless of what rocks one is on, hard old granite, or soft younger shale, it has all been planed off to an almost flat, featureless landscape – called the Springbok Flats.

As you get to roads branching off the N1 to Settlers and Codrington, about 80 km north of the Magaliesberg, note the first real hills since leaving Pretoria, ahead and coming in from the left. By now you have crossed progressively younger Karoo formations and are on basalts, the same rocks that cap the 'Roof of Africa', the Drakensberg. This accounts for the heavy, dark soil you may see in any open ploughed lands around here.

The hills as you approach Bela Bela (formerly Warmbaths) and its turn-off from the N1 are made up of lavas and sediments of the Rooiberg Group, lying at the top of the Transvaal Supergroup, though you won't get to see any of those rocks near the road. How, you might ask, since you're travelling over Karoo volcanics nearly two billion years younger than those ancient strata of the Rooiberg Group, can you be at the same level as, or slightly lower than them? The answer is that the younger Karoo formations have been down-faulted against the older rocks. The existence of deep faults is revealed by the numerous hot springs in the area, with hot ground water seeping up faults and emerging on the surface. As you go past Bela Bela, to the left in the shadow of the hills, note that the higher hills to the north of the town, which you will see to your left for a while, are sedimentary formations of the Waterberg Group. This is a somewhat younger basin, and quite distinct from the Rooiberg rocks that make up the southernmost range. Just north of the bridge where the Modimolle- (formerly Nylstroom) Marble Hall road passes over the N1, and the Kranskop Toll Plaza is situated, there are some good outcrops in a road cutting of mauve Waterberg quartzite that are worth stopping to look at.

Kranskop, just east of the road shortly after the Kranskop Toll Plaza, shows reddish-weathering sandstones and subordinate conglomerates of the Waterberg Group.

THE BUSHVELD COMPLEX:
IGNEOUS TREASURE HOUSE WITHOUT EQUAL

The Bushveld Complex of South Africa, best known for its intimately interrelated mafic intrusive bodies, is the most extensive, and by far the thickest, structure of its kind in the world.

Intrusive bodies are formed from liquid magma that was intruded into the rocks of the Earth's crust at some depth, allowing the magma to cool slowly. Certain minerals crystallise from the melt before others, while the temperature is still around 1 000°C. If they are significantly denser than the magma itself, these crystals will sink through it and settle near the bottom.

This means that thick mafic intrusive bodies are generally differentiated or layered. The heaviest minerals, such as olivine and pyroxene, and any sulphide minerals (usually of iron, nickel, copper and platinum-group elements), and oxide minerals (like magnetite and chromite) concentrate towards the base of each layer. Lighter minerals, such as feldspar and quartz, tend to form at the tops. This is a general trend observed in big mafic and ultramafic intrusive bodies around the world, and the Bushveld Complex is, as we have said, the largest and most dramatically layered of them all.

FIGURE 13

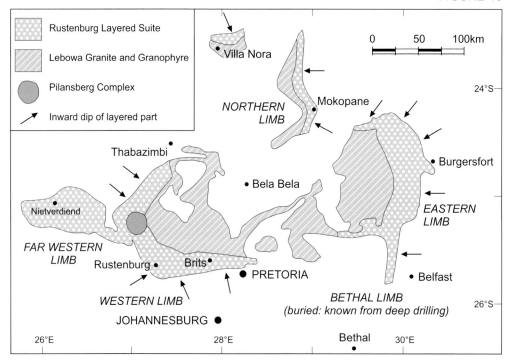

The Bushveld Complex extends over 440 km east-west, from Burgersfort to Nietverdiend; and for nearly 350 km north-south, from Villa Nora to Bethal. It is made up of five distinct limbs (or lobes) which comprise two very different but genetically related geological formations, namely the Rustenburg Layered Suite (Mafic Phase), and the Lebowa Granite and Granophyre (Acid Phase). It is not believed that the limbs are connected in depth. Much of the complex is covered by older or younger rocks.

From east to west, the complex measures about 440 km, and 350 km from north to south, though its roughly ring-shaped outcrop at the surface is anything but continuous, as the sketch (fig. 13, opposite) shows. The rocks intruded by the complex occur in the centre (called roof rocks) and around the outside of the complex (called floor rocks).

The Bushveld Complex comprises an Acid Phase, called the Lebowa Granite Suite, occurring towards the centre of the complex, and a Mafic Phase, called the Rustenburg Layered Suite. Though very different in many respects, the two parts are closely linked geologically and are close in age; and there is no doubt they are different phases of the same igneous intrusive event.

It has been proposed that, as the centre of the huge basin of Transvaal sediments sank into the granitic crust, a dome of hot, mantle-derived material (of mafic to ultramafic composition) was rising towards it, melting the crustal material as it rose. It pushed through the crust, producing conical fractures in the basin. The acid material, lying centrally over the middle of the rising dome, exploited the fractures towards the middle of the basin while the heavier, mantle-derived material was left to intrude up fractures around the side of the crustal melt and towards the edges of the basin. In other words, the portion that makes up the Layered Suite did not come up through a single, huge conduit and spread out when it was near the surface; it came out through separate feeders, tapping a single parent source. The Rooiberg lavas occurring at the top of the Pretoria Group sedimentary pile are currently interpreted as being derived from the crustal melt.

The Layered Suite, the source of an immense wealth of platinum, chrome and vanadium, comprises six quite distinct zones. The overall thickness of the suite may exceed 7 km.

The most spectacular of the six zones of the suite are the Lower Critical Zone and the Upper Critical Zone. The former contains the extraordinarily extensive, but thin, layers of chromitite, consisting largely of the mineral chromite, an oxide mainly of chrome and iron, and contains at least 60 per cent of the world's known chrome reserves. The Upper Critical Zone is the source of platinum, from both the narrow but famous Merensky Reef, and even richer Upper Group 2 (UG2) Chromitite Layer. These two 'reefs' between them mean that South Africa contributes about half of the world's platinum-group elements (platinum, palladium and four others that are chemically related) or PGE production and known reserves.

Interlayered black chromite seams and pale anorthosite in this world-famous locality at Dwarsrivier, near Steelpoort, vividly illustrate the phenomenon of magmatic differentiation, whereby markedly different minerals crystallise from the same magma under different conditions.

Not far north of the Kranskop Toll Plaza, you'll see why the toll is thus named: the lone inselberg, walled by kranses, is just to the right of the road ahead **(geosite 2, map 4)**. If you've got binoculars with you, it's worth stopping and training them on the bare cliffs. You should pick out at least one conspicuous bed of conglomerate: note the pink to mauve-brown colour of the sediments, telling of considerable iron pigmentation and deposition in an oxidising atmosphere, probably similar to today's – and quite different from that of earlier times, when the Earth, its hydrosphere and atmosphere were in a primitive stage of evolution. Even from this distance you'll see that these horizontal Waterberg sandstones differ conspicuously from the hard, grey Witwatersrand sediments.

The next big cutting (low but long), about 13 km north of Kranskop, is worth a stop to see the way manganese and iron can invade rocks, given enough of the relevant minerals, time and the right conditions **(geosite 3, map 4)**. This exposure is particularly interesting and very beautiful. The manganese minerals are generally black, the iron hydroxides red or ochry and rust-coloured. What happens is that groundwater, somewhat acidified by carbon dioxide in the air, dissolves iron and manganese from the rocks it passes through and in which these metals occur as extremely lean scatterings or disseminations. Once in solution, the iron and manganese are moved into areas of lower pressure, in this instance into every crack in the rock that's formed by fault- or bedding- and joint-planes. Slowly the fluids lose their dissolving capabilities and evaporate, leaving the new minerals, iron and manganese hydroxides, high and dry. And there they stay, now in equilibrium with their surroundings.

The rocks that have been pervaded are lavas of the Rooiberg Group and, after about 3 km of cutting, there are quite coarse-grained volcanic sediments that are also worth stopping to look at **(geosite 4, map 4)**. These are pyroclastic rocks, made up of fragments of material of a range of sizes that have been blasted out of volcanoes and have settled in sheets around them, sometimes dry, sometimes underwater.

As you proceed along the N1 here, you will notice signposts first to Bela Bela (formerly Warmbaths), then Modimolle (formerly Nylstroom) and lastly to Mookgophong (formerly Naboomspruit). These small towns nestle against the hilly country to the west of the road, while to the east lies the flat country of the Springbok Flats, broken only by gentle rises and the Kranskop inselberg. Now, though, as you approach Mokopane (formerly Potgietersrus) it becomes clear that you are going into hilly country, which extends quite far to the east of your line of travel.

ABOVE: *Volcanic sediments (pyroclastics) from the same set of cuttings as the manganese staining shown below.*
BELOW: *These five pictures amply illustrate the beautiful effects that result from the passage through rocks of solutions of manganese (black) and iron (yellow, pink, mauve and crimson). Note the frond-like manganese dendrite in the picture second from the left, a precipitation effect and not a plant fossil, as it might seem to be.*

An essential detour off the N1 at Mokopane

We strongly recommend a short detour via Mokopane, a town named after the Kekana chief, corrected from its earlier 'Makapan'. Makapan's Valley is a great drawcard for palaeoanthropologists from around the world to visit South Africa. The caves in this broad, dolomite-filled valley, 12 km north of the town of Mokopane, are a vivid revelation of three – perhaps four – million years of history **(geosite 1, map 5)**. To find them, take the R101 and you'll see the turn-off to the east after underpassing the new N1.

The past comes dramatically alive as you wander among heaps and heaps of limestone breccia packed with fossil bones. In a system of shallow caves in the old limeworks you can see the layers of sediment with bones and how the various generations of fossil-bearing limestone have formed. Because the caves are shallow and widely open to the surface, no torches are necessary; sunlight illuminates the story perfectly.

When you've seen the 3.3 million-year-old bones of *Australopithecus africanus* or *Paranthropus robustus* in the system of shallow caves called the Limeworks Cave, the guides will take you to the Cave of Hearths along the contour of the same hill. There you can relive more recent hominid evolution as you look up at the limestone slopes marked with the different stages of occupation by *Homo habilis* (Early Stone Age Man), 2.5 to 2 million years ago, and the first hominid to use tools; then *Homo erectus*, also a user of stone axes, diggers, scrapers and arrowheads; then, in the Iron Age, in historical times, *Homo sapiens* frequented the cave, starting around 500 AD.

And there's another corner to round, literally and metaphorically – to discover who Mokopane was, and his connection with these caves. It makes a fascinating epilogue to the story of Makapan's valley. Application for World Heritage Site status has been made and should soon be a reality, making this valley an icon of Limpopo Province.

Before leaving the 'valley of the caves' you should put on your geological hat again. Like the Sterkfontein Caves, the Makapan's Caves were formed many millions of years ago in Malmani dolomite near the base of the Transvaal Supergroup (see cave formation, pp. 280–281). Have a look

At Makapan's Caves, fossil teeth of a bushpig are some of the many indicators of the diet of the ancient cave-dwellers.

at some of the structures in the dolomite en route to Makapan's hideout. Ask your guide to show you the stromatolites, quite common in the Malmani dolomites, but which you might not yet have seen in these parts. Stromatolites reflect vast algal colonies that for a long time puzzled geologists, but which are now universally accepted as 2 500 million-year-old fossil remnants of the simplest single-celled organisms, and earliest producers of Earth's oxygen (see text box, p. 283). Before you visit Makapan's valley, contact the tourist information office in Mokopane to organise a guide, and spend time at the local museum where there is much background information about the caves that will make your visit there more meaningful.

LEFT: *Scouring of the surface limestone at the caves continues to yield valuable material.*
ABOVE: *Careful excavation of debris in the Cave of Hearths has enabled workers to demarcate the occupancy levels of the cave over the millennia.*
BELOW: *Stromatolites over two billion years old that mark fossil algal colonies put Man's brief tenure of these parts into perspective.*

The Firstborn (Eersteling): from prehistory to gold rush

Not many kilometres north of Makapan's valley, South Africa's first important gold mine was set up in 1871 on what was the Marabastad gold field, and is close enough for a visit **(geosite 2, map 5)**. Travelling northwards along the old N1, now the R101, the next turn-off to the east (14 km after the turn-off to the caves) is marked 'Eersteling Monuments'. Drive almost 5 km along a good dirt road before you find another entrance to the right, marked 'Monuments', which, after less than a kilometre, will bring you to the old dressed-stone smokestack. On your way there you will have driven first past dark greenstones, then quite intensely veined, very weathered granite, then fresher granite. From around 4 km along the dirt road you will catch, through the bush lining the road, glimpses of the Eersteling gold-mine headgear down to the right, the first evidence that you're in gold country. Once you've turned off and admired the stone smokestack, read the three descriptive and informative plaques.

With a neat farmhouse in its immaculate garden a stone's throw away and extensive citrus orchards across the valley, it's hard to imagine the spirit of adventure, the courage, the dogged determination that drove prospectors Messrs Edward, Button and Goodwin to travel to London in a bid to float the Transvaal Gold Mining Company, and to bring in a stamp mill hundreds of kilometres by oxwagon. Remember, there was little here other than a small Boer settlement over the hills to the south – with its memories – and they had but the barest inkling of what lay beneath the ground. And it was long before Pilgrim's Rest and Barberton had shown that gold mines could be made to pay in this remote and virgin land.

Towering above those citrus orchards are quartzite kranses of the Wolkberg Group that in these parts form the basal unit of the Transvaal Supergroup and which are not found further south. Over to the west is the pair of tall ironstone-capped hills called the Ysterberg, which lies immediately west of the Ysterberg Fault, and is part of the same 3 200 million-year-old Pietersburg Group greenstone belt that hosts the Eersteling gold mine. Around Eersteling itself, the ground is gently rolling. Remember that these formations form the floor rocks of the thick quartzites to the south and are a billion years older. Then, looking across at Ysterberg, consider how high it stands now, way above the base of the sandstones. That's what the faulting has done: it's pushed everything west of the fault up, relative to the base of the Wolkberg quartzites east of the fault.

The oldest gold-production smokestack in the country, part of the boiler-house used to drive a steam engine, which was required for rock crushing and possibly water pumping – and reputed to have been built with stone imported from the United Kingdom.

MAP 5

The Nyl Toll Plaza to Beitbridge

The break between the flats south of Mokopane and the hilly country north of it is caused by the Zebediela Fault, which has dropped the whole of the Karoo Basin, to the south, against older rocks to the north, so that the basalts abut against folded and upturned Precambrian formations.

The low, hummocky hills just east of the toll plaza are made of the same rock as the low hills on the flats north of Pretoria, Main Zone gabbro of the Bushveld Complex Layered Suite. Just behind them is a low ridge of Magaliesberg quartzite, then another quartzite ridge, and finally the curved ridge that dominates the scenery here, made of quartzites of the Timeball Hill Formation. Here, 300 km north of Pretoria, you are looking at ridges built of the same rock formation as that in Pretoria. However, because you're going from inside the saucer-shaped basin of the Bushveld Complex into the Transvaal Supergroup floor rocks on the outside, you cross the geology in the reverse order now, from younger to older.

If, before you got into the hilly country, you noticed some old dumps a short distance to the east, you might have wondered what they were. They are the last vestiges of the Grasvally chrome mine of Samancor, and if you have travelled on the N4 west of Pretoria, you will have seen the same sort of dumps between Brits and Rustenburg. Perhaps this scale of things will help you understand why geologists, both from academia and industry, come from around the world to see the Bushveld Complex. It is, indeed, one of a kind.

After going through the toll and past 'Engen One-Stops' on either side of the road, you see a low koppie close to the road and to the right, and then you pass under a bridge. Two hundred metres after this there is a cutting at the base of this higher ground where there are good exposures of fresh gabbro norite of the Main Zone.

From the 70.2 to 70.6 km beacons you pass a low cutting to the right of white Magaliesberg quartzite, before reaching the main gorge through a high pass at the 72.2 km beacon. Here, for a few hundred metres, is a jumbled mess of south-dipping sediments, mostly shales with minor quartzites and diabase. Everything except the quartzites is deeply weathered, perhaps largely because of the fracturing of the rock by the Ysterberg fault, which has formed the poort. Immediately after the feeder road from Mokopane joins the N1, and just north of the Sebetiela Toll Plaza, the rock faces in the road cutting to your left show dolomites and chert (chemically precipitated silica) still close to the fault and, as a consequence, in a chaotic pattern of dips and strikes. These belong to the Malmani Subgroup, part of the Chuniespoort Group, which lies below the shales and quartzites of the Magaliesberg Formation that you've just seen.

If you look for them, you will notice near-vertical surfaces in the dolomite where surface weathering has given rise to the 'elephant-skin weathering' characteristic of the dolomite in these climatic conditions. You will see much better examples at other places where the Malmani dolomite occurs, so be patient. You're soon out of these grey rocks into a cutting that has quite a different look about it. These are sandstones of the Black Reef Formation, right at the base of the Transvaal Supergroup, and they show extensive bedding surfaces of ancient ripple marks, the surfaces shaped by material wafting in the gentlest of currents over 2.5 billion years ago (**geosite 3, map 5**).

Not long after leaving this cutting you cannot help noticing a fairly major mine-working off to the left; and no sooner have you wondered whether this is Mokopane's newest big mine opening up, than you'll see to the right of you a smokestack and a board advertising Midway Bricks. This is a timely reminder

Mohs Scale of Mineral Hardness

One of the reliable diagnostic tests used by geologists to identify minerals in the field is the scale of relative hardness. The hardness of minerals varies greatly, and the scale attributes 1 to the softest and 10 to the hardest.

Hardness	Mineral
1	Talc
2	Gypsum
3	Calcite
4	Fluorite (Fluorspar)
5	Apatite
6	Orthoclase Feldspar
7	Quartz
8	Topaz
9	Corundum
10	Diamond

Gypsum will scratch talc, calcite will scratch gypsum and so on. Try it out, and if you are keen on identifying minerals, it's easy, over time, to make up a set for yourself of minerals with factors of hardness from 1 to 9.

A good example of ripple-marked sandstone of the Black Reef Formation occurs north of Mokopane.

that, just as much as the world needs chrome and platinum, people need bricks to build houses. The brick clay being quarried is derived from rocks of the Pietersburg Greenstone Belt, which you will travel over for some 10 km, with a fresh road-cutting exposure from the 81 km beacon for quite a few hundred metres. These are mostly metavolcanics, with nothing remarkable enough about them to warrant your stopping, except that at the 81.6 km beacon there is a talc schist that merits a closer look. It seems like an ordinary enough rock, but wait: see if you can scratch it with your fingernail. You'll find you can do so quite easily. And you'll understand why, in the scale of hardness of minerals (see text box on opposite page), talc is the softest. Talc is a metamorphic mineral formed from non-aluminous magnesium silicates like olivine, which in its gem form is called peridot. This is one of the less common semi-precious stones, with an unusual grassy green colour. You can understand why talc-rich rock (often called soapstone because of its slippery feel) is favoured among African rock carvers, especially those from Zimbabwe, where talc rocks are common.

Metamorphic minerals and metamorphism

You've looked at the softest mineral on the scale. At Blaauwkop, 20 km south of Musina, you should be able to find corundum, the hardest but one. Both are metamorphic minerals, occurring in metamorphic rocks, both the result of the process called metamorphism. And both, incidentally, appeal to our vanity: talc for cosmetic reasons, and corundum by other names. Add traces of chromium to corundum and it becomes ruby; add traces of cobalt, iron and titanium, and it becomes sapphire.

But back to metamorphism. We've mentioned examples of low-grade metamorphism in the Malmesbury sediments around Cape Town, and in the ancient sedimentary rocks around Johannesburg. From here, though, you'll see them in profusion, and in no cryptic expression. The talc you've just seen is in a schist, towards the lower end of the metamorphic scale. Ahead we'll see high-grade gneisses galore: both are metamorphic rocks par excellence – they bear little resemblance to the rocks from which they formed.

The process has a parallel in the animal kingdom: insect metamorphosis. And sometimes the geological results – a star sapphire, for example – are quite as beautiful as the Monarch butterfly that started life as a lowly caterpillar. But where metamorphosis of caterpillar to butterfly is time-triggered, it is change of temperature and/or pressure that induces the process of metamorphism in the Earth. The first minerals to form in a sedimentary rock as it solidifies, or lithifies, or in an igneous rock as it cools and crystallises, are in equilibrium in that environment. Raise the temperature or apply pressure, and the equilibrium goes: the minerals change to others that are stable at the new temperature and pressure. And, having changed, they don't change back as soon as the heat and the pressure are off, just as bread does not change back to dough when it comes out of the oven.

And that is a useful analogy. Just as the lumps of dough that go into the oven have nothing added or subtracted in order to become scones, so shale may become schist, or even gneiss, with practically no material addition or subtraction. Atoms and molecules reorganise themselves in response to the changed environment. New minerals form, intimately intergrown in a new fabric. Chemical analysis shows gneiss to be insignificantly different from the shale from which it formed: all the sodium, calcium, iron, aluminium and silica in the shale are there in the gneiss. The rocks are as different to look at, though, as chalk and cheese. It has all happened in the solid state, with no melting, rather like dough turning to scones. Melting may happen with temperatures that are high enough and sufficiently sustained, but it is not the norm. Metamorphism on a vast scale can – and does – take place without it.

A granite koppie, symbol of the African veld, looms above the settlement at Mphakane.
This Matopos Granite intrudes the slightly older gneiss to the north and south.

What happens to change the temperature-pressure environment on a regional scale is a combination of tectonism – causing folding, thrusting and faulting – and igneous intrusion, mainly in the deep, hot root zones of fold belts, where the tectonism plunges rocks to depths far greater than those at which they were formed, and melting starts to happen. Heat given off by big intrusions like the Bushveld Complex is another important source of metamorphism, and the stresses and elevated temperatures when crustal blocks grind against each other are the third main factor. Any temperature-pressure environment sufficiently more pronounced than those under which the rocks were formed will lead to grades of metamorphism, giving new minerals and new textures.

After the 85 km beacon there is a prominent granitic hill to the left, made of what's known as Geyser Granite, part of the Basement granite-gneiss. Here it is a pink to red rock, mostly fine grained and tough, tending to resist erosion and form high-lying country. It shows an interesting feature further on, between the 87.0 km and 87.2 km beacons, where a roof pendant of much darker amphibolite (a rock composed largely of hornblende, one of the minerals of the amphibole family) has been caught up in the granite **(geosite 4, map 5)**. Picture molten granite forcing its way upwards into the rocks above it, mostly pushing them up ahead of it, until a block of the rocky crust works loose and breaks off, sinking into the ascending granite. It is heated by the granite until it's about the same temperature and can be consumed around its edges by the granite, with the granite, in turn, being contaminated by a material with a very different composition. See how the granite grades from its naturally pink colour to dark greyish pink and, finally, to dark grey before you get into the black amphibolite.

Soon after this you breast a rise and start your gradual descent to the plains which stretch ahead towards – and beyond – Polokwane (formerly Pietersburg). Stretched to your right across the flats are large hills of the Pietersburg Greenstone Belt. We have been passing to the west of this 70 km-long, northeast-trending belt since just north of Mokopane. Like Barberton and other greenstone belts,

The cutting edge

Just north of Mphakane, near the Tropic of Capricorn, and after you cross the Dwarsrivier, which you'd be exceptionally lucky to see flow, you are in a different kind of Basement gneiss, known from radiometric age dating to be older than that which you were on before the granite koppies. This rock, the Goudplaats or Baviaanskloof Gneiss, has more dark minerals (biotite and hornblende) in it, and a more banded look. In a quarry entered by a road to the right, about 2 km after the Dwarsrivier, blocks of this rock are extracted for dimension stone. You will be able to see the smooth-cut surfaces of rock from the N1, and perhaps a spread of huge rectangular blocks of rock, upwards of 50 tons, waiting to start on their long journey overseas for cutting into slabs and polishing. It is intriguing to see how the koppie is literally being carved up into these blocks. To an extent, breakage of quite a clean surface is achieved by drilling holes spaced 15 to 25 cm apart, then loosening the almost-free block with a light charge of explosive. Otherwise the rock is sawn through using a diamond-coated cable run over a pulley on a little petrol-driven motor, and threaded through holes drilled into the rock. It's hard to imagine, mind-boggling to see: never again will you walk past a granite- or gneiss-cladded building without realising the effort involved.

Gneiss from this koppie north of Polokwane will be admired in the furthest corners of Europe. The linear grooves on the blocks in the foreground are from the drilling to loosen them.

it has excited prospectors for well over a century with its tantalising showings of gold, including at Eersteling (see p. 94). This greenstone belt is capped by beds of hard, banded ironstone, like the Ysterberg hills over your right shoulder, and also referred to earlier along this route.

Once you've been on the flats for a few kilometres and between the 11.0 and 11.2 km beacons, the road cuts through some good outcrops of the Basement in these parts, which are light-coloured, banded granite-gneiss, with conspicuous pegmatite, the very coarsely crystalline late-stage phase of these rocks **(geosite 5, map 5)**. These are quite typical of a huge stretch of country west, north and east of Polokwane, as far north as the Soutpansberg.

Leaving Polokwane, there are some large, rounded hills ahead of you and slightly to the left. You will drive though the eastern end of these hills, known as Rhenosterkoppies, a large remnant of greenstone belt, now at a somewhat higher metamorphic grade than that to the southeast. There is some good-looking magnetite quartzite in the low cutting to the right of the road, which is dense and will pull a magnet, if you have one handy **(geosite 6, map 5)**. The large, undeveloped iron-ore deposit at Sandrivierspoort, owned by heavyweight Kumba Resources, lies in the hills to the west. It is based on a vast tonnage of high-grade, magnetically recoverable iron ore.

As you descend back onto the flats, the Soutpansberg range looms in the far distance. And, much closer, are impressive granite koppies on either side of the road. You enter them at a large settlement called Mphakane. Named the Matoks Granite, they are part of a granite pluton that is dated at 2 670 million years old, a little younger than the granite-gneiss you've travelled over for most of the last 50 km, and intrusive into them. From Dwarsrivier onwards, the granite and gneiss you drive over are poorly exposed and there's little to see, either in road cuttings or on nearby hillsides. The mountains ahead are getting closer by the minute, though.

The Soutpansberg (see fig. 14, opposite) is an east-west range made up of several ridges trending in the same direction. This succession of rocks, called the Soutpansberg Group, consists of basalts and coarse-grained sediments, mostly quartzites that are gritty in part, and including some conglomerates. The kranses that crown the range behind Makhado (formerly Louis Trichardt), and along the crest in both directions, are made up of reddish brown quartzites. The evidence points to this elongate depositary having formed within a broad, fault-bounded rift valley, with features similar to those to be seen in the East African Rift Valley today, but 10 000 times older.

In the Soutpansberg, strike faulting, parallel to the ridges, is common. At the time of formation, faulted blocks dropped down to accommodate coarse material washed off the valley sides, and the fault systems reached deep enough to tap into magma chambers from which issued a series of flows of basalt. During the 1 750 million years of history that followed, the harder, younger Soutpansberg range has withstood the forces of erosion more resolutely than the gneisses on either side, to form, slowly but surely, the range of high scarps and shallow dip slopes that can be seen from tens of kilometres on all sides. Remember, it is not that they have been lifted up; the reason for their prominence is that the surrounding gneissic countryside has been worn down. Having said that, there is little doubt that faulting, now in the reverse sense, was active to the north of the range after Soutpansberg sedimentation, with the gneisses to the north having dropped down intermittently.

North of the range, in the Limpopo Lowveld, you don't get straight back into the highly metamorphosed ancient rocks which once formed the high hinterland abutting the rift valley; instead, you encounter Karoo rocks, faulted against and overlying the Soutpansberg rocks. As is generally the case, the faulting that gave rise to the Soutpansberg rift valley did not stop at the end of that event, but continued, probably both during and after Karoo sedimentation and volcanism.

NORTH-SOUTH GEOLOGICAL CROSS-SECTION
THROUGH THE SOUTPANSBERG

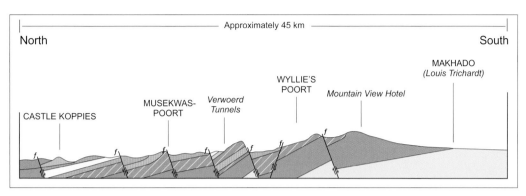

This north-south geological cross-section across the Soutpansberg runs more or less parallel to the N1, from just south of Makhado to past Castle Koppies in the north. The area is strongly block-faulted as the sediments of the Soutpansberg Group were deposited in a rift valley. The corresponding geological map shows a number of east-west trending normal faults that cause repetition of strata and related mountain ridges, notably the prominent Wyllie's Poort quartzite. Note that to the north there are much younger Karoo Supergroup formations. Although block faulting started during Soutpansberg times, it was reactivated much later after the deposition of the Karoo strata.

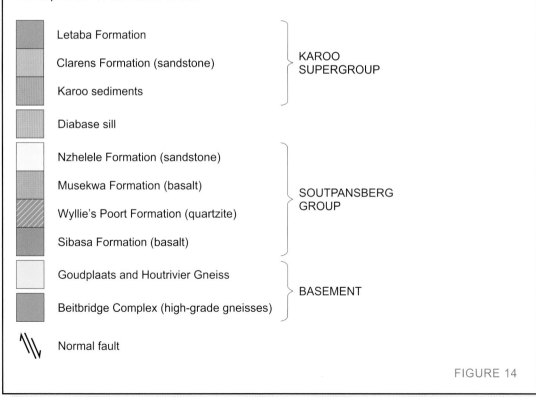

Letaba Formation

Clarens Formation (sandstone)   } KAROO SUPERGROUP

Karoo sediments

Diabase sill

Nzhelele Formation (sandstone)

Musekwa Formation (basalt)

Wyllie's Poort Formation (quartzite)   } SOUTPANSBERG GROUP

Sibasa Formation (basalt)

Goudplaats and Houtrivier Gneiss

Beitbridge Complex (high-grade gneisses)   } BASEMENT

Normal fault

FIGURE 14

The southern of the two Hendrik Verwoerd tunnels cuts through mauve Wyllie's Poort quartzites of the Soutpansberg Group. Note how intensely fractured these sediments are, due to strong east-west faulting at this location.

But back to roadside geology: as you leave Makhado, you will see float of fresh, dark grey volcanic material to your right. As you proceed with the early part of the climb, most of the reddish brown, weathered, rounded float blocks are from diabase sills intruded into the Soutpansberg Group. By the time you reach the Mountain View Hotel, you have passed well-bedded sandstones of the same group, both gritty and bouldery in part. They are easy to tell apart: the sandstones (hard quartzite in places) form bigger, more angular blocks and breakage surfaces, compared with the smaller, rounded diabase, usually seen in deeply weathered, red-brown soil.

By the time you're off the pass and have just about reached the end of the valley floor stretch that follows it, vertical slopes loom ahead, which appear to hem you in completely. Drawing closer, you'll see that the way out is through a tunnel – two, in fact – still called the Hendrik Verwoerd Tunnels. Just before the first one is a cutting to your right, through fresh-looking dark grey rock, a good example of fresh diabase. It appears not to extend across the road or as far as the tunnel, which is cut in hard mauve quartzitic sandstone, called the Wyllie's Poort Formation after the gorge where it is so beautifully displayed. Note that here the bedding of this formation may not be as evident as it was further back and that there is a strong vertical component to the rock fracturing. This reminds us that we are in an area of abundant faults, though not all show much displacement.

After the tunnels, you wind around in the hills for a while and pass through Masekwaspoort, showing a repetition of the hard Wyllie's Poort quartzites, before making a long, sharp right turn, which brings you into much more open country. A couple of kilometres ahead, and to the right of the road, is another steep-fronted ridge parallel to the main range. The precipitousness has much to do with the fact that the face you can see marks a fault between the Soutpansberg sediments, making the north-dipping ridge; and to the south of it, in the flat-bottomed valley, Karoo sediments that contain thin beds of carbon-rich rock, formed at the same time as the coal seams further south, but without economically viable concentrations of plant life in these parts.

After going past the western end of the ridge, you're pretty well out on the wide plains again. Except not quite: there are some low, flattish ridges on both sides of the road whose general coloration and weathering surfaces might ring a bell if you are familiar with the countryside around Bethlehem and Golden Gate. The pale, fine-grained, yellowish-weathering sandstones making up the low hills you are passing between, going by the name of Castle Koppies, belong to the Clarens Formation of the Karoo, and display characteristic large-scale cross-bedding, a clue to their wind-blown origin. Today it's difficult to think of two parts of South Africa more different than where you are now and the area around Clarens. Two hundred million years ago, these places shared the same wind-swept desert environment. (For more on the environment of these times, see table 5, p. 176.)

An interesting point here is that some parts of the Karoo succession, like the Dwyka tillite, are missing, and that the rest have been substantially condensed. You would have to climb over 1 000 m to get to Clarens from the Ecca coal fields around Newcastle: here, a few tens of metres of sedimentary rock separate the carbonaceous sandstone and these Clarens sandstones. Either the supply of sediment was less here, or the agencies of transport and deposition were not as active, or both.

The telescoping of Karoo formations here is dramatically emphasised by finding, a couple of kilometres after these hills, basalt float alongside the road – the same, to all intents and purposes, as the rocks capping the Drakensberg (see ch. 17, p. 294). Thinking stratigraphically, what would be about 2 000 m in KwaZulu-Natal's Karoo geology has here been shrunk to a tenth of that.

About 9 km after the Nzhelele Dam turn-off to the east, you're on the Beitbridge Complex and have just gone between low hills on either side, when you see masses of loose rock float alongside the road. This is of a variety of rock types, but you might find it worth scratching around to see if you can find some of the coarsely crystalline white marble, which contains quite a lot of garnet in places **(geosite 7, map 5)**. If you have a pen-knife – or even a key will do – and you scratch the big white rhombohedral crystals of calcite, you will see how soft they are, always an immediate test for the difference between calcite (whose crystallinity does not always give it away as much as it does here) and quartz, which is so hard that, instead of a scratch on the rock, you will find a streak of metal on it. From here on, although the countryside is generally flattish, there are scattered low hills and you pass through low cuttings of deeply weathered gneiss. The next place you might want to stop and have a look is about 1.9 km after a sign showing 'Musina 20 km', just after the Sand River Safaris entrance. In a cutting on the west side there is an unusual-looking speckled rock, which, on closer examination, will turn out to be a coarsely crystalline biotite-plagioclase feldspar-pegmatite, with minor quartz, next to a much finer-grained biotite gneiss **(geosite 8, map 5)**.

By now you are dropping towards the Limpopo River and in the very heart of baobab country. The countryside is becoming quite dissected and you find yourself passing through a number of cuttings, mostly showing gneiss of one kind or another. About 7.5 km after the 'Musina 20 km' signboard, you go through a deep cutting that's worth slowing down for. To your right, you will see strongly banded gneiss, the banding just about vertical, with a white quartz vein, about a third of a metre thick, cutting horizontally across it, and the whole lot cut by a fine-grained, dark dyke. After foliation of the gneiss, there was further activity, including cross-cutting by the quartz vein and, much later, intrusion by a feeder dyke related to some volcanic episode.

The complex geology of the Beitbridge Complex around Musina is best seen south of the town in the Musina Nature Reserve, an area also well known for its many spectacular ancient baobab trees. Here the high-grade metamorphic gneisses of the complex show incredible patterns of ductile deformation, and are best seen in the bed of the usually dry Sand River. This world-famous and accessible geosite, located close to the road bridge along the R508 to Tshipise, some 8 km southeast of Musina, is definitely worth a visit **(geosite 9, map 5)**.

Suddenly you're on the edge of Musina, and you are immediately reminded that this is, as much as anything else, a mining town. Or was, anyway, from the mine tailings and other dumps you see on the right-hand edge of the town. If you were to speak to the townsfolk of Musina today, the younger ones would not even remember the mining days, when Messina and Palabora and Okiep were names synonymous with South African copper.

North towards the border, the extremely complex geology of the Beitbridge Complex is poorly exposed. Two quite imposing hills in the corner between the N1 and the R572 to Alldays consist of Archaean metasediments, akin to a greenstone belt, here comprising much quartzite and magnetite quartzite. But from the car, the stretch between Musina and the Limpopo offers low-lying country of mostly deeply weathered, highly metamorphosed rock, grist to the mill for only a handful of geological specialists.

ABOVE: *This area of spectacular geological exposure occurs in the usually dry Sand River within the Musina Nature Reserve and has been listed as a possible Heritage Site. Here, well-layered metasedimentary gneisses and migmatites of the Beitbridge Complex have been deformed into a variety of complex fold structures.*

RIGHT: *The headgear and waste dump in Musina are a reminder that this was once a mining town accounting for an important part of South Africa's copper production. Now its proximity to De Beer's Venetia mine has given it a new lease on life.*

Musina: destined to be a mining town

As you pass through Musina (meaning 'place of copper', discovered here in ancient times), en route to Beitbridge, you will probably notice signboards referring to another mine, Venetia, on which appear the familiar words 'A diamond is forever'. Although 70 km to the west of the town, the mine that is De Beer's biggest South African producer of diamonds has no closer commercial and residential centre of any importance, so Musina has taken on a new lease of life.

Venetia is not only De Beer's largest mine in South Africa, it is also its newest and richest. As ideas of the origin of diamonds were evolving, a critical realisation was that only the very deep-tapping kimberlites would have brought diamonds up from the mantle (see text box, p. 242). The shallower parts were not suitable for the formation and preservation of these extraordinary crystals of carbon. Conventional wisdom had it that diamonds would form under the deep, stable cratons in ancient shield areas which, whether deeply eroded or not, have roots that extend down as much as 300 km into the Earth's upper mantle. Regions between the cratons, usually elongated 'mobile belts', where there has been strong deformation and metamorphism in post-Archaean times – so-called off-craton areas, as they are known to diamond explorationists – were not regarded as prospective. It was considered that, while such areas might well host kimberlites, they were unlikely to be diamondiferous. And, for a long time, the Limpopo Belt was regarded as just such an off-craton mobile belt, sandwiched between the Kaapvaal and Zimbabwe Cratons. Of its widespread shearing, extreme deformation and high-grade metamorphism in post-Archaean times there is no doubt.

So when the diamondiferous Venetia pipe was discovered in the mid-1970s, serendipitously, some may say, just where it ought not to have been, a re-evaluation was called for. With better understanding of the geology of the Limpopo Belt, it is now believed that the apparent cratonic break at the surface is not reflected in the upper mantle, and that the two cratonic roots were annealed in late Archaean times.

5 N1: Johannesburg to Cape Town

GEOLOGICAL OVERVIEW

This portion of the N1 crosses the industrial heartland of South Africa and is a reminder that the country is founded on minerals: gold as you leave Johannesburg, iron as you pass Vanderbijlpark with its steel mills, and coal as Sasolburg slips by to the east.

The granite-gneiss tor not far to the west of the road as you leave Sasolburg is a clue that you are passing over the eastern edge of the Vredefort Dome, manifestation of the world's biggest known meteorite impact, which happened some two billion years ago and is unquestionably worth a detour. As you head across the Karoo Basin, frequent cuttings, particularly as you get further into the basin, show a range of sedimentary rock types and structures and, cutting across them, dolerite dykes and sills. It is this dolerite that saves the Karoo from scenic monotony, with ridges and flat-topped hills whose bush cover contrasts strongly with the grass and scrub of the plains. The range of fossil species – particularly of mammal-like reptiles – from this central part of the Karoo is unequalled anywhere and has made it famous in palaeontological circles around the world.

MAIN PICTURE & INSET: *South of Sasolburg, this Basement granite-gneiss – floor to the Witwatersrand sediments – was brought from great depth to the surface by the impact of the meteorite that gave rise to the biggest such structure known on Earth, the celebrated Vredefort Dome.*

After Beaufort West, upended strata catch your attention for the first time as you enter the Cape Fold Belt. This is a magnificent field laboratory for structural geologists; for the lay person, it's a delight to the eye, as you drive slowly through the cuttings just west of Laingsburg and, later, down the syncline carved out by the Hex River. By the time you start your descent out of the Karoo, you're into sediments of the Cape Supergroup. And, an hour or so later, with Table Mountain visible ahead, you're crossing the pre-Cape Basement of Malmesbury Group sediments and the Cape Granite intrusive into them. The latter is most conspicuous as you pass Paarl, with its typically domed granite hills.

MAP 6

Geology of the route

Johannesburg to Kroonstad

We've covered the first part of this journey in the section on Greater Johannesburg, so until you reach the Sasolburg-Parys crossover, we suggest you turn to ch. 1, p. 34, and follow the route there.

From the Vanderbijlpark-Potchefstroom flyover, with the major industrial complex of Vanderbijlpark prominent to your left, far ahead and further to the left you'll see the tall stacks and other structures of Sasolburg, its grey dump of waste-ash conspicuous alongside it. A little later you'll pass the turn-off to Sasolburg, and that's as close as you'll get to the most notable success story the industrial history of South Africa has to offer.

Sasol industrial complex in the early morning.

SUPERLATIVE SASOL: FORTUNE FAVOURS THE BOLD

SASOL is superlative, not in the sense that the purely Earth-based South African industries are – the gold, diamonds and platinum – but in the technological realm. It's not that Sigma Colliery and others supplying the essential coal are the biggest: it's what is done with the coal that makes SASOL a world leader.

By 1950, global post-war industrial expansion was gathering momentum: motor cars were being produced and new oil fields opened up on an unprecedented scale. But the prospects for finding oil in South Africa were very poor, according to the geologists. Another fossil fuel, coal, was locally available in vast quantities, but the rocks were wrong for oil.

The idea of using coal in an oil-deficient geological environment had been born in Germany's Ruhr Valley early in the twentieth century, but the technology had not progressed much beyond the laboratory in Europe and the USA. In South Africa, since 1935, Anglovaal had been making petrol on a limited scale from small deposits of shaley, coal-like material called torbanite, which yields oil on heating. When the 2nd World War

broke out, Anglovaal was poised to take the technology up a gear and apply the Fischer-Tropsch process to coal. The war and events soon after it changed all that, though, and the mid-point of the century saw Anglovaal hand the venture to the newly formed parastatal South African Coal, Oil and Gas Corporation, soon shortened to SASOL.

More than 50 years later, it is difficult to imagine the boldness of the decision to spend £20 million on such a project on the African Highveld. But, in an age of burgeoning industrialisation, it was simply not strategic to be completely dependent for fuel, the very lifeblood of national existence, on powers that might not always be friendly.

A group of bright young South Africans applied themselves tirelessly to perfecting the nascent technology. They struck up partnerships with pioneers in the field of petrochemicals in Europe and the United States, and step by step they drew closer to building a commercial-scale oil-from-coal complex. Where to build the plant, though? Principal requirements for the chemical processes involved in the gasification of coal, were, firstly, huge reserves of coal of a specific quality; secondly, abundant water; and, if such a plant could be close to the industrial heartland of the country, Johannesburg, so much the better. With a coal field close to the Vaal River and just south of Vereeniging, Sasolburg located itself.

Involving courage as much as chemistry, the development took place against a background of unrest in the oil-rich Middle East and growing international hostility towards the then South African regime's policies – and the threat of oil sanctions. Developing local capacity to produce liquid fuel, from jet fuel to diesel, was a technological triumph. As proof of the profitability of the initiative, Sasolburg's much bigger brothers at Secunda, far over the eastern horizon, established computerised coal mining on a scale unequalled anywhere, and petrotechnology that's revered throughout the industry.

Noting that the Sasolburg-Parys crossover is at the 69.2 km beacon, look out for the 65.2 km beacon. (These roadside kilometre marker boards or beacons are invaluable tools for pinpointing interesting sites. Highway sections are generally numbered from south to north.) About 100 m further on you'll see some outcrop in the low road cutting **(geosite 1, map 6)**. This is the first outcrop you've seen for a while, and it's none other than the Hospital Hill quartzite of the Witwatersrand Supergroup. The granite in the next few cuttings – and on a bush-covered koppie off to the east that looks as though it might have been transplanted here from deep in the bushveld – is the ancient floor to the Witwatersrand Basin. We've seen it exposed in northern Johannesburg and around Midrand; here it has been brought to the surface by the impact two billion years ago of the meteorite that has given us the Vredefort Dome, centre of the oldest and biggest impact crater on the face of the planet (covered in more detail in the chapter on Greater Johannesburg, ch. 1, p. 34).

This fresh granite in a low road cutting south of Sasolburg is an invitation to explore the Vredefort Dome.

There's little to see in the way of rocks as you travel across the Highveld, until you get into Kroonstad. As you drive through the centre of the town you'll see a couple of quite high cuttings. They show beautiful trough cross-bedding in the beige, lower Beaufort Group sandstone of the Karoo Supergroup, a sedimentary structure that's worth a closer look **(geosite 2, map 6)**. Each trough represents a channel within the river system in which sand was being carried and, ultimately, deposited. As the channels, or troughs, became filled with sand, new courses were sought out by the anastomosing or braided river system, to one side or the other and incrementally slightly higher, and slowly the stack of sandstone you now see was built up.

SHAPING THE FACE OF SOUTH AFRICA

We touched on some of the principles of landscape evolution in the Introduction. Now is a good time to go into more detail. Lowering of the landscape happens by back-cutting into high ground from base levels such as sea level and the valley floors of major drainages crossing the interior (see fig. 4, p. 23). It is a process of 'parallel scarp retreat', not a general, overall wearing down, as is sometimes assumed.

Africa was the central piece in the Gondwana jigsaw before it broke up. It stood higher than the surrounding parts when continental drifting got under way, but even before this, there would have been considerable relief on the Gondwana surface: hills, ridges and valleys. The highlands of Lesotho are remnants of that Gondwana surface scenery, as are the various quartzite ranges in the southern and western Cape, the Outeniquas and other rugged mountain chains. But the first convulsions started to shake Gondwana, and rift-bounded valleys opened up, along which the southern and eastern coasts of the country were shortly to be formed (up to 400 km from the coast we know today). Now, as the other continental landmasses were pushed away over the horizon, gullies formed on the primeval African cliffs towering over the storm-lashed virgin coast. Over time the ravines were cut back and widened by weathering and erosion – further and more quickly where the rocks were soft, or where rift valleys cut the coastline; centimetre by centimetre where the slopes were buttressed by hard quartzite. Pioneer rivers cut back through the retreating scarp to intersect and 'capture' the old rivers of Gondwana. Along these rivers, higher, new base levels formed above the nick-points where the rivers cut through the scarp, and the resulting valleys eventually stretched to form their own wide plains, traversed by meandering tributaries, old and new. The retreating cliff faces that had started at the coast with the break-up of Gondwana were pushed steadily back at the head of the widening coastal plain – and are still retreating today in the Drakensberg.

A period of stability lasting 100 million years, through the Cretaceous and the early part of the ensuing Tertiary periods, led to the development of extensive flat land surfaces or peneplains, formed by ongoing erosion. These were at low elevations along the coast, at higher levels in the interior, behind the Great Escarpment. We call this family of land surfaces, formed at the same time and so genetically closely related, the African Surface. Below the African Surface, deep and pervasive weathering took place – complete decomposition of the rock that had been there. On the African Surface, resistant duricrusts were formed – hard deposits of silcrete (silica crust) or ferricrete (iron cap). These consisted of the cemented uppermost part of the soil profile, and speak of prolonged stillstand, showing no erosion and no accumulation. Think of the African Surface as a geomorphological time marker; all other extensive surfaces are younger. During the Miocene, about 18 million years ago, and again in the Pliocene, 2.5 million years ago, there were renewed periods of uplift of the African Surface, which was cut into over wide areas.

What happened to the quantities of earth stripped off as the surface was lowered and the escarpment retreated? Offshore oil exploration has shown that some of the basins on the continental shelf have accumulated as much as 10 000 m of sediment since the African coastline formed. That's where it went.

Were the cycles of erosion and new base levels initiated by the land rising or sea level falling? Probably both, not equally and not continuously, but spasmodically or episodically. On the one hand, forces deep in the mantle continued to exert their influence on the surface and below the ocean. On the other, subtle changes in the tilt of the Earth in its journey around the Sun resulted in icing and de-icing of the poles and in variations in ocean temperatures – a slight, but critical effect on the huge volume of Earth's water, and on world climate. Cycles of warming and cooling, of glaciation and deglaciation are ongoing, and have manifested themselves in sea level changes in a time frame measured in thousands, rather than millions, of years.

MAP 7

Kroonstad to Springfontein

Not far south of Kroonstad, at Ventersburg, you will see signs to Welkom and Virginia off to the west and, although there is little other evidence, you are passing the Free State or Welkom gold field. Deep below the surface, under a cover of some 1 000 m of Karoo sediments and Ventersdorp volcanics, lies the southwestern margin of the Witwatersrand Basin. After a long period of prospecting, a viable deposit of gold was discovered in 1938. Exploration and development was delayed by the 2nd World War, and production commenced in the early 1950s, leading to the establishment of the city of Welkom. Where once there was only farmland, more than 20 mines now exist, and gold mining continues to this day.

Other than the cuttings in Kroonstad, outcrop is sparse. Crossing the Sand River – which has cut a pronounced valley – you'll see more sandstone of the Beaufort Group, here conspicuously well bedded (**geosite 1, map 7**). Then you're back on the grassy rolling plains. Further south, Karoo dolerite koppies and ridges abound, adding some vertical dimension to the landscape, but here even the dolerite is muted in its expression, showing as flat ungrassed pavements with rounded boulders and cobbles strewn over them. They illustrate how the same rock type expresses itself differently in different climatic regions.

That difference is starting to manifest itself as you approach Bloemfontein – with the geographic Karoo not very far ahead. You can't miss the change in the topography, and to some extent in the vegetation, as bushed hills start to appear in the landscape. The scenery is more varied than anything you've seen for hours, mainly because Bloemfontein is situated on one of the biggest dolerite sheets in these parts, and the countryside shows it.

Soon after passing the Free State capital you're off the island of dolerite-dominated country and back into open, gently undulating grasslands, now on the African Surface. The road passes through low cuttings at intervals, mostly showing horizontal sediments, here and there cut by a dolerite dyke or capped by a sill. The sediments are mainly shales and mudstones, with some sandstones, and are generally pale grey to cream, more rarely medium grey or dark purple: typical Beaufort sediments in other words, that cover some 20 per cent of South Africa's surface area. The grassland is punctuated by scrub-covered low hills and ridges that show where the dolerite has cut through the sediments.

As you approach Edenburg, glance to your left (**geosite 2, map 7**). The low hills quite close by are more than just low Karoo hills: they are substantially enriched in uranium. For three or four years in the late 1970s, the whole of the area centred on Edenburg

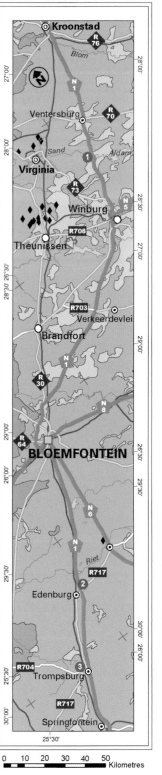

was the scene of intense exploration, with farms being optioned, drills operating around the clock, and consultants uttering wise pronouncements. Similar uranium mineralisation had been discovered north of Beaufort West five years earlier, and around Victoria West, but faraway Edenburg was a surprise, a latecomer. In the end, the uranium price did not maintain the levels it had held for a decade. It was no longer viable to open a mine – or a series of small mines – and the quest was all over. Peace descended on the upper Karoo once more.

ABOVE: *The supermature topography of the Highveld leads to subdued expression of even relatively resistant rock types, such as the Karoo dolerite seen here.*
LEFT: *That resistance is well illustrated by the blocky jointing in the same rock type seen here in the big sheet that outcrops around Bloemfontein.*

Still waters

Some of the farms at the southern edge of the Edenburg 'uranium field' had seen drilling 30 years earlier, this time with platinum the target. A national gravity survey mounted by the South African Geological Survey in the late 1940s had shown a singular anomaly: a gravity high, centred directly on the town of Trompsburg (**geosite 3, map 7**), *which lies 38 km south of Edenburg. The gravity anomaly, some 60 km across, had a similar profile to the mafic-ultramafic intrusion in Zimbabwe, known to geologists around the world as the Great Dyke of Zimbabwe, which is platinum bearing. Mafic and ultramafic rocks contain a high percentage of minerals that are significantly denser than average and, provided they are big enough, will show clearly in a gravity survey. Furthermore, geologists noted that the Trompsburg Anomaly lay in a straight line with the elongate Great Dyke and the enormous Bushveld Complex in the northeast of South Africa (see p. 88). With the Bushveld Complex already – in the 1940s – yielding most of the world's platinum, it was inevitable that the Trompsburg Anomaly would attract the attention of every mining company in the country. The problem was that, according to the gravity survey, the anomaly was covered by about 1 100 m of Karoo sediments. One company, though, decided the risk was worth taking, and drilled eight boreholes, revealing a large, layered intrusion, between 1 800 to 3 000 m thick. Gabbro varieties were the main rocks encountered, analogous with those of the two intrusions further north, but no platinum was found. However, numerous layers of titanium-bearing magnetite were discovered that also contained significant amounts of vanadium. But who knows what else is hidden in what is now called the Trompsburg Complex? It continues to taunt and tantalise mining companies.*

Only 40 km northwest of Trompsburg lies the town of Jagersfontein, a name well known to any 'diamantaire'. It has a man-made hole that rivals Kimberley's and has produced enough big, top-grade stones to have immortalised the name of the farm where the excitement began over 130 years ago. In the spring of 1870, a farmer named De Klerk began prospecting on the farm Jagersfontein, and within a week recovered a 50-carat diamond. This was the first locality where diamonds were

Beaufort shales are seen in extensive outcrops where the N1 crosses the Orange River.

MAP 8

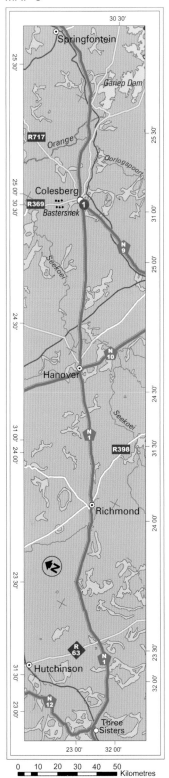

recovered from their source rock, kimberlite – a bonanza soon to be repeated at what was to become Kimberley. Remarkable large stones like the 997.5 carat Excelsior (the second-largest gem diamond ever found), the 657 carat Jubilee, the 637 carat Reitz, and many others were found here.

It's a remarkable small triangle of the upper Karoo. In its floor, at Trompsburg, long before the first Karoo sediment settled, was an igneous complex, giving us a gravity anomaly unique in the country. During the waning days of its sedimentation, brines significantly enriched in uranium deposited their load in the porous sandstones around Edenburg. And then, long after the last sandstorm had blown itself out and the whole basin had been covered in a sea of Drakensberg lava, explosive volcanoes of 'blue ground' or kimberlite, containing carbon crystals plucked from deep in the mantle, burst through to the surface at Jagersfontein.

After Trompsburg, the next village close to the N1 as you head towards Cape Town is Springfontein, and soon after you have passed this turn-off, the country becomes noticeably more broken, with bush-covered dolerite hills and ridges making up much of the topography. You are dropping down towards the Orange River, though you are not yet in the typical Great Karoo landscape, and will notice that between the koppies and ridges (remnants of higher ground), the undulating grasslands persist.

Springfontein to Three Sisters

You're getting close to the heart of fossil country. Lying near the top of the Beaufort Group, the sediments you see here formed near the end of the Permian Period (Palaeozoic Era), around 245 million years ago, just before the Mesozoic Era (in the International Dating System – see table 4, p. 21). During this time, and in the Beaufort depositional environment, life flourished. Rivers wound their lazy way over the plains: on the floodplains, seasonal pools were home to a variety of fishes and on the swampy ground between them roamed a range of reptiles, big and small. This part of the Karoo has yielded a wealth of fossils that make us the envy of the collecting world. The animals and plants here foretold of the extraordinary biodiversity that is still reflected in Africa today. And, equally important, the environment was stable enough for their remains to be preserved. Painstaking work by palaeontologists has given us a good idea of what the creatures looked like and of the world they inhabited. Some of the wonderful books written on the subject are listed at the back of this guide; they give a more comprehensive idea of what it was like. All that is possible in a general treatment like this is a brief summary.

DEM BONES, DEM BONES

In terms of its fossils, the Karoo sequence has been described as one of the great natural wonders of the world. For 50 million years, from 240 to 190 million years ago, a regime of quiet sedimentation persisted almost unbroken, with practically no removal of material, at a time when life on land was young and with the whole Gondwana supercontinent to fill. Think of it as a unique window of evolutionary opportunity, a continuum practically without equal throughout time and around the globe. Fifty million years of continuous fossil record was created and preserved. Now the different levels are presented at the surface, well exposed and easily accessible, reflecting different time periods.

From just above the glacial tillites to almost the highest sandstones below the basalts that cap the Drakensberg, spanning nearly the entire thickness of the sedimentary Karoo sequence, the sediments are fossil-bearing, with plants, invertebrates, fishes and, most importantly, reptiles. And although the Karoo reptiles include the most celebrated of all fossils, the dinosaurs, in these parts they are outranked by another group – a group that filled a vital evolutionary niche and, marginally predating the dinosaurs, was far better represented. These were mammal-like reptiles, the family called Therapsida, representing a transitional stage between reptiles and mammals. As to the lesser importance of the dinosaurs in the Karoo beds, only the early part of their evolution included Gondwana; the later part of their story had to be played out in the northern hemisphere, where they were spared the tides of red-hot lava that rumbled in the south. Until, that is, the awful event that signalled the end of the Cretaceous Period, and – for the dinosaurs and a host of others – the end of their world.

Struthiocephalus, *Bradysaurus* and a host of other mammal-like reptiles dominated the plains of Gondwana long before the arrival of the dinosaurs. Later, *Tyrannosaurus* was to rule half the world, and *Massospondylus* and his bigger (12 m-long) cousin *Melanorosaurus* – both vegetarian dinosaurs – roamed the Triassic veld of central Gondwana. But the mammal-like reptiles were the ancestors of the order that was to succeed the dinosaurs at the end of the Cretaceous Era, and still has dominion today – the mammals. Dozens of species of mammal-like reptiles have been collected from the Karoo, some big, some small, some vegetarian, some fiercely predatory, short-tailed, long-tailed, beak-mouthed with tusks, robust or delicate, smooth-backed or carrying high, sail-like crests from neck to tail, solitary or gregarious.

This group provides the link between two of the most important groupings in the vertebrates of the animal kingdom today. This form of life was transitional, bridging the gap between egg-laying reptiles and mammals that give birth to live young. They were skeletally intermediate – showing features of both reptilian and mammalian skeletons. An iguana and an otter might look structurally related, but their skeletons, and particularly their skulls, are quite different, reflecting their divergent evolution and particular lifestyles. And it is not just that the mammal-like reptiles lie somewhere in the gap between early reptiles and mammals: they fill the gap. In other words, within the Therapsida family, there is a steady progression from more truly reptilian in the lower sediments of the Beaufort, to more mammal-like fossils in the Stormberg sandstones far above them.

Fossilised footprints, thought to have been left by Bradysaurus, *found near Fraserburg.*

'Woolsack' weathering, such as that shown above, is wonderfully exemplified in the koppies around Colesberg.

The main centre you pass in this section of the route is Colesberg. You may well be stopping there since it's close to being the mid-point between Johannesburg and Cape Town, with an abundance of excellent accommodation options. Colesberg nestles around a few koppies of dolerite **(geosite 1, map 8)**: in these parts Karoo dolerite makes up a large proportion of the surface geology. In fact, around the Vanderkloof dam, which is 60 km northwest of Colesberg, and which you will see signposted, you could hike for 50 km, crossing dolerite very nearly all the way.

Note the blocky weathering of the dolerite sill around the town, a fine example of 'woolsack' weathering. As the dolerite cooled and solidified after its molten intrusion, joints formed, approximately at right angles to one another. When these rocks were exposed at the surface, more than a hundred million years later, the rainwater seeped down and along the joints, and the rocks began to weather inwards from the joints. As the process continues and material washes away, the formerly sharply angular block-edges become rounded, giving the impression of rows of stacked-up wool sacks or, to use a more local metaphor, bags of mealies.

Three Sisters to Laingsburg

Since about Colesberg you have been in the Karoo geographic region. Now you are descending into what is known as the Great Karoo, reached not long before you enter Beaufort West. At the N1-8 30.2 km beacon, the Great Escarpment is now clearly recognisable to your right. It forms a towering scarp, reaching an elevation of nearly 2 000 m above sea level in places, a full 1 000 m above the plains around Beaufort West (**geosite 1, map 9**), and very different from the stepped-down, broken country we have come through: the difference between a non-negotiable towering wall and the step-by-step ascent or descent the pioneers of old were able to pick their way through.

Out on the flats southwest of Beaufort West note that, for the first time since the northern Free State, dolerite is conspicuous by its absence. You won't see this rock at close quarters again, this builder of ridges and plateaus that caps the mighty escarpment to the north and provides a resistant barrier to erosion and down-cutting by streams. Look to the countryside for a clue as to why this is. As fast as the high ground recedes to the north as you head southwestward, mountain ranges to the south are closing on your direction of travel. This is the Swartberg range, the first of the Cape Fold Mountains, and just as it forms a high barrier to travellers, so its roots delve deep into the crust (see fig. 20, p. 244). Drive over this range and you will see folding in abundance. Before you are in the mountains, though, and even before you get to the next big centre, Laingsburg, you will see the folds. These folds resulted from the compression of the Cape and lower Karoo strata by far-distant subduction. The southern tip of what would become South America was wrapped around what we know as the Cape, and the plate-collision process that still builds the Andes was just getting under way.

The first sign you see of the folding, here of Beaufort sediments, is soon after Prince Albert Road. As you pass the turn-off to Dwyka siding, shortly after which you cross the railway line, you cannot miss it (**geosite 2, map 9**). From here you will be in folded sediments until you enter the Breede River valley just before Worcester. As you head towards Cape Town, you get closer to the main axes of Cape folding and the folds become tighter.

In the distance lie the Cape Fold Mountains, seen looking south from the bridge over the Dwyka River. Note the smooth tops on either side of the Gamkapoort cutting, telling of a planation that bevelled high mountain ranges long before the break-up of Gondwana.

MAP 9

SEE KEY FOR MAP ON INSIDE BACK COVER FLAP

119

FOLDING: SOME ESSENTIAL TERMS

We have not yet looked at folding in any depth, but it is now opportune to introduce some of the basic terms geologists use in describing what we will see as we approach Cape Town and elsewhere in the country where folding occurs.

Beds of sedimentary rocks, or **strata**, that are not horizontal, are said to **dip**, the angle of dip being measured from the horizontal, which was their original attitude. A dip of 70° would be described as steep, of 15° as flat.

Simply folded strata are shaped into **synclines**, or troughs, and **anticlines**, or domes. Strictly speaking, these terms apply to individual features, but we'll see that, in nature, folds seldom occur individually. The folds we see in road cuttings or on the slopes of hills are almost without exception parts of bigger structures that are kilometres or tens of kilometres across, termed **synclinoria** (singular synclinorium) and **anticlinoria**. The **axial plane** is the imaginary plane cut through the middle of a fold, separating the opposing **limbs**, and the **axis** is where this plane intersects any bed. Folds may be **open**, where dips of the opposing limbs are shallow – less than 45°; or **closed**, where they are steeper than 45°. Similarly, folding – where one talks of a system, or pattern, of adjacent folds – may be **open** or **tight**. When they are so tight that the limbs are parallel, both having more or less the same dip, folds are called **isoclinal**. A term we will hardly use, but which we should have up our sleeves in case of need, is the **plunge** of a fold, where the fold axis is not horizontal, and where the troughs and ridges themselves dip into the ground, instead of lying horizontally. For our present purposes, the folds you will see are mostly folded about horizontal axes, which means that they do not plunge. You only see the **fold closures** themselves where these horizontally disposed folds are exposed in the slopes of hills or in road cuttings; on the flats all you see are the limbs, where the dip of the sediments changes, and the sequence is mirrored, across the axial plane, as the sketch opposite illustrates.

A feature you will see in areas of folding is **cleavage** (most commonly parallel to the axial plane and called **axial plane cleavage**), where the buckling of hard rock has been accompanied by fracturing, often quite intensively developed and penetrative through the strata.

Folding of lower Ecca shales just west of Laingsburg.

SOME GEOLOGICAL TERMS APPLIED TO FOLDING

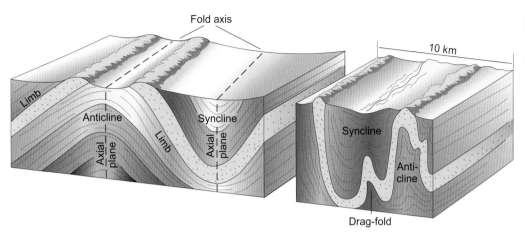

A. An open fold, showing an anticline and syncline, fold limbs, fold axes and axial planes

B. A tight, or isoclinal fold, showing subsidiary drag-folds

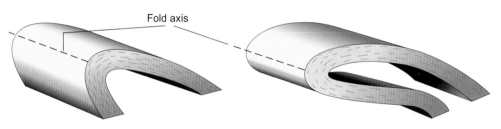

C. An overturned fold

D. A recumbent fold

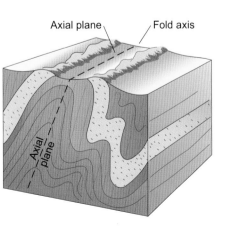

E. Slaty cleavage – also called axial plane cleavage – develops in tightly folded shales and their metamorphic equivalents. Sandstones interbedded in the shales commonly do not show any conspicuous cleavage. In the fold limbs the cleavage will be broadly parallel to the bedding: in the fold closures, or noses, cleavage will cut across the bedding

FIGURE 15

MAP 10

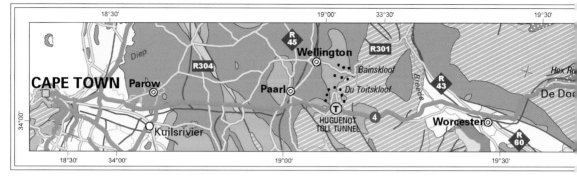

SEE KEY FOR MAP ON INSIDE BACK COVER FLAP

Look south as you cross the Dwyka River, not far after the railway crossing (**geosite 3, map 9**). Note the flat tops on both sides of the Gamkapoort, and the conspicuous break in the distant mountain rampart where the Gamka River cuts through the ranges after being joined by the Dwyka. Those flat tops, unusual in a range of mountains as hard and rugged as these, tell of a very ancient erosional surface, long predating the break-up of Gondwana. It is from the Dwyka River in these parts that the glacial Dwyka Group got its name.

As you drop in elevation, you get into older and older sediments. Ever since leaving Kroonstad, you have been travelling on sediments of the Beaufort Group. After the Dwyka River, you cross over onto another unit in the Karoo Supergroup, the Ecca Group, well known further north for its coal deposits (see p. 198). Here, though, because of the Cape mountain building, conditions were less stable, with much finer sediment deposited in the deep trough flanking the rising mountains to the south – not the forested coastal plains far to the north that favoured the formation of coal.

After coming off the flats that stretch westwards from Beaufort West into more and more broken country, suddenly there is quite a deep valley to your left as you approach Laingsburg. But one of the real treats of the journey awaits you before you get into town (**geosite 4, map 9**). Thin sandstone beds dipping southwards towards the road show text-book ripple-marked bedding planes over areas of many square metres – an extravagant display of a sedimentary process frozen in time. Imagine light water currents wafting the sand into those shapes, and their preservation as the next load of sand was deposited, the water squeezed out, the individual grains cemented together; and then, over millions of years, the whole package turned on its side, to be laid bare by the forces of erosion eons later, producing a snapshot of Ecca sedimentation. Here you are on the northern limb of a syncline, or trough.

Laingsburg to Cape Town

As you leave Laingsburg, look out for the small subsidiary syncline – a drag-fold – in the last cutting to the north of the road, elegantly shown off by the finely bedded shales and siltstones (**geosite 1, map 10**). The structure is complicated from here and we won't attempt to unravel it. But just beyond Matjiesfontein, there is one of the delights of the Karoo Supergroup: the tillite of the Dwyka Group, the glacial deposit that was one of the main keys to unlocking the story of continental drift. Field geologists recognise it in these parts by its so-called tombstone weathering, well exhibited near the road at the 46.6 km beacon (**geosite 2, map 10**). Two kilometres after this are beautiful exposures of fresh tillite in the cutting south of the road (**geosite 3, map 10**), where you can get an idea of the completely unstructured nature of this rock, with clasts – the fragments of rock that make up the sediment – of all sizes, from boulders as big as a third of a metre across,

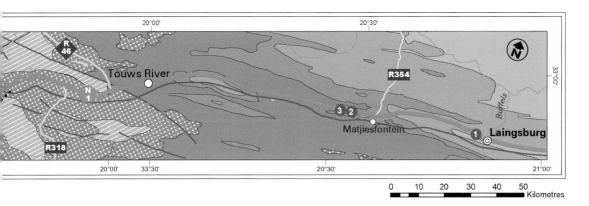

The Dwyka tillite around Matjiesfontein shows what is very aptly named 'tombstone weathering'.
With eyes half closed, you could easily imagine yourself in an extensive graveyard.

The 'White Band' and Matjiesfontein Chert

Between Matjiesfontein and Laingsburg you cannot miss a thin sedimentary band that runs for kilometres, standing above the surrounding countryside like a low, cream-coloured farm wall. It is, in fact, a thin turbidite band (up to half a metre thick) with a high component of volcanic material, and is called the Matjiesfontein Chert. It lies near the base of the Ecca Group, just above the white-weathering Whitehill Formation (formerly loosely known as the 'White Band'), and of which it could be considered to be a part. It stands up as it does because the whole sedimentary package in these parts has been upended into a (sub)vertical attitude by Cape folding.

floating in the finest clay. Other than the fact that it is around 300 million years old and so hard that it is favoured by engineers for road foundations, it is no different from the glacial till that covers large parts of Canada and was left by the last Ice Age, almost in living memory. It is a tribute to the abrasive power of the ice sheets that they ripped not just sand and clay off the surface they ground over, but quite big fragments of rock, to be carried along and dropped as the ice melted.

Around the 23.0 km beacon, you will start to notice impressive rock slopes dipping steeply towards the road on the left-hand side, reaching 40 or 50 m in height. You won't find much better examples of true dip slopes, where hard sediments dip at an angle that is just steeper than the normal angle of repose of weathered rock and soil, and the bed itself makes the slope; these are in sandstones of the Bokkeveld Group, part of the Cape Supergroup. Note that, around Touws River, you pass briefly between sandstone hills made of the topmost unit in the Cape succession, the Witteberg Group; and that you have seen the last of the Karoo Supergroup for this trip. You are moving steadily down in the stratigraphy into older and older formations as you drive westwards.

As you come into the top of the Hex River valley, you are entering a big northeast-opening syncline, the axis of which you will travel roughly along until leaving the valley. The dip slopes on the north side of the valley are striking, composed of sandstones of the Table Mountain Group.

On the northwestern side of the Hex River valley, Table Mountain sandstone dips beneath the recent valley-fill sediment on which is grown a large part of the country's table-grape crop.

On the south side, there are no dip slopes, but as you catch glimpses of some of the deeply incised kloofs cutting into the slopes – well along the valley – you will see that on this side, too, the bedding dips down towards the road. Fix this experience in your memory: you may not find yourself driving along the axis of a mega-syncline like this again soon.

When you are out of the tight kloof that links the valleys of the Hex and Breede Rivers, you may see that the rocks making up the slopes just to the right of you are different from anything you've seen before on this journey. These are metamorphosed sediments of the Malmesbury Group, significantly older than the Cape sediments and already folded and eroded by the time the latter were laid down. They were refolded during Cape folding and their cleavage is something you won't have seen this conspicuously before. Note that these Malmesbury sediments support a prolific growth of aloes, in which they differ conspicuously from the Cape rocks you have passed over.

Old Man River

A striking feature of the Breede River valley is its width, compared to the relatively minor river that has carved it. It may help to know that this is a very old valley, dating back at least 170 million years to the days of the inception of continental rifting and drifting, around the middle of the Jurassic Period. It follows, around here, the ancient system of deep faults that stretches from Tulbagh all the way to Mossel Bay. Over the eons, the ground south of the fault has dropped and dropped, and dropped some more, until a 6 000-m 'drop' has been notched up. But normal erosional forces level the ground continuously, so that for a while there will be a small drop, until it is levelled off by erosion; then as the fault is reactivated there will be a drop again, which is gradually levelled off, then reactivated, levelled off, and so on ad infinitum. And it may occasionally still move, as those startled from their slumbers in Ceres and Tulbagh in September 1969 by the Ceres earthquake will attest – a quake that registered a magnitude of 6.3 on the Richter Scale.

Ahead are ranges even more towering than those you have just come through. But as you get closer to them, you will see that there is none of the folding that was evident in the Hex River valley. In the foothills across the Breede River, note the occurrence, particularly to the south, but in one excellent exposure to the north as well, of the Cedarberg shale, the smoothly fynbos-covered slopes making a striking contrast with the craggy, rocky mountainsides that are the norm in these parts.

As you enter the tight Molenaars valley, approaching Du Toit's Kloof Pass and the Huguenot Tunnel, keep a lookout for the granite in a few low cuttings to your left (**geosite 4, map 10**). It's weathered and not at all like the crystal-clear outcrops at Sea Point or on Paarl Rock, but it's useful to get an idea of what weathered granite looks like, especially as it's easily distinguishable from the metamorphosed sediments of the Malmesbury Group, through which it cuts, or of the Table Mountain Group, which overlies it. You will notice, too, if you cast your eyes upwards, that the Table Mountain sediments show that you are out of the folding now. That's because you are into what geologists call the syntaxis zone, the geological equivalent of the eye of the hurricane. You are in the zone between the north-south and east-west ranges of intense folding and thrusting. The dips of the beds are flattening from their steep inclinations in the fold belts, until, as you emerge from the Huguenot Tunnel, there is the perfectly flat-topped Table Mountain far ahead. But directly in front of you are the Cape Granite domes of Paarl Rock, the 'pearls'. For more about the Cape Granite we suggest you look at the chapter on Cape Town (ch. 2, p. 62). In the meantime, welcome to the Cape.

6 N2: Cape Town to Port Elizabeth

GEOLOGICAL OVERVIEW

This route has a dominating geological theme: from start to finish, you will be driving over the Cape Fold Belt. And for most of the way you will be in sight of the fold mountain chain that resulted from a collision of crustal plates, far to the south, during the assembly of Gondwana. The route is arguably South Africa's most scenic drive, and part of it, from Mossel Bay to Storms River, is appropriately known as 'the Garden Route', a favourite among tourists, with its spectacular mountains and passes, indigenous forests, splendid lakes and stunning coastal scenery. The route shows considerable coastal geology and land-forming processes. You will see clear evidence of the changing position of the South African coastline, and of the power of erosion acting over many millions of years. Long stretches of the route from Mossel Bay to Port Elizabeth are within sight of the sea; and modern coastal dunes, and their fossil predecessors, are a conspicuous feature of the landscape, as are coastal lagoons between Wilderness and Plettenberg Bay.

The flat top in the distance is a remnant of the African Surface, shown here by a hard layer of silcrete (or 'surface quartzite') produced by weathering. Such remnants are common in the southern Cape, where they usually overlie folded Bokkeveld shales.

The other feature of coastal geology well displayed on the N2 is the development of robust conglomerate of the Enon Formation, particularly as you enter the town of Knysna. These bouldery sediments are noteworthy in that they formed during the early break-up of Gondwana and the evolution of the first South African coastline. And as you pass Mossel Bay, the large oil-from-gas plant will remind you that offshore, not far over the southern horizon, is South Africa's only commercial gas field, in rocks formed at the same time as the formation of the conglomerate.

In summary – with the exception of the granite seen at George, this entire drive is a wonderful illustration of a range of sedimentary and coastal erosion processes.

INSET: *In strong contrast to the main picture, this flat top in the Karoo owes its presence to a hard sandstone bed, and is unrelated to any land 'surface'.*

These Table Mountain sandstones near the top of the Houw Hoek Pass are an excellent example of cross-bedding, formed as the sand is deposited. The clearly defined horizontal layers represent successive phases of deposition.

Cape Town to Riversdale

As you leave Cape Town on the N2, the only geology you will clearly see from your car window is the amphitheatre of high quartzite mountains, composed of rocks of the Table Mountain Group. On the Cape Flats surrounding you, only glimpsed through the rampant alien vegetation, is windblown sand, hardly consolidated, and geologically young. As you approach the Hottentots Holland range and Sir Lowry's Pass, also composed of Cape Supergroup sediments, note how broken the rock is: the sedimentary layering, so clear in Table Mountain, is not nearly so easy to pick up here. This is because you are well and truly in the zone where the Cape Fold Belt changes its direction from north-south, following the Atlantic coast, to east-west ahead of you, running parallel to the southern coast. This transitional zone of deformation is typically characterised more by brittle fracturing than by folding.

Soon after you have started the climb up Sir Lowry's Pass, at around the 11.0 km beacon, you'll see some outcrop of fresh Cape Granite in the road cutting to your right. At and beyond the 11.8 km beacon, steeply dipping Table Mountain quartzite can be seen in the cutting to your left **(geosite 1, map 11)**, reminding you of the folding that tilted the horizontally deposited sediments into a variety of attitudes. Here, only 50 km from Cape Town's table-flat monolith, the quartzite is already up to 60° off horizontal. You'll see steep dips to the top of the pass, continuing for a while over the top.

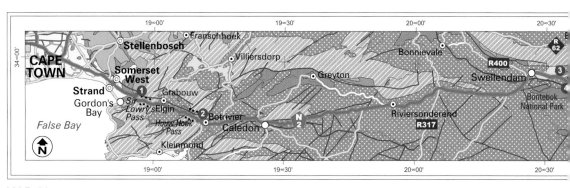

MAP 11

SEE KEY FOR MAP ON INSIDE BACK COVER FLAP

Silcretes (or 'surface quartzite') of the Grahamstown Formation, developed on the African Surface of erosion, support a vigorous growth of aloes east of Swellendam.

By the time you have crossed the Steenbras River you are into some complicated geology – both folds and faults in shaley rocks of the Bokkeveld Group – until the road divides for the Houw Hoek Pass, where you are back in quartzites of the Table Mountain Group for a while. Note the beautiful cross-bedding in these quartzites, particularly near the beginning of the dual carriageway **(geosite 2, map 11)**. Down on the flats, in the wheatlands of what are known locally as the 'ruens', you are back in Bokkeveld sediments, a situation that will persist for most of the way until Mossel Bay. The shales show a variety of reds, mauves, pinks, browns and yellows and are generally highly cleaved, as well as showing more bedding than earlier along the route.

After Caledon, not only do the shales show a dappling of their colours, they also show conspicuous pock-marking in places. Both effects tell of varying porosity of the rock, causing the chemicals, mainly iron and silica, to settle in some places and not in others.

For a long way you'll see mountains far off to the north, and hills closer, all of them Table Mountain quartzites, but the rolling hills you drive over are composed of Bokkeveld shales, mostly soft and easily sculpted. Where they have been subjected, during the folding that pervades these parts, to conditions of higher pressure, they have been slightly hardened and some of the wheatlands seem to show more broken rock than soil; as far as the farmers are concerned, the stone is soft enough to be broken by their rippers and ploughs, and there is enough nutrient-rich soil in there to support the crops they grow.

Colours in sediments and Liesegang banding

The shales of the Bokkeveld Group show off quite extravagantly the range of colours to be found in rocks. In the most general terms, dark grey shales are rich in organic material (that is, in carbon) – the darker the richer. Thick sequences of such rocks will have formed in still water and we classify them as either deep-water marine or lacustrine (lake-deposited) sediments. Red rocks are iron-rich and deep-water marine, generally deposited by rivers or along the coast under oxidising conditions. Black bands in very ancient (Archaean) sediments generally comprise iron oxide, often magnetite; and the black coatings or leaf-shaped dendrites seen on joint or bedding planes are of manganese oxide.

All other colours – the greens, purples, etc. – are mainly a function of the amount of iron and its state of oxidation. Many common rock-forming minerals have some iron in them, which can be released from the minerals at any stage as iron oxide, and distributed through the rock. Most other elements present, which find their way into the fabric of the rock in exactly the same fashion, form white or colourless minerals, and while they may lighten the tone of the final rock, they do not colour it in any way.

Some of the most eye-catching colour banding we see in weathered rock exposures is called Liesegang banding. Although easily mistaken for bedding, a close look will usually show that this banding is, in fact, something quite different. It tells of the movement of waves of groundwater through the permeable rock, and along bedding and joint planes. Over long periods of time, the water leaches soluble material – mainly iron – from the rock and carries it along in solution. Sooner or later the water evaporates or the chemical environment changes, the material is no longer stable in solution, and it precipitates. Water moves along a 'front', as though in a wave. If everything were equal, these fronts would be straight. However, there are subtle but important differences in permeability, so the front becomes distorted and sinuous. The result of all this may be either colour banding, sometimes in very beautiful, brightly hued patterns, or hardening alongside joint-planes, giving rise to the pitted, box-work appearance seen, for example, in road cuttings around Caledon.

This Liesegang banding occurs in Bokkeveld shale east of Grabouw.
It may be seen in a wide variety of rocks, from young to ancient.

This unsorted, unbedded appearance is typical of the Grahamstown Formation.
Such rocks form from the prolonged silicification of an ancient soil profile.

As you start your descent to the Breede River crossing, with Swellendam visible ahead, you will see the rounded boulders and cobbles of the ancient river that are now perched high above the present river level and tell of a time long before lowering sea level had dropped the base level to where it is now. If you were to drive to Malgas, or further, to Witsand at the mouth of the river, you would find beautifully rounded, river-worn cobbles strewn liberally over the flats, further testimony to this ancient, higher level of river flow.

With Swellendam behind you and the Buffeljags valley coming up, you will notice, both north and south of the road, planed-off river terraces, generally edged by scarps that, though low, mark quite a distinct break in the surface. Such flat, scarp-edged surfaces, where close to rivers, almost invariably tell of old river terraces (see profile 'C', fig. 4B, p. 23). They are most conspicuous where the underlying bedrock is quite soft, like the Bokkeveld shales, and are common in the southern Cape, where late Jurassic sedimentation that was the precursor to the break-up of Gondwana took place, the barely consolidated sediments providing little resistance to the forces of erosion.

So it won't come as a surprise that you are crossing one of these late Jurassic basins, part of the rather diverse Uitenhage Group, as you head east from Swellendam. It's not a big basin and you won't see much of the coarse Enon Formation conglomerate that characterises the lower part of these basins. As you drive along the straight section of road on the Buffeljags flats, though, and just before the secondary road to Suurbraak and Barrydale turns off to the left, there is a low cutting with some of this conglomerate well displayed **(geosite 3, map 11)**. It's worth a stop if you've got the time.

As you climb out of the valley, you are coming into a belt of country where there are high-standing remnants of the African Surface, capped by Tertiary-aged silcretes (thin surface quartzites) of the Grahamstown Formation. Generally ringed by slopes that are steeper than anything else you'll see around here, these residual cappings are a common feature of the landscape **(geosite 4, map 11)**. They offer a glimpse into the distant past, the only reminders of the vast coastal plain that once joined all these isolated mesas; in a few million years they, too, will be gone.

MAP 12   SEE KEY FOR MAP ON INSIDE BACK COVER FLAP

Riversdale to Storms River

Past Riversdale and approaching Albertinia, with the railway line close on your left, you can hardly miss the piles of golden rock and sand at the Resiesbaan siding **(geosite 1, map 12)**. You may have noticed the quarry a couple of kilometres to your right just before this. It produces agricultural lime, quarried from Tertiary dune rock, with calcium carbonate derived from tiny fragments of shell and other marine organisms. It is used by farmers in the hills to the north to neutralise the very acid soil that forms over the Table Mountain quartzites, which are just about pure quartz. Remember: the more quartz in a rock, the more acid it is, and if that becomes a problem in the soil such rocks make, nature also supplies the remedy.

The dumps at Resiesbaan are a reminder that South Africa is a country with a long mining heritage. Here, though, there is no shining treasure awaiting release: what you see is what you get – yellow limestone. It is used to unlock the potential from the soil that is otherwise too acid to produce rich harvests.

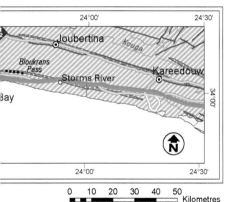

Around Albertinia, and especially east of it, as far as Mossel Bay, you will notice extensive, smoothly planed flats off to your left. These ancient coastal plains were cut into by early rivers, which, slowly but surely, and over millions of years, have opened their valleys to the profiles we see today. In its last 25 km, from under the N2 to its mouth, the Gouritz River falls by a little more than 5 m, this flatness eloquent testimony to the millions of years it's had to do its downcutting.

Not long after crossing the Gouritz River, the flames of burning waste gases from tall PetroSA (formerly Mossgas) stacks are in view. Like the flat gradient of the Gouritz, this giant production facility relates to events that followed the break-up of Gondwana. The main reason the gorge of the Gouritz, as well as those of rivers in the Tsitsikamma, have cut so deeply is that there was a time when the coastline lay far beyond today's shipping lanes (see more about sea level changes in the chapter on Cape Town, ch. 2, pp. 66 & 72). During the Cretaceous Period, the coastline transgressed, to a maximum of 120 m above today's sea level, and regressed, as far as the edge of the continental shelf at times, again and again. Rivers cut down during regressions, and are partially backfilled during transgressions, over many millions of years. And it was during the regressions that the scene was set for the formation of the offshore gas fields of the Agulhas Bank.

OIL AND GAS IN SOUTH AFRICA

The search for a South African oil field was mounted – and relentlessly pursued – during the period of international sanctions against South Africa's apartheid regime. For a time the sediments of the Karoo Supergroup were targeted, without anything resembling a potentially productive oil reservoir being discovered. Unrivalled source of fossils it might be, but exhaustive geophysics, drilling and high-tech analysis of data suggested that the Karoo was not a promising oil-bearing formation.

With the North Sea and other continental shelf areas receiving growing attention from oil companies at the time, it did not take the parastatal Soekor long to take the search offshore. In 1970, Placid Oil Company drilled a borehole 85 km south of Mossel Bay on the Agulhas Bank, as the large offshore Cretaceous sedimentary platform had become known. They found only a small quantity of gas and the search was discontinued. Soekor's first hole into what became known as the 'F-A gas field', drilled 10 years later and just over 3 km away from Placid's hole, gave sufficient encouragement for systematic drilling to start to define a reserve. The decision was made to build a major plant at Mossel Bay to convert gas to liquid fuels and other products using Sasol's Synthol Process, and the first gas flowed onshore in 1992. The Mossel Bay synfuel plant is currently the only commercial gas-to-liquid facility in the world, supplying eight per cent of our domestic fossil fuels.

Ten years after the gas discovery hole was drilled, another exploratory hole penetrated what would turn out to be an economically viable reservoir of natural oil, some 45 km south-southwest of the F-A field. Production at the Oribi Field started in 1997 and at the adjacent Oryx Field in 2000, with oil transported from a floating production facility by a shuttle tanker. In 2003 the Sable Oil Field, 18 km west of Oribi, commenced oil production to a dedicated floating and storage facility.

As to why the fields south of Mossel Bay have accumulated oil and gas at all, and why they have not delivered the fabulous reserves that the North Sea or the Arabian or Texan fields have, there's no easy answer. A number of factors have to combine for oil and gas to form, and to collect in a suitable reservoir. The sediments need to have had a generous quota of organic remains of the right sort; after burial and lithification, the rocks formed have to be heated – usually by burial – for the oil to form and move, but not to be vaporised completely. There have to be porous reservoir rocks above the source rocks into which the oil and gas will move, and these need to have been shaped into traps so as to concentrate the hydrocarbons, usually by folding or faulting. And finally, there needs to have been an impermeable 'cap-rock' to prevent the oil and gas dispersing upwards. All of these requirements must be met for an oil field to form: the greater the extent to which they are all met, the bigger the oil field.

A big ask it may be, but it's far too soon to be pessimistic. PetroSA, the Petroleum Oil and Gas Corporation of South Africa, was formed in July 2000 from a merger of the businesses of founder companies Mossgas and Soekor. PetroSA's role is to develop and exploit crude oil and gaseous hydrocarbon resources of South Africa and beyond our borders.

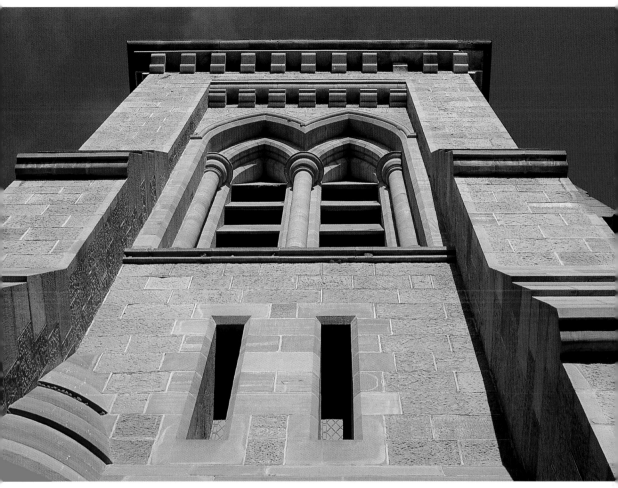

Kirkwood sandstone from nearby Cape St Blaize has been used in all the handsome older churches in Mossel Bay.

If you need a break at about this point in your journey, do yourself a favour and drive into the town of Mossel Bay. It's a place with a disproportionate depth of history for its size, as well as being one of the major growth centres in South Africa. But it is the stone buildings in Mossel Bay that should draw your attention. With very rare exception, they are built from sandstone of the Kirkwood Formation of the Jurassic to Cretaceous Uitenhage Group that is found in a restricted outcrop around the lighthouse on Cape St Blaize. Being geologically relatively young, these sandstones lend themselves to easy working, and the beds at the Point, just outside the town, must have proved a boon to the settler builders. If you have seen Oudtshoorn's splendid stone buildings and these strike you as similar, it's for good reason: the source rocks are geologically the same.

Back on the N2, soon after joining the dual highway you will find yourself at the top of the long slope down almost to sea level. Here you will cross the sediments of the Uitenhage Group that filled Mossel Bay when it was a much bigger bay than it is today. Imagine the sea level more than 100 m higher, with young, steep rivers carrying loads of boulders and cobbles to dump them not far from their source, the sand drifting further out. The headland that makes Cape St Blaize would have been much longer then, the bay indenting the coastline more than 30 km to the west of where we see it today.

Note, from about the 96.8 km beacon next to the road, the peculiarly shaped hills quite far off to your left: they will ring a bell if you've travelled around Oudtshoorn at all, for they are cut in Enon conglomerate, also part of the Uitenhage Group (see also p. 250). You can see the grey grits and maroon mudstone of this group at the end of the road cutting on your left just after you cross the Groot Brakriver. Drive slowly and you'll see the grey granites of the Maalgaten Pluton in the next road cutting, and quite regularly from here on for a while **(geosite 2, map 12)**. This pluton belongs to the Cape Granite Suite, the same general family as those around Paarl and Cape Town, intruded into folded sediments that are not very much older than they are, and then planed off to form the floor of the basin of Cape Supergroup sediments.

George and its environs are up on the smoothly planed Miocene platform, part of what was the offshore continental shelf around 20 million years ago. You'll see much more of this surface after Plettenberg Bay, when you've climbed out of the Keurbooms River valley and will be on the plain long enough for it to make an impression. Here you are on and off it so quickly that you hardly have time to appreciate its exceptional flatness. Note that here, the platform is carved on granite, whereas further east it's on the even harder quartzites of the Table Mountain Group.

In the meantime, soon after George you are on your way down to sea level again. To get there you have to go down into the Kaaimans valley just before getting to Wilderness, with some long stretches of tightly cleaved and folded metamorphosed sediments in the cuttings on both sides of the river. Known as the Kaaimans Group, these sediments are the same age, broadly speaking, as the Malmesbury metasediments to be seen around Worcester, or at Sea Point, on Robben Island or in the Cango Caves. It's worth having a good look at these as you drive by them, to see their general similarity to the rocks you may have seen at some of the other places mentioned, and to think that, although you are a long way away, things have not changed much.

From Wilderness until you have climbed out of the Knysna valley, you go through a stretch of lake country that is unusual in South Africa, not only scenically, but geologically as well. It's a little two dimensional if you stick to the N2; to get a fascinating glimpse of the third dimension, you need to take the train from George to Knysna – well worth it if you can make the necessary arrangements.

Before you even get into Knysna, the signpost to the Millwood gold field may catch your eye, and your curiosity **(geosite 3, map 12)**. The site has recently been restored and, if you have a couple of hours to cover the 26 km from the N2 and to have a look around, it's worth the detour. Now set in tranquil pine forests and cooled by sea breezes, the spot is about as different from the Witwatersrand as can be imagined. The only building surviving from the mini-gold rush, which first hit the Cape Town newspapers in 1887 and had played itself out 13 years later, has been converted into a museum and tea room, and some of the extraction equipment is on display near the entrance to an old mine shaft. The gold, having been discovered by prospectors panning the stream sediments, was soon traced to its primary source in the hard rock higher up the valley. Together with pyrite, it had been carried by the quartz veins which intruded into the quartzitic sandstone of the Table Mountain Group during the Cape folding. In all, a production of some 127 kg of gold was declared, small by any standard.

The Heads linking the huge Knysna Lagoon to the sea are, in contrast to the dune-enclosed lakes, a break in a forbiddingly rocky stretch of coastline. Here the relatively deep channel stays open, offering an inviting refuge to sailors buffeted by wild storms in the open ocean. Even before you get to the turn-off to the Heads you will have seen the roadside cliffs of Enon conglomerate. Knysna's depositional history goes back into the Jurassic Period, and the proposal has been made

The curious phenomenon of coastal lakes

Why do coastal lakes occur here, when they are found nowhere else along the coast until you get onto the wide coastal plains of northern KwaZulu-Natal 1 000 km away? The answer lies in the combination of coastal rock formations and sea level fluctuations.

During marine regressions, when the coast moves far offshore from where we see it now, erosional and river down-cutting processes are at work and valleys are carved out, very easily where the coastal geology comprises soft, usually quite young formations. During the ensuing marine transgression, when the sea moves inland, these valleys become filled or 'drowned' with coastal sediment. This results in wave-cut platforms that are quite extensive if the building process is given long enough. As the next regression gets under way and the sea level retreats southwards again, these platforms are left high and dry. One of the main reasons for regression is glaciation, where climates become colder and drier and, being at the southern end of the continent, perpetually windy. Dune cordons build up along the coast. Again, the sea level rises with the next transgression, and the valleys behind the dune belts become drowned, to some extent with further sediment but, more importantly as far as we're concerned, with water. Much of that water is from rivers trying to breach the dunes to reach the sea, but the dunes are quite permeable, added to which, the water in the lakes is at such a low elevation that they are tidal anyway.

As to why these coastal lakes and lagoons form here, and not elsewhere – it is partly climatic and partly because the underlying geology permits it here and not elsewhere. Being soft, the rocks here are more susceptible to valley formation than is possible in hard granites and quartzites, where deep, vertical-sided gorges are all that the rivers can manage. You've just seen the deeply weathered, highly cleaved schists and phyllites between George and Wilderness – you hardly have to be told that they are soft and easily incised, compared to the quartzites that lie along the coast up ahead. It's a good illustration of how manifestly geology continues to shape the world we live in.

Groenvlei Lake with the barrier sand dune behind it, taken from near the top of the sand dune inland of the lake and the N2.

that the resistant barrier of Table Mountain quartzite closing the lagoon, and breached at the Heads, was pushed up after the Enon conglomerate and sandstone were deposited. The conglomerates to be seen extensively in Knysna were river-deposited, though probably reworked by offshore currents. As you drive through Knysna, give a thought to the antiquity of this basin, which is probably not very different today from the way it was in late Cretaceous times, 65 million years ago.

Plettenberg Bay is different from the other bays along the Cape south coast in one respect: the Robberg cape, or headland, that closes off the 'half-heart' bay, is built not of resistant Table Mountain quartzite, but of far younger late Jurassic sediments called the Robberg Formation. These intertidal sediments are mainly a variety of sandstone, lesser conglomerates and breccias. In some places, it is true, a basement of folded Table Mountain quartzite can be seen quite a few metres above sea level on Robberg, and it could be argued that, without this ultra-resistant rock at sea level, the peninsula would have been reduced and ultimately obliterated – but that is speculation **(geosite 4, map 12)**.

Heading eastwards, note the Enon conglomerate towering over the Bitou River on the far side, and only a little further on, as you cross the Keurbooms River, the opposite slope is cut in Bokkeveld shales. Then you climb off the coastal plain of today onto that of yesteryear, 200–300 m higher. And

These Enon sediments in the Knysna Basin, seen here as you enter the town from the west, show alternating coarse- and fine-grained layers not typical of Enon conglomerate elsewhere and are thought by geologists who have studied them to have been reworked since their first deposition.

you'll stay on it for most of the way until you're on the outskirts of Port Elizabeth. We've already said that the rocks so perfectly planed off are mostly quartzites of the Table Mountain Group. That such hard formations were reduced to featureless flats tells how prolonged was the period they were under water, and how the surf must have crashed against the foot of the high mountain slopes visible just inland. That they have not been carved up into hills and valleys in the last 20 million years – that the only valleys cutting them could be spanned by man in a single structure – speaks clearly of their durability. For most of the way, these are the same quartzites that tower over Table Bay, there so perfectly horizontal, here upended.

From the Beacon Isle Hotel, the long headland that makes the Robberg Peninsula is atypical of headlands along the southern Cape coast, which are mostly carved from resistant Table Mountain quartzite. This promontory is made of sandstone and conglomerate of the Robberg Formation lying on the much older quartzite, which is exposed at sea level.

Storms River to Port Elizabeth

After George you travel for some time along a strip of coastal plain sandwiched between the mountains and the sea. About 30 km west of Humansdorp, though, that starts to change. The mountains, by now more like hills, peter out completely and you have the Krom River valley ahead of you. Unlike the series of steep gorges you have recently crossed on magnificent arched bridges, this is a wide valley cutting obliquely across the mountain range as it leaves the Langkloof, on its way to the sea. Although the Krom River is not much more than a stream, it's been at work for eons, carving out a valley of significant proportions, as you'll know if you've ever followed it along the alternative Langkloof route.

Just after passing to the north of Humansdorp, you'll see the sweep of St Francis Bay in front of you. The coast is starting to change direction, from the roughly east-west direction it has maintained since you left Cape Town to one more northeast–southwest, which continues to beyond the Mozambican border, with only minor fluctuations in direction.

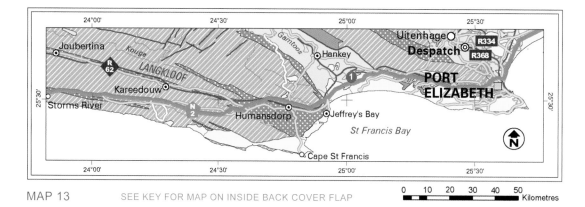

MAP 13   SEE KEY FOR MAP ON INSIDE BACK COVER FLAP

0 10 20 30 40 50
Kilometres

Like the other 'half-heart' bays on the Cape coast, St Francis Bay was considerably more elongate in the past. It stretched way inland of its present coastline, so that Jeffrey's Bay and the other resorts around the mouth of the Krom River (but not Cape St Francis) would have been deep under water. Since the late Jurassic Period, which was more than 100 million years ago, it has been filled with sediment that you'll drive over as you head towards the Gamtoos River. It is the Gamtoos that has

helped carve out the formerly much longer bay, and you'll see as you cross it how it was able to do so: it's the confluence of major rivers draining the interior – the Groot, the Baviaanskloof and the Kouga rivers. See the low sand dunes at the river mouth as you cross it, and a tiny window of Enon sediments in the steep opposite bank to your left **(geosite 1, map 13)**. The younger, covering dune rock or aeolianite you cut through as you leave the Gamtoos is bush-covered, so you won't see it here, though there's lots of it to be seen in cuttings between Port Elizabeth and Grahamstown.

After quite a stretch of broken country east of the Gamtoos River, you find yourself back on the same marine terrace you were on west of Humansdorp. Here there are scattered hills to the north of the road, not the continuous mountain range you've been travelling alongside for a while. But you're not off that ancient coastal platform yet, and the crossing over the Van Staden's River is very reminiscent of the Keurbooms and other spectacular crossings further west. Dropping down to lower levels in Port Elizabeth, you'll notice you're in the same white Table Mountain quartzite you've seen so much of since leaving Cape Town.

Marine gravels lying on the gullied surface of Table Mountain quartzites just east of the Van Staden's River bridge. The cobbles and pebbles have been beautifully rounded and sorted by wave action through a number of cycles, starting some 30 million years ago.

7 N2: Port Elizabeth to Durban

GEOLOGICAL OVERVIEW

The route northeast from Port Elizabeth shows surprising geological variety. Algoa Bay's hinterland is a large Cretaceous basin, well known for abundant marine fossils, particularly in the Sundays River valley. Folded Cape and lower Karoo Supergroup sediments offer some dramatic exposures around Grahamstown, and the progression from folded to unfolded sediments can be tracked on the way to King William's Town. This provides an excellent opportunity to see good exposures of normally flat-lying Karoo sediments. In a general sense this change mirrors another that is conspicuous if you look for it, and that is the first appearance of Karoo dolerite; it is not present in the compressional fold belt, but well developed where horizontal sediments allowed the tensional opening of fissures that were the forerunners to the break-up of Gondwana.

Past East London, your route will take you through the rolling, wide-open spaces of the Transkei, underlain mainly by Karoo sediments, and you will see more evidence of dolerites and of donga formation. Dropping from Kokstad towards the KwaZulu-Natal coast takes you down through a good section of the Karoo Supergroup, then

the pre-Karoo Msikaba Formation and, briefly, through Precambrian granite. Along the quite severely faulted KwaZulu-Natal coast you will see gneisses of the Natal Metamorphic Province that forms the Basement in these parts, together with Karoo sediments again and, near Durban, sandstone of the Natal Group. On part of the journey, from Port Shepstone to Durban, you will be within sight of the sea; and modern coastal dunes and their fossil predecessors are a conspicuous feature of the landscape.

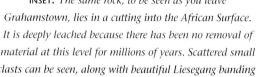

BELOW: *This Dwyka tillite, east of Harding, is conspicuously unweathered – revealed because the soft surface material (see inset) has been removed by active erosion along the coastal strip.*

INSET: *The same rock, to be seen as you leave Grahamstown, lies in a cutting into the African Surface. It is deeply leached because there has been no removal of material at this level for millions of years. Scattered small clasts can be seen, along with beautiful Liesegang banding.*

MAP 14   SEE KEY FOR MAP ON INSIDE BACK COVER FLAP

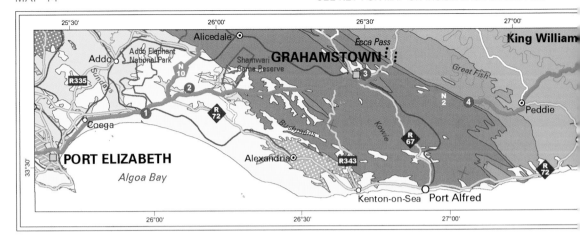

Geology of the route

Port Elizabeth to East London

Algoa Bay is the last of the 'half-heart' bays that characterise the southern coast, and also the largest, shaped by both the Swartkops River and the biggest river you'll cross on the Cape south coast, the Sundays River. This bay, too, reached far deeper into the interior in the geological past and, like those further west, it has largely been filled with sediment washed off the mountains of the interior, on and

The highest dunes in South Africa that relate to the present coastline are to be found in this dune field along the coast northeast of the Sundays River, itself not far northeast of Port Elizabeth, the 'Windy City'.

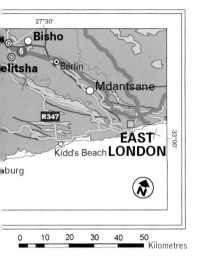

Bisho
6
elitsha Berlin
Mdantsane
R347
EAST
Kidd's Beach LONDON
33°00'
burg

0 10 20 30 40 50
Kilometres

off over the past 150 million years. Thickest of these sedimentary packages is the Uitenhage Group, deposited during the late Jurassic and early Cretaceous, around 140 to 120 million years ago. On a lesser scale, sedimentation continues to this day – the beaches of Algoa Bay are sandy in contrast to the rocky coastline along the Tsitsikamma and north of Kenton-on-Sea. Long, sandy beaches in a windy environment mean sand dunes, and even before you cross the Sundays River, only a few kilometres from the coast, you'll see the dune field **(geosite 1, map 14)**. To an extent, the dunes are vegetated, but by no means entirely, and flanking the mouth you'll see slopes of shifting, bare sand, reminiscent, for those who have visited it, of Swakopmund. From just east of Port Elizabeth there is a stretch of 100 km of modern Quaternary coastal dunes, some just about as high as you'll see anywhere.

Aeolianite (rock formed from wind-blown sand) of the Nanaga Formation north of where the N10 and R72 leave the N2. The high angle of cross-bedding in this cutting identifies the rock as wind-laid as opposed to water-laid, where the maximum angle of repose of sand is significantly lower.

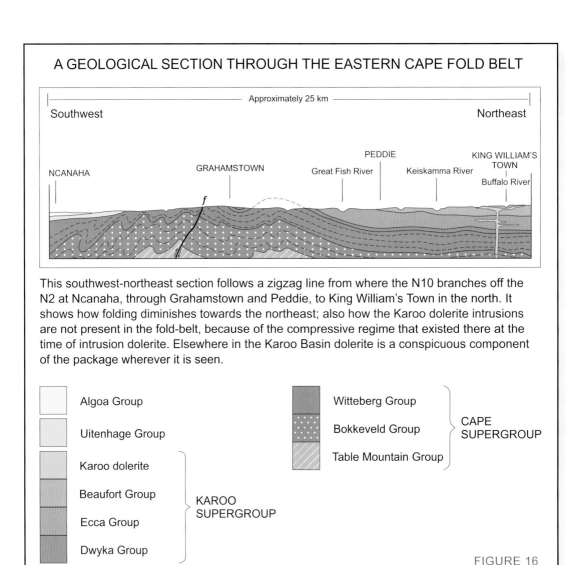

A GEOLOGICAL SECTION THROUGH THE EASTERN CAPE FOLD BELT

Approximately 25 km

Southwest

Northeast

NCANAHA   GRAHAMSTOWN   Great Fish River   PEDDIE   Keiskamma River   KING WILLIAM'S TOWN   Buffalo River

f

This southwest-northeast section follows a zigzag line from where the N10 branches off the N2 at Ncanaha, through Grahamstown and Peddie, to King William's Town in the north. It shows how folding diminishes towards the northeast; also how the Karoo dolerite intrusions are not present in the fold-belt, because of the compressive regime that existed there at the time of intrusion dolerite. Elsewhere in the Karoo Basin dolerite is a conspicuous component of the package wherever it is seen.

Algoa Group

Uitenhage Group

Karoo dolerite

Beaufort Group   KAROO SUPERGROUP

Ecca Group

Dwyka Group

Witteberg Group

Bokkeveld Group   CAPE SUPERGROUP

Table Mountain Group

FIGURE 16

As you climb out of the Sundays valley you're on older Tertiary dunes **(geosite 2, map 14)** – now lithified to aeolianite – for a long way, the last of them quite close to Grahamstown. They're easy to identify where exposed in the cuttings, generally covered by very red soil, and themselves showing as buff-coloured, cross-bedded sandstones that are quite soft, not yet having been compacted by deep burial or hardened by metamorphism. As you get onto the higher ground, you will see scattered outcrops of harder, older rock – quartzite and shale – which make up an increasing proportion of the exposed geology. Now that you are travelling in a more northerly direction, you are cutting across the fold structures on your way out of the Cape Fold Belt. The rocks of which you catch increasingly frequent glimpses as you approach Grahamstown belong to the topmost member of the Cape Supergroup, the Witteberg Group. They are distinguished from the other Cape sediments you've seen thus far by being a more mixed package, predominantly quartzitic sandstone, but with shale not uncommon.

Although on your way out of it, you are still in the Cape Fold Belt, as demonstrated by these folded Witteberg sediments seen just southwest of Grahamstown.

As you approach and pass Grahamstown, the folding in the bedded Witteberg Group shales and sandstones is manifest; but after passing the off-ramp into the town centre, you find yourself in a high cutting through unbedded Dwyka tillite **(geosite 3, map 14)**. Parts of it near the beginning of the cutting are comparatively unweathered, but mostly it is highly kaolinised and you have to look hard to see it is, in fact, tillite. In places, though, the clasts have not weathered and tend to stand out in the softer matrix. The flow of solutions through the rock have produced spectacular Liesegang banding. Half a kilometre on, as you're leaving the valley in which Grahamstown nestles, you will see the silcrete of the Grahamstown Formation at the top of the cutting. This occurs between Swellendam and Riversdale, but there you wouldn't see the highly kaolinised bedrock as well as you do here.

The silcrete is a relatively recent Tertiary surface phenomenon, formed as the weakly acid ground water rises by capillary action, bringing with it minute amounts of dissolved silica, which leave a deposit as the water evaporates. That the rock below the silcrete has been so intensely kaolinised, and that quite a conspicuous capping of silcrete has developed, tells geologists that this is the African Surface of erosion. The plateau surface above Grahamstown, as in this area generally, is typically capped by the silcrete layer. The development of extensive white kaolin, as a result of palaeo-weathering of Witteberg, Dwyka and Ecca sediments during the prolonged period of Tertiary peneplanation, has given rise to numerous good-quality kaolinite deposits, and resulted in a local pottery industry.

An outline of pre- and early Karoo sedimentation

Conditions during the deposition of the Witteberg Group sediments were more variable than those when the Table Mountain Group was laid down. By around 330 million years ago, the Cape Basin was filling up, with alternating periods of more and less energetic flow – and carrying capacity – of the rivers. Soon sedimentation would stop altogether, closing a major chapter in South Africa's geological history.

As consolidation of the sediments continued, Gondwana was drifting southwards into polar latitudes. Glaciation began in the mountains, and ice sheets spread over the lower ground, both from the north and south. A new landscape was being shaped, and on it the Dwyka ice sheets were doing their work: glacial till was deposited as moraine on land, and was forming a tillite in the early Karoo sea, with a maximum thickness of some 800 metres in the south. The ice melted and, as Gondwana drifted northwards again, the vast Karoo inland basin accumulated thousands of metres of sediment. Even while the southern part of the basin was filling, the mountainous hinterland feeding it with sediment was convulsed by phase after phase of folding, as the Cape Fold Belt formed. What you see around Grahamstown is the infolding of a wedge of Dwyka tillite at the base of the Karoo, into the topmost sediments of the Cape, an intimate intermixing of these two sedimentary sequences. (Also see Karoo Supergroup summary in ch. 9, p. 176.)

The wide range in size and angularity of the pale-coloured clasts set in a blue-grey matrix of glacial flour in this Dwyka tillite near Harding in KwaZulu-Natal is a reflection of the tillite's glacial origin. Unlike water and air, ice offers no potential for sorting of different-sized material ripped off the floor over which the ice sheets move.

The Ecca sediments seen as you drop into the Great Fish River valley have been uptilted into a vertical attitude by folding, showing that you are still in the Cape Fold Belt. The sediments comprise soft shales, here dark with carbon, and harder, more massive sandstone.

After travelling across the gently rolling plateau for 20 km, you start the first part of the descent into the Great Fish River valley. You've long since passed out of the in-folded tillite and are back in the steeply north-dipping sandstone and shale of the Witteberg Group. Then you're on a flattish spur protruding out into the valley before the second part of the descent. You will notice conspicuous flat-topped mesas to your left, standing above the valley but away from the plateau. Their shape – perfectly flat tops, carved from steeply inclined formations, and concave edges – gives them away as being capped by the same hard silcrete that you saw just outside Grahamstown, in other words, part of the ancient African Surface of erosion.

At the 95 km roadside beacon, you start to go into a cutting that shows you're back in Dwyka tillite again. You've gone from tillite just outside Grahamstown, through older sediments of the Witteberg Group, now back into tillite, so you've gone through an anticline. But that's the last tillite you'll see for quite a way, because slowly but surely you're getting out of the fold belt. It will be a while before you're in horizontal sediments, though, as the steeply dipping Ecca sandstone and shale in the cutting after the 96 km beacon attest **(geosite 4, map 14)**. Here, the thin, lowest part of the Ecca is predominantly sandstone, though after a few kilometres you'll be crossing the thicker upper part, which consists almost entirely of shale. You won't see much Ecca shale, which is quite soft, except in cuttings as you go through the river valleys, with good exposures around the 101 and 102 km beacons, and again as you climb out of the Great Fish River valley.

The country you're travelling through is dissected by several deep rivers such as the Great Fish and, not far ahead, the Keiskamma; but, as you approach Peddie, you can see in the distance the same peneplain last observed around Grahamstown. The African Surface ahead makes for very smooth topography, with the ancient Amatole Mountains standing above the plains in the far distance. And, though you wouldn't have been aware of any change, the sediments you're crossing by the time you get to Peddie are the mudstones and sandstones of the Beaufort Group. The distinction between the Ecca and Beaufort sediments is subtle, but tells of a distinct palaeo-environmental change. Some of the Ecca sediments were deposited in deep water in the Karoo Basin, while the Beaufort muds and sands were generally deposited in river channels, ponds and lakes on the fringes of the inland Karoo sea. Although the Beaufort is famously fossiliferous (best known for its mammal-like reptiles, see p. 116), it is in the arid Karoo geographic region, with its generous abundance of outcrop and low rainfall, where most of the discoveries have been made. The Beaufort covers more of South Africa (about 20 per cent) than any other group, and you will cross its mudstones and sandstones, which are interrupted only by the dolerite that cuts through them, from here until some way beyond Kokstad in KwaZulu-Natal.

But where's the dolerite? Keep your eyes open because you'll soon cross the first outcrop on this entire route about 15 km before King William's Town **(geosite 5, map 14)**.

The distribution and identification of Karoo dolerite

The southern strip of South Africa, with its history of folding and thrusting and mountain building, did not favour the intrusion of dolerite, which was happening on a grand scale over the whole of the rest of the Karoo Basin: the rock formations were too tightly packed, with less of a regime of tensional cracks opening up than was prevalent further north. By the time you are close to King William's Town, though, you are almost out of the fold belt. You might have noticed the gentle folding in the sediments as you went down into the Keiskamma valley, but in general now, the dips are much flatter, and at the town they are effectively horizontal. The dolerite gives itself away, here and generally, in a number of ways, notably by its:

➤ massiveness, meaning it shows no internal structure like bedding;

➤ colour – dark grey to almost black, on a fresh surface, sometimes with the crystalline texture visible;

➤ rounded shape (may also weather spheroidally) – boulders on surface;

➤ very conspicuously red soil that forms over it; and

➤ positive topographic expression, forming ridges and cappings.

Other rocks, especially some of the sediments in this part of the world, also weather spheroidally and have to be scrutinised quite carefully before you can be certain they're not dolerite, but a combination of the above criteria should help ensure correct identification.

There's much dolerite from here on, occurring mostly as big sills and inclined sheets, only very occasionally as vertical dykes. East of King William's Town is perhaps the most interesting dolerite exposure on the whole route. As you leave the town, the first few cuttings are through clearly bedded sediments, with the first dark grey, massive dolerite evident after just a few kilometres. Stay alert because the particularly interesting dolerite exposure is in the third cutting through dolerite after leaving King William's Town. It's to the north of the road, and comes after you've passed a few cuttings through sandstone and mudstone **(geosite 6, map 14)**. At this exposure, there are two

In this dyke of sandstone – the first east of King William's Town – blocks of dark, fine-grained dolerite, from the contact of the sill with the sandstone it has cut through, contrast conspicuously with the much coarser-grained, slower-cooling dolerite from the interior of the sill.

pale dyke-like features intersecting the medium-grey intrusive rock, and they're both worth a closer look as they show an unusual reversal of geological roles, where a sedimentary rock has intruded into an igneous rock. If the sediment is not fully lithified when the dolerite comes rumbling hotly through it, the heat is transferred from the dolerite to the sediment. This renders it 'plastic', and therefore capable of flow. The dolerite contracts slightly as it cools and shrinkage joints may form, into which the sediment can flow.

The first pale dyke is nearly a metre thick and has a blurred contact with the dolerite. It shows, in addition, inclusions of two kinds of dolerite in the sandstone: one dark and very fine-grained, the other mottled and coarsely crystalline. The result is an extremely 'mixed-up' rock: a sediment that has not only intruded an intrusive rock, but has collected fragments of the 'host' dolerite in doing so. The second dyke is 30 to 40 cm thick and uniformly white, with sharp contacts with the dolerite. They are pleasing illustrations of just how bizarre nature can be, in an exposure that shows an unusual phenomenon extremely vividly.

The African Surface peneplain first visible before you reached King William's Town is very noticeable in these parts, and will remain so, in patches, as far as Butterworth, and again when you approach the South Coast of KwaZulu-Natal from the more rugged landscape around Kokstad.

MAP 15

East London to Kokstad

The combination of dolerite and sediment you'll see in and around East London continues, with variations in proportion – of dolerite to sediment, and sandstone to mudstone and shale – until you're well past Kokstad. The colours will differ, and the way the dolerite looks – whether fresh or weathered – will change, but you're in mixed Beaufort Group sediments and dolerite for approximately the next 450 km. You'll see mudstone that's bright purple, green, pale grey and brown, shale that's practically black, and sandstones that are cream, pale grey and beige, either massive or finely bedded. You'll see sparkling dolerite that's hard to break with a hammer, and deep red soil that looks nothing like the rock from which it was formed, but which was once dolerite.

As you get further from the coast you will start to notice conspicuous dongas – modern erosion gullies, to give them their more scientific, but less evocative name – on the hill slopes.

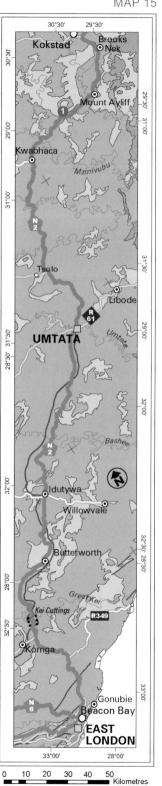

These Ecca shales – dark with carbon – on the north side of the Great Fish River valley are subhorizontal, though you're not quite out of the folding yet. Their tendency to weather spheroidally is quite common among sediments in these parts.

Dongas: a geological phenomenon triggered by man

You cannot fail to notice the dongas in these parts. They are a manifestation of soil erosion, which is particularly bad here for a variety of reasons. These include:

> climate – occasional winter frost; rainfall that's lower than along the coast and against the mountains and that often falls in heavy storms;

> geomorphology – the relatively hilly terrain favouring rapid gully formation;

> geology – the sediments of the Beaufort Group are susceptible to breaking down to unbound and generally quite thin soils;

> and mainly unsuitable land-use practices, including overgrazing and an over-frequent burning cycle for fresh pasture, followed by premature grazing of recently burned veld.

On a more positive note, the pastoralists here appear to have learned from the mistakes of the past, and there are more cases of old dongas slowly grassing over than of new dongas forming.

Decades of overgrazing of low-value grassland have exacerbated the negative effects of soil low in natural nutrients and a climate characterised by violent summer thunderstorms.

Karoo dolerite continues to impose itself on the scenery, from the ridges visible in the distance to material in the cuttings, and loose blocks on the surface near the road. Map 15 indicates a very extensive dolerite sheet around Butterworth, and this shows itself conspicuously in cuttings. But it is further north that dolerite intrusion reaches its maximum effect on the geology of South Africa. About 13 km (check the kilometre beacons alongside the road) after Kwabhaca (Mount Frere), you start to see a major massif off to the left, with high, rocky, south-facing slopes that are almost vertical **(geosite 1, map 15)**.

As you get closer, climbing as you do so, you see that the slopes swing round till they're more or less east-facing, and that they extend into the distance. This massif is known as Insizwa, arguably the best-documented body of Karoo dolerite in the country. It's about 1 000 m thick and its emplacement was not very different from that of the Bushveld Complex in the north of South Africa, although on a smaller scale and much later. The dolerite magma apparently entered the sediments in separate pulses, and crystal settling during its cooling and crystallisation produced olivine-rich gabbro layers at the base. There is enough copper, nickel, platinum and palladium in

The Insizwa dolerite sheet, seen in the background of this picture, is thick enough to have accumulated tantalising amounts of copper and nickel at its base. The weathered product, seen in the road cutting, holds equally tantalising traces of the aluminium ore, bauxite, where it underlies very ancient land surfaces.

these mafic rocks for there to have been considerable interest shown in the basal contact zone of Insizwa. Prospecting by early entrepreneurs, and subsequent considerable underground and surface exploration by mining companies, took place over a number of decades, with numerous boreholes drilled, but without economic success.

Most students of the area agree that the four distinct mafic massifs around Mount Ayliff, east and south of Kokstad, in fact comprise remnants of a single 1 800 sq km intrusive sheet of dolerite, broken up by erosion of the higher, domed parts of the original body. From Mount Frere, for most of the next 120 km, you will be no more than a few kilometres away from one or other of the remnants of this singular vast Karoo dolerite phenomenon. If you've tried to break off a piece from a fresh outcrop of dolerite, you will know it's a hard rock, and you will better understand why it builds high ranges and plateaus, and why the country around Kokstad is as rugged as it is.

Kokstad to Port Shepstone

It is not only for its base and precious metals that this area has attracted interest from mining companies. It has been prospected for aluminium, too (see text box, opposite page). So this large dolerite sheet is unusual in ways other than its size: it has been mineralogically anomalous in both its infancy and its maturity. Over 180 million years ago, metallic sulphides were settling out to gather near the floor of the giant sheet while the dolerite was still semi-molten. Eons later, after the top of it was no longer rock, but porous soil, the aluminium in its weathered minerals would, slowly but surely, concentrate near the surface of the ground.

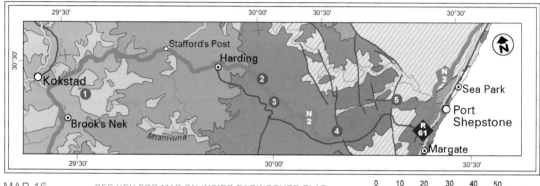

MAP 16   SEE KEY FOR MAP ON INSIDE BACK COVER FLAP   0 10 20 30 40 50 Kilometres

East of Kokstad, you emerge from the land of the Xhosa and Pondo people into the verdant farmlands of KwaZulu-Natal. There's a subtle change in topography and weather patterns, and most of the road cuttings are soil-covered and grassed over, with not much outcrop around. The change from Beaufort Group sediments to those of the Ecca Group, just after you've passed Harding, is not one you'd notice, but the Ecca is thin in these parts and you're quite soon onto the Dwyka Group again. Remember that, since leaving Port Elizabeth, you have climbed – stratigraphically – from the base of the Cape Supergroup until you were high in the overlying Karoo Supergroup on the Beaufort, where you remained until a few kilometres back. Now, as you drop towards the coast, you're also dropping stratigraphically, off the Beaufort Group, through the Ecca and back onto the Dwyka, last seen near Grahamstown.

Ten kilometres east of Harding, slow down or stop and look at the Dwyka tillite in the road cutting at the 72.2 km beacon (**geosite 2, map 16**).

The abundant pale clasts in this rock cutting east of Harding give it away as tillite; otherwise, at a glance, you might mistake it for dolerite.

It's fresh and you can clearly see the clasts, or inclusions, of a wide range of rock types in the tillite, up to 15 cm across in this outcrop. A word of caution: tillite and dolerite in this region of high rainfall and often intense weathering can look very much the same until you examine them closely. Both are darkish grey on a fresh surface, and massive, and both weather with rounded surfaces and an ochry brown to yellow colour; sometimes there remains just a skin, sometimes just soil, with the hard rock lost altogether. The soil over dolerite is usually a more vivid red than that over tillite, though, and if you can still see some rock, the clasts contained in the tillite, or the crystallinity of the dolerite, will tell you what you're looking at.

At the 82.8 km beacon there's an outcrop of tillite that's worth a closer look **(geosite 3, map 16)**. It's noteworthy for two reasons: firstly, its style of presentation. The blocky break-up of what was a massive rock into orthogonal blocks of almost geometric precision is closely analogous to the way that dolerite may behave – and just another way in which these rocks mimic one another. The second thing you'll see is how conspicuous the clasts are, with the biggest coarsely crystalline boulder nearly a metre across. So although if you sped past without sparing the cutting more than a glance you might pass it off as dolerite, it is, in fact, textbook tillite.

Alumina – another Achilles heel

Few people realise that the country's burgeoning aluminium industry – no small player in the national economy – is completely dependent on imported alumina (Al_2O_3), the starting material of aluminium production, that is refined from the low-cost, naturally occurring primary ore called bauxite (a hydrated aluminium oxide).

In nature, bauxite forms over an extremely prolonged period, and as a weathering product. It forms:

➤ *over rocks rich in aluminium silicate minerals such as feldspar;*

➤ *where a climate of extremely high rainfall prevails;*

➤ *and particularly in equatorial or tropical latitudes.*

Most bauxite deposits occur where the climate required for its formation still prevails, such as in South and Central America, West Africa and Queensland. The climate in which the South African bauxite formed, millions of years ago, has changed; and because South Africa today generally has a relatively dry climate, it had never – until the 1970s – been considered prospective for bauxite.

How, then, did we come to have an aluminium industry if we have no bauxite? While the conversion of bauxite to alumina is a relatively simple and low-cost operation, smelting and electrolysis of the aluminium oxide to produce the metal requires access to sustainable, low-cost power, making it a logical industry for South Africa to consider developing.

*In the mid 1970s the supply of alumina to the South African market by foreign producers was considered to be under threat, as global efforts to bring the apartheid regime to its knees gained momentum. A Natal entrepreneur, Helmut Redinger, teamed up with soil scientist Dr Martin Fey to identify potential areas of bauxite formation in South Africa, and invited multinational Rio Tinto to form a joint venture to explore that potential. The team confirmed that there were indeed resources of low-grade bauxite formed at a number of localities over dolerite sheets in the high-rainfall escarpment region of KwaZulu-Natal. In the end, the resources were rated too small and too low-grade to elevate a submarginal project to viability, and the exploration was discontinued. The vibrancy of South Africa's aluminium industry today is eloquent vindication of the decision not to proceed with the hugely messy business of mining a thin surface layer of bauxite in some of the most beautiful parts of the country, including the area near Weza, east of Kokstad **(geosite 1, map 16)**.*

MAP 17

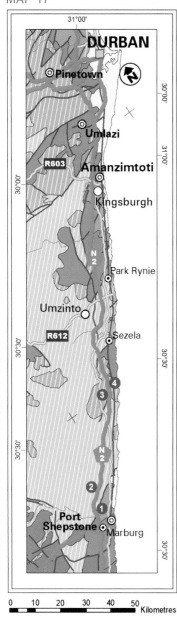

From here on, the scenery is reminiscent of that west of East London – the flat plains of the African Surface of erosion well preserved for the first time for hundreds of kilometres. They are dissected by a number of small rivers heading towards the coast, but the concordant plateau levels between the valleys are obvious, nonetheless. For the first time, from about the 89.4 km beacon, you will see the pale, horizontal sandstone of the marine Msikaba Formation, dated at around 350 million years old (**geosite 4, map 16**). This unit, contemporaneous with – but quite separate from – the pre-Karoo Witteberg Group, is widespread in southern KwaZulu-Natal. Its resistant lithology means that it is frequently seen in high, vertical cliffs.

Within less than 20 km, you'll have climbed down out of the hilly country onto the coastal plains where you cross gently undulating country with occasional outcrops of quartzite, as well as exposures of it in cuttings. From the 14.2 km beacon, you see more cuttings as you start dropping towards the coast, and 2 km after this you'll see weathered granite in a cutting (**geosite 5, map 16**), the first since way back in George, if you've come that far. You have been cutting down through the stratigraphy as you have lost elevation, and now you're on the ancient crystalline basement.

Port Shepstone to Durban

Now that you're at the coast, the geology is broken up by regular faulting, related – in general terms – to the formation of the coastline, by rifting and the break-up of Gondwana 150 million years ago. You'll cross from one formation to the other, and back to the first, as you travel northeastwards up the coast.

Dolerite is still an important part of the geology; behind the off-ramp toll booth on the south-bound lane, where the Port Shepstone-St Faith's fly-over crosses the N2, you'll see a thick dolerite sheet cutting the Ecca shale (**geosite 1, map 17**). The south-dipping dolerite is at the northern end of this high cutting, with the clearly bedded shale – ochry brown where weathered, black where fresh – quite flat-dipping, but clearly disturbed by faulting, and completely broken up at the extreme southern end of the cutting.

Five kilometres after this – at the 41 km beacon – is the first gneiss of the Natal Metamorphic Province next to the road (**geosite 2, map 17**). It's a beautiful fresh rock, and worth a close look to remind yourself of how new minerals are formed and redistributed during really intense tectonism. The rock is well banded with dark minerals – hornblende and biotite – and pale bands consisting mainly of feldspar, well separated, while on the northbound side of the road, the darker rock predominates. Just after crossing the Mzinto River there's a small outcrop in a cutting that is mostly grassed over, of very attractive granite of the Sezela Suite, mostly feldspar with a little biotite and quartz. Note that the formation of these high-grade metamorphic basement rocks is dated at around 1 100 million years ago.

At the 36.0 km beacon you'll see a good example of the Natal Group sandstone, correlated in age with the Table Mountain Group seen in the Western and Eastern Cape (**geosite 3, map 17**). This sandstone is the same as that which has been cut through to get from Durban to Kloof and the hinterland (see the chapters on Durban and the N3, chs. 3 & 9), most illustratively seen in the Field's Hill and Inchanga cuttings. These are fluvial (coastal plain) sediments, as their mixed and impure character testifies. They are slightly older than the Msikaba Formation sandstone seen further south and were apparently formed quite separately from them.

Within less than 2 km note the cutting in red sand to the east of the road (**geosite 4, map 17**). It's a subtly different colour from the red of typical dolerite soil and is the first sighting – and one of the best – of what used to be called Berea Red Sand, now known as the Berea Formation. These are dune sands formed about 10 million years ago, during the Tertiary, and a good example of how a little iron oxide can impart a vivid red colour to the material with which it occurs. At that time, the sea level was higher than it is now. Behind the beaches large dunes accumulated, made mainly of quartz grains, but with shell fragments and silicate minerals as well, all blown off the beaches. The shell fragments released their calcium carbonate to the slightly acidified groundwater which, as conditions varied, came out of solution and cemented the other grains. With time and a wetter climate, and countless more rainstorms, the cement was dissolved from the grains and the iron-bearing silicate minerals released their iron to tinge the whole package red. And that's what you see in this cutting, and perhaps on the Berea in Durban if you should find yourself near any excavations.

And as you head northwards you'll see more of most of the rock units we've covered so far: Basement gneiss, Natal Group sandstone, Dwyka tillite, Ecca shale, and, at a distance, Berea Formation ridges. It's a telescoped selection of South African geology, from the Precambrian to the Quaternary. Complementing beautiful coastal scenery, it turns a good drive into a great one.

Gneiss of the Natal Metamorphic Province can be spotted on the west side of the freeway, some 6 km north of Port Shepstone.

8 N2/N17: Durban to Johannesburg

GEOLOGICAL OVERVIEW

The geological bonus this alternative route to Johannesburg offers is a good section through the volcanic top of the Karoo Supergroup. This is in northern Zululand, where the road leaves the coast and is in the shadow of the Lebombo Mountains. Another interesting aspect to the route is that you start crossing Basement rocks of the Natal Metamorphic Province, an off-craton mobile belt; later, you cross over onto the Kaapvaal Craton, whose gneisses and granites you will see near Pongola. Lying on these are sediments of the Pongola Supergroup, equivalent in age and the environment of their deposition to the gold-bearing Witwatersrand, the big difference being that there was an insignificant supply of gold into this basin.

Near the coast there are high dunes of various ages to be seen and, as you pass Richards Bay, you will be close to one of the world's major deposits of titanium and zirconium. Still in the field of economic geology, the last section of the journey, across the Highveld, will take you through the Ermelo coal field and, as you approach Johannesburg, the Evander gold field. A little further north along the Zululand coastal plain lies the Greater St Lucia Wetland Park, a World Heritage Site. An ecosystem of considerable importance, it's a fine example of young coastal geology.

Large-scale mining and processing of the coastal sand dunes by Richards Bay Minerals produces big tonnages of the heavy minerals ilmenite, rutile and zircon. After mining, the high coastal dunes are refashioned and the coastal dune forest is rehabilitated, resulting in the development of an ecological system similar to that which existed prior to mining.

MAP 18

Geology of the route

Durban to Mtubatuba

For the first 13 km north of Durban, the N2 crosses poorly exposed, faulted blocks of both the Dwyka and Ecca Groups of the Karoo Supergroup. Much of the first part of the freeway is carved out of the red, compacted and well-vegetated dunes known as the Berea Formation – or, more informally, as the Berea Red Sand. This formation, which extends inland for up to 5 km, occurs almost continuously along the entire KwaZulu-Natal coast. Named after its type area on the Berea Ridge in central Durban, it consists of an old dune cordon made of Tertiary wind-blown beach sand. It was first calcified as a buff-coloured aeolianite and then, during millions of summers of soaking rains, became decalcified and coloured red by iron leached from minerals in the dunes. The Berea Red Sand makes for good sugar-cane land and, more recently, prime building sites along the booming Dolphin Coast. Much of the first part of the N2 north of Durban is carved out of this soft formation, in places exposing Karoo rocks at the base of the fossil dunes.

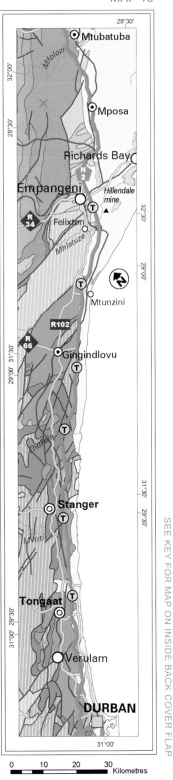

New building developments abound on what was once sugar-cane fields, north of Umhlanga Rocks. The dark red sand represents 'fossil' coastal dune cordons, now well above sea level, and are heavily pigmented by oxidised iron minerals.

Now occurring inland and on ground well above sea level, this part of the N2 near Ballito is carved out of old red coastal dunes. Commonly called Berea Red Sand, this young, compact formation is free of hard rock, making it good news for road engineers.

When you get to a high point, look inland and in the distance you'll see flat 'table mountains' formed by remnants of the older Natal Group sandstone, with the valleys between them exposing granitic basement rocks. By the time you reach the Tinley Manor Beach turn-off, the geological map shows that you are directly on Karoo rocks again, and you'll notice that the soil is now much browner, although red dune sand is still noticeable in places. After crossing the alluvium-filled Mvoti River valley – look out for Karoo sediments here – and passing the Blythdale Beach turn-off, you will be on hard rock geology again, faulted blocks of both Karoo and Natal rocks. The considerable faulting is a result of the major rift zone that developed during the Gondwana break-up around 150 million years ago. The broad Thukela River valley marks your crossing into Zululand. Originating at Mont-aux-Sources on the high Drakensberg, 260 km to the west, this river has cut a deeply incised, meandering path through Ecca and Dwyka rocks; also look out for the blue-grey tillite of the Dwyka Group in the cutting just north of the bridge.

From south of Mtunzini there are prominent hills north – and inland – of your direction of travel, and the geological map will show that a new formation makes its appearance here. These are the rocks of the Natal Metamorphic Province, dated at around 1 100 million years ago, when the ancient Kaapvaal Craton in the north collided with another crustal plate to the south, forming a geologically complex, mobile belt as it was thrust over the stable craton. The end result was a fold mountain chain of Alpine proportions, made of highly metamorphosed and intensely deformed sedimentary rocks and lavas, and a range of intrusive granites and metamorphic gneisses. This is thought to be part of the mobile belt extending from the Namaqua Metamorphic Province, 1 000 km to the west, underneath the Karoo all the way to KwaZulu-Natal. To see some of these spectacular rocks, take the R66 to Eshowe, onto more hilly ground.

After passing Mtunzini you'll be at the start of the now ever-widening coastal plain that extends northwards into Mozambique. The terrain is flat to gently undulating and the sandy soil, coupled with the coastal climate, makes it ideal for eucalyptus trees, of which you'll see extensive plantations. Where you pass Felixton and cross the Mhlatuze River, the coastal plain is about 10 km wide. Here, just to the east, you'll notice an opencast mining operation in Berea Red Sand, as well as mine tailings dams on the wide flood plain in the foreground. Hillendale mine produces a rich crop of heavy minerals – ilmenite ($FeTiO_2$), rutile (TiO_2) and zircon ($ZrSiO_4$). These minerals were concentrated by wind action millions of years ago within coastal sand dunes after being eroded out of the granites, dolerites and basalts of the hinterland. Richards Bay, South Africa's largest and deepest port, is close by and is the location of one of the world's largest heavy mineral mining operations from younger coastal dunes. Richards Bay Minerals is a pioneering company in post-mining dune rehabilitation and provides fascinating tours of their operations. Initially built as an export coal terminal, Richards Bay now boasts two aluminium smelters and several other primary industries.

Maputaland – once a haven for giant ammonites

The coastal plain here is covered by young redistributed sand and alluvium, and by older Tertiary sand in some areas. These are jointly grouped as the Maputaland Group. Underlying these relatively thin sands is the Zululand Group, a thick sequence of Cretaceous siltstones and minor sandstones with shelly layers. Outcrops of this group extend from Hluhluwe northwards, on the eastern side of the Lebombo Mountains, and are not seen along the N2. Representing the first marine sediments deposited in the newly opened-up Indian Ocean – once Antarctica had split away from what is now the KwaZulu-Natal coast – this unit is well known for its abundant ammonite fossils. These now-extinct, flatly spiralled molluscs, reaching up to 1 m in diameter, thrived in the tropical ocean. Their sub-class Ammonoidea suffered the same end-Cretaceous fate as the dinosaurs, the only distantly related survivor being the fragile Paper Nautilus that occasionally gets washed up on our beaches. A good place to see the Zululand Group and its fossils is along the shore of Lake St Lucia, a famous conservation area and a World Heritage Site. You'll pass the Greater St Lucia Wetland Park turn-off at Mtubatuba – visit it if you can for an unforgettable ecotourism experience.

This is an example of an unusual fossil ammonite, called Myloceras serotinum, *that came from Cretaceous sediments in KwaZulu-Natal. Note that it is coiled at both ends (about 130 mm long).*

MAP 19

Mtubatuba to Pongola

Near Mtubatuba, the N2 crosses the broad Mfolozi River floodplain and, surprisingly, you'll see typical Drakensberg lavas in the valley, known here as the Letaba Formation, part of the Lebombo Group. You are on these rocks for the next 8 km, before returning to the coastal plain for a while. About 10 km south of the Hluhluwe-Umfolozi Game Reserve turn-off, you will be back on poorly outcropping Letaba lava, which forms a characteristic dark, clayey soil. By now you may have noticed a north-south trending line of hills about 10 km west of the N2. The geological map will show that these are in fact the equivalent of the Stormberg sediments, consisting of the Clarens, Elliot and Molteno Formations (for details, see the section on the Drakensberg, ch. 17, p. 290). So you are seeing upper Karoo Supergroup geology, these being the easternmost outcropping sediments, which dip shallowly eastwards as part of the Lebombo Monocline or Natal Arch (see text box, p. 168) under the Letaba lavas. These formations, here considerably thinner than in the main Karoo Basin and conspicuously faulted, extend northwards as far as the Pongola River.

Running for over 600 km, the Lebombo Mountain range forms much of South Africa's eastern border. The lower slopes are of softer, more easily weathered basalt of the Letaba Formation, and the upper cliffs are of more competent rhyolitic rocks of the Jozini Formation.

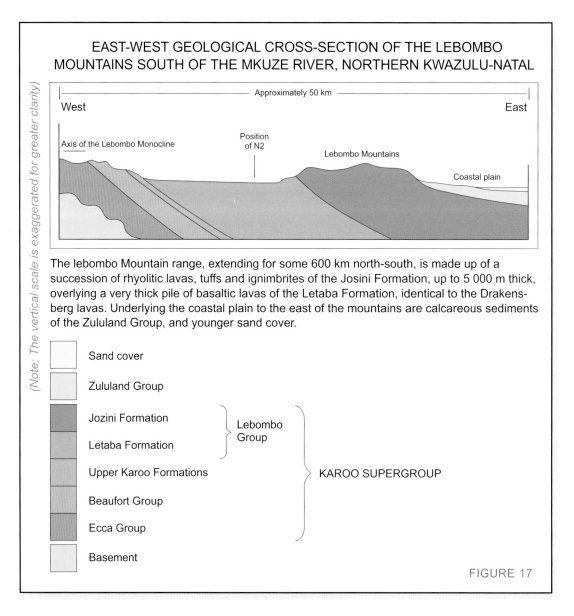

EAST-WEST GEOLOGICAL CROSS-SECTION OF THE LEBOMBO
MOUNTAINS SOUTH OF THE MKUZE RIVER, NORTHERN KWAZULU-NATAL

(Note: The vertical scale is exaggerated for greater clarity)

Approximately 50 km

West   East

Axis of the Lebombo Monocline

Position
of N2

Lebombo Mountains

Coastal plain

The lebombo Mountain range, extending for some 600 km north-south, is made up of a succession of rhyolitic lavas, tuffs and ignimbrites of the Josini Formation, up to 5 000 m thick, overlying a very thick pile of basaltic lavas of the Letaba Formation, identical to the Drakensberg lavas. Underlying the coastal plain to the east of the mountains are calcareous sediments of the Zululand Group, and younger sand cover.

Sand cover

Zululand Group

Jozini Formation   } Lebombo
                                Group
Letaba Formation

Upper Karoo Formations   } KAROO SUPERGROUP

Beaufort Group

Ecca Group

Basement

FIGURE 17

The Lebombo Group consists of lower basaltic and upper rhyolitic lavas, with an extraordinary combined thickness of over 7 000 m. About 35 km north of Mtubatuba you will be on Letaba basalts again, characterised by dark, clayey soil and thick bushveld vegetation, including abundant yellow-trunked fever trees. The Letaba basalt has been carved into a broad valley that's 10 to 15 km wide, with the N2 running approximately down the middle. From Hluhluwe onwards, you will start to notice another mountain range to the east, getting progressively higher northwards. This is the beginning of the Lebombo Mountains which from here run for over 600 km through Swaziland and Mozambique. The upper part of the range is made predominantly of hard rhyolite (felsic volcanic rocks) lavas, and varieties of pyroclastic rocks and breccias, all of which resist weathering, unlike the basalts in the valley. Known as the Jozini Formation, they are the youngest rocks of the Karoo sequence.

ABOVE: *The road to Jozini takes you up the western side of the Lebombo range. Excellent exposures of Letaba basalt flows are seen (right foreground), and are overlain by harder Jozini rhyolites (upper background).*

BELOW LEFT: *The lower part of Pongola Pass shows the Letaba Formation, the equivalent of the Drakensberg lavas, and is built up of many thin basalt flows that are characteristically amygdaloidal, and dip gently to the east.*

BELOW RIGHT: *The Jozini Formation overlying the basalt is made of harder, more competent felsic volcanic rocks such as rhyolite flows, welded tuffs and agglomerates, commonly showing signs of flow banding.*

To better see these volcanic rocks, make a short detour off the N2, preferably the road to Jozini at the Pongolapoort Dam. Here you will see individual amygdaloidal basalt flows (**geosite 1, map 19**). Take a drive through the entire rhyolite succession to the town of Jozini, where the narrow Pongola River gorge has been dammed to provide irrigation water to the Makhathini Flats to the east. Near Mkuze village, look out for the legendary Ghost Mountain or Tshaneni, burial place of Shangaan kings.

The Natal Arch – end of the Rift Valley?

The dominant structure of the region, formerly called the Natal or Lebombo Monocline, and more recently the Natal Arch, extends all the way from the Limpopo River in the north to southern KwaZulu-Natal, and is related to rifting associated with the break-up of Gondwana. It can be visualised as an axis of uplift, where the arching resulting from the uplift causes the development of rift valleys along the axis. However, in the case of the Lebombo axis, the rifting did not lead to the dropping down of valleys. Instead, major faulting took place, with large blocks to the east of the faults dropping down in stepwise fashion, tilting eastwards, from 5° to 15°. The geology is further complicated by close-spaced oblique faults, also related to continental break-up.

Near Jozini, in the narrow gorge where the Pongola River cuts through the Lebombo Mountains, a major dam wall was constructed in the 1960s. Today the dam is a great attraction, with the Lebombo Mountains on the east, and is part of the Pongola Nature Reserve.

North of Mkuze the N2 passes the big Pongolapoort Dam to the east, backed by the impressive, scarp-like Lebombo Mountains **(geosite 1, map 20)**. Soon you'll have crossed the entire – but minimally exposed – basalt sequence, and will enter hilly ground made up of east-dipping upper Karoo sediments, replicated by faulting, through which the Pongola River has cut its path. A stop at the river will reveal water-worn sediments of the Beaufort Group, after which follows a ridge of mainly Ecca shales, the ridge being called Rooirante because of its red colour derived from the capping of weathered Karoo dolerite dykes and sills. It's a telescoped section of quite a significant chunk of the Karoo Supergroup. Up to Pongola, the road continues on Karoo sediments that soon disappear beneath the thick river alluvium, which regularly produces bumper crops of sugar-cane.

Pongola to Ermelo

West of Pongola there is a complete change in geology after crossing a major fault line. About 2 km from the town, quartz-mica schists of the Pongola Supergroup make a brief appearance, soon followed by Basement gneisses and granites, one of which, although unnamed, is dated at 3 553 million years old, making it one of the oldest rocks in the country. The road takes you upwards through a well-defined granitic valley showing typical exfoliation weathering, to the Highveld. About 32 km from Pongola, stop on the flatter ground at the top of the climb close to the Swaziland border, and have a look at the dark, rounded boulders of somewhat younger coarse-grained, porphyritic, biotite-rich Kwetta Granite, which extends from here into Swaziland **(geosite 1, map 20)**.

To the south of the road you'll see the thick sedimentary sequence of the Mozaan Group of the Pongola Supergroup. It consists of shales, quartzites, iron formations, conglomerates and lavas, and is similar in both age and composition to the Witwatersrand Supergroup. The similarities between the Pongola and Witwatersrand Successions led to a run of historical gold prospecting and the discovery of some small gold deposits. Fabulous gold-rich conglomerates in the Pongola formations were no more than a dream, though. The Mozaan sediments are exposed along the road some 43 to 55 km from Pongola, and you would be excused for thinking you were in true Witwatersrand geology. After this, the underlying Nsuze Group, mostly of volcanics, outcrops poorly along the road. About 33 km from Piet Retief, exposure of a massive dark igneous rock is seen in a road cutting: this is gabbro of the Usushwana Complex that intruded the Nsuze rocks **(geosite 2, map 20)**.

After this you'll be on poorly exposed Basement granite until 60 km beyond Piet Retief, approaching Sheepmoor. The landscape of flat to gently undulating grassland is part of the old African Surface, and then you're back in timber country.

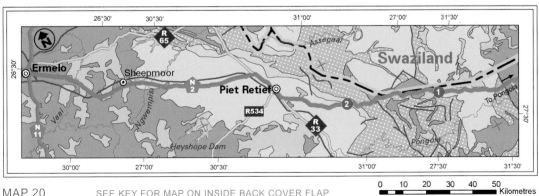

MAP 20   SEE KEY FOR MAP ON INSIDE BACK COVER FLAP

0   10   20   30   40   50
Kilometres

ABOVE: *The N2 west of Pongola shows a variety of granites, often weathered in a typical domal manner. One of these granites has been dated at 3 553 million years old, one of the oldest yet recorded in South Africa.*

INSET & BELOW: *After rising up the somewhat subdued escarpment from Pongola, outcrops of this pinkish, coarse-grained, biotite granite make their appearance. This is one of the younger, non-gneissic granites, dated around 2 700 million years old.*

The amount of Karoo dolerite increases significantly as you head westwards; an example close to the road, about 6 km west from Ngwempisi station, is a prominent hill called Spitskop, capped by a dolerite sheet. Close to Sheepmoor, the N2 moves off the Basement and back onto Ecca sediments of the Karoo, and soon you'll be in the Ermelo coal field. From here, Ecca sediments, broken by big expanses of dolerite, continue all the way to Gauteng. Between Sheepmoor and Ermelo the dolerite-capped hills provide the main geological interest along the road. The terrain becomes hillier, and occasionally thick, flat-lying sandstone layers are seen within the Ecca shales. About 20 km before reaching Ermelo, Camden Power Station comes into view. Built in 1962, it was one of the earlier mega-power stations, supplied with coal from the nearby Usuthu colliery.

Ermelo to Johannesburg

Ermelo marks the end of the N2, and alternative routes to Gauteng are available, either the N11 to Middelburg and then the N4 or N12 (see relevant sections, chs. 4 & 13) or the N17 via Bethal and Springs. The following short description covers the latter route. From Ermelo to Bethal and beyond, the N17 continues across Ecca sediments, which host an exceptionally high proportion of Karoo dolerite. About 4 km out of Ermelo, an impressive dolerite sill can be seen to the north of the road, overlying a thick, well-exposed sandstone layer in an eroded valley. At about 35 km, look out for the Richards Bay railway line, which crosses the road overhead, and is dedicated to moving export quality coal to the coast using ultra-long coal trains. Close to Bethal you will see coal mines and, in the distance to the north, two power stations located in the Witbank coal field, as well as another to the south. (See text boxes on power generation and coal, pp. 197 and 231 respectively.)

After Bethal, as you approach Trichardt, you can't miss the smokestacks and production plants of Sasol II and Sasol III rising out of the Highveld at the relatively new town of Secunda. These enormous plants produce a significant portion of South Africa's liquid fuel needs, and a host of other petro-chemicals, using coal mined directly in the area. (See the text box on Sasol on p. 109.)

The next town is Kinross, and to the south of the N17 you will notice a few typical Witwatersrand gold-mining operations: these are located on the Evander gold field, discovered as recently as the 1950s. The field is completely covered by Karoo rocks and is a small outlying basin of the main Witwatersrand Basin. Exploration was largely by geophysical techniques, followed by core drilling. Mining started in 1958 and is still in progress, more than 45 years later. The road to the great metropolis continues on Ecca and dolerite as far as Springs, where Malmani dolomite makes a minor appearance. Ecca shales continue right up to Brakpan, overlying thin Dwyka tillite.

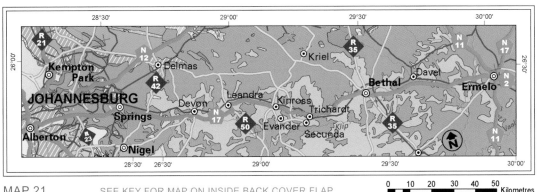

MAP 21   SEE KEY FOR MAP ON INSIDE BACK COVER FLAP

0 10 20 30 40 50 Kilometres

9 N3: Johannesburg to Durban

GEOLOGICAL OVERVIEW

Not only does this route take you from the rolling plains of the Highveld to the rolling waves of the Indian Ocean: it takes you across a full spectrum of nearly three billion years of Earth history. Your journey starts on sediments of the Witwatersrand Basin, laid down 2 900 million years ago, past volcanic hills that are a little younger as you pass Alberton, and, soon after that, over somewhat younger Malmani dolomite of the Transvaal Supergroup. Not far past Heidelberg you are onto the considerably younger Karoo sequence, and will see a decommissioned power station that is a monument to the coal-bearing strata of this sequence. And it is on the Karoo Supergroup, which takes its name from this great basin, that you stay until you are past Pietermaritzburg. Around there you will see tillite of the basal Dwyka Group, with the memory still fresh of the basalts that cap the Drakensberg, discussed in the previous chapter.

This stretch of travel offers a good look at the Karoo, the country's most widespread sequence. As you drop towards the coast, you descend stratigraphically, too, with mesas of the pre-Karoo Natal Group very evident between Pietermaritzburg and Durban; and in the valleys carved through these horizontal sandstones, you'll see Basement gneisses of the ancient Natal Metamorphic Province. When you see the sea for the first time, you may realise that the hills of the Bluff and the Berea are made of dune sands formed only a few million years ago. They are relatively fresh, compared to the rocks we've crossed since leaving Johannesburg that are hundreds and thousands of millions of years old. The drive is a full geological experience.

This impressive mountain near Harrismith, known as Platberg, is an outlier of Clarens Formation sandstone, topped by a dark layer of what was previously thought to be Drakensberg basalt. However, the apparently columnar structure and seemingly transgressive lower contact suggest that it is a Karoo dolerite sill.

MAP 22

Geology of the route

Johannesburg to Harrismith

As you travel southwards out of Johannesburg on the N3, you will notice the mine dump reclamation in progress, where low levels of gold are being recovered at the major ERGO plant near Nigel. The geology you are driving across is the Central Rand Group, the upper quartzite- and conglomerate-rich formations of the Witwatersrand Supergroup. (Details on this area can be found in ch. 1.) In the built-up areas there is generally little outcrop to be seen from the N3, but around Alberton the dark koppies mark the start of the overlying lavas of the Ventersdorp Supergroup. Directly to the southeast of Alberton, the N3 crosses the Black Reef Formation at the base of the Transvaal Supergroup, where the major reed-filled Natalspruit wetland has formed on Malmani dolomite, just younger than – so immediately overlying – the Black Reef. The burgeoning towns of both Katlehong and Vosloorus are located on the dolomite.

Some 10 km to the south of Vosloorus, the Ventersdorp rocks reappear in the distance as the prominent Suikerbosrand range, with Perdekop the highest spot in the entire Witwatersrand region at 1 902 m. The Suikerbosrand Nature Reserve provides over 13 000 hectares of rugged and pristine Highveld wilderness, and is of considerable geological interest. A trip through the reserve is well worthwhile to see the variety of dark volcanic rocks of the Klipriviersberg Group.

In Johannesburg, old gold mine dumps, untouched for many decades, now offer new value as they are profitably reprocessed to recover minute amounts of gold. At the same time, valuable city land is released for property development.

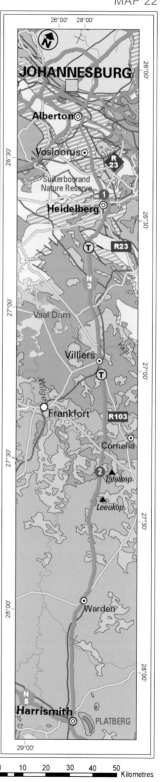

The hills directly north of Heidelberg reveal a thick succession of north-dipping, orange-weathering quartzite and quartz pebble conglomerate, identical to that seen around Mondeor in Johannesburg.

As you pass the town of Heidelberg, which pre-dates the gold rush, you will notice typical orange-brown weathering quartzites of the upper part of the West Rand Group that you crossed near Alberton, but now dipping to the northwest **(geosite 1, map 22)**. You have crossed the major syncline that holds the East Rand gold field. Just to remind us that we are still in 'gold country', a derelict concrete mine headgear of the old Witwatersrand Nigel Mine stands sentinel almost in the centre of Heidelberg.

Directly to the south of Heidelberg the ground flattens out as you drive onto remnants of Karoo sediments that partly fill the valley, thought to be of glacial origin. The hills a bit further south are north-dipping West Rand Group quartzites again, from which a little gold has been mined. Some 12 km from Heidelberg all these formations have been cut off by the major east-west-striking Sugarbush Fault, just to the north of the Suikerbosspruit, with down-faulted Ventersdorp lavas south of the fault. On the next ridge, north-dipping Witwatersrand rocks reappear, and about 20 km from Heidelberg they make their final appearance as a more subdued grassy ridge to the east of the N3. Some 40 km southeast of Heidelberg lies the South Rand gold field, hosting probably the last shallow, untapped gold resource in the Witwatersrand Basin. A resource of 16 million ounces of gold has been shown by drilling.

SUMMARY OF THE ESSENTIAL GEOLOGICAL FEATURES AND FORMATION OF THE KAROO SUPERGROUP IN THE MAIN KAROO BASIN

AGE*	GROUP	THICK-NESS	MAIN ROCK TYPES	ENVIRONMENT OF DEPOSITION	COMMON FOSSILS AND OTHER MARKERS
183 Ma	Drakensberg Group	>2 000 m	Basaltic lava flows, fed by Karoo dolerite dikes	Continental scale rifting and eruption of flood lavas	No fossils
198 Ma	Clarens Formation ('Stormberg Group')	<300 m	Fine-grained sandstone and siltstone	Wind-blown, dune-covered desert with occasional wadis	Dinosaur and fish fossils in places
215 Ma	Elliot Formation ('Stormberg Group')	<500 m	Red-maroon to green mudstones, with interbedded sandstones	Sinuous river systems on a semi-arid to arid alluvial plain	Dinosaurs, *Massospondylus* and *Euskelosaurus*, and the earliest tortoise
240 Ma	Molteno Formation ('Stormberg Group')	<600 m	Alternating sandstone, mudstone and shale, minor coal beds	Braided river systems on a vast flood plain, with lush vegetation	Abundant plants and insects, early dinosaur traces plus coal seams
250 Ma	Beaufort Group	<7 000 m	Mainly grey-green to reddish mudstones, some thick, river-channel sandstones; beds thin to the north of the central Karoo Basin	Extensive alluvial floodplains crossed by meandering north-flowing rivers, and inhabited by diverse primitive land-dwelling reptiles; deposition was mainly from the southern highlands of the rising Cape Fold Belt	Abundant vertebrate fossils, notably the *Therapsids* or mammal-like reptiles; divided into 8 'assemblage zones' of distinct fossil populations; the Permian/Triassic extinction boundary is in the Upper Beaufort
260 Ma	Ecca Group	<3 000 m	Dark shales, some sandstone layers and coal seams; deep-water sediments in the south grading to shallow-water sediments in the north	Deep-water basin and submarine fans in the south; shallow-water shelf and rivers and deltas in the north	*Glossopteris* flora and thick coal beds in the north; *Mesosaurus*, one of the earliest reptiles; Whitehill Shale marker in the south
300 Ma	Dwyka Group	<700 m	Unsorted tillite, minor shale; thickest in the south	Glacial moraine and floating ice sheets	Glacial striations on Basement rocks in places

(Note: This diagram is not to scale)

* AGES SHOWN IN MILLIONS OF YEARS AGO (Ma) ARE APPROXIMATE

TABLE 5

By this stage you will see the cooling towers of the decommissioned Grootvlei Power Station in the distance, east of the road. The geology has changed and you are now driving over very much younger sediments of the Ecca Group of the Karoo Supergroup, comprising shale, mudstone and sandstone layers. This power station was based on coal from the Springfield Mine, part of the South Rand coal field. Here a wide, glacially scoured valley became colonised by temperate forests as Gondwana moved out of the polar region. And there they grew for geological time, accumulating enough plant debris to form coal seams up to 25 m thick (see p. 231 for more about Karoo coal).

The Karoo geology (summarised in the table opposite) is reflected by the mainly flat and featureless grassland terrain that continues far

A good exposure of a fresh dolerite sill seen in a road cutting near Tafelkop. Many such exposures are seen along the N3. The fresh rocks are dark grey but weather dark brown and may have reddish iron oxides on joint surfaces.

to the south, almost to Harrismith, before which, at Villiers, you cross the Vaal River and enter the Free State. Watch for roadside borrow-pits and road cuttings, and you will see occasional flat-lying layers of weathered sandstone and shale. Without knowing it, about 25 km south of Villiers you cross from the Ecca Group onto the Beaufort Group. The latter consists of mudstone and sandstone beds, formed from material deposited mainly on extensive flood plains. This Group reaches a thickness of nearly 3 000 m in the central part of the vast Karoo depositional basin, and covers some 20 per cent of South Africa.

The most conspicuous exposures are of numerous sills of intrusive Karoo dolerite, indicated by the presence of reddish brown soil and flat-topped hills; south of the Frankfort turn-off and about 40 km south of Villiers, you pass the appropriately named Tafelkop. This is a good example of a resistant dolerite-capped hill – and look for the same intrusion in the road cutting **(geosite 2, map 22)**. A further 6 km southwards you will see fresh, dark, even-grained dolerite close-up in another road cutting. Still further south, about 40 km north of Warden, a hill called Leeukop provides another good example of the landscaping effect of these ubiquitous 183 million-year-old intrusions.

Southwards, the terrain becomes hillier and you'll see pale yellowish sandstone beds and khaki-weathering shales in road cuttings and water courses and in the prominent hillsides 10 km north of Warden. You are cutting stratigraphically upwards through the Karoo Supergroup into ever younger formations, and in the far distance you may catch a glimpse of sandstone mountains ahead. Notice, too, that a lot of the older farmhouses are built of blocks of this same sandstone.

Closer to Harrismith there are many exposures of flat-lying sandstones and shales alongside the N3. The most impressive of these is the flat-topped, 10 km-long mountain outlier called Platberg directly northeast of the town. It is composed of two formations not mentioned before: towards the base is the Clarens Formation, a thick unit of hard, pale-coloured sandstone and, above this, a thin, dark capping of basalt of the Drakensberg Group, with conspicuous columnar jointing sometimes seen in dolerite sills. Here, isolated by erosion from the rest of the Drakensberg, we have the two main geological components of the major mountain range to the south. If you catch a glimpse of mountainous terrain far to the southwest, you have spotted the Golden Gate area (see ch. 17, pp. 298–299).

MAP 23

Harrismith to Durban

About 18 km after Harrismith, close to Swinburne village, and lying to the south of the N3, is Rensburgkop, peaking at 2 236 m above mean sea level. This is another striking example of a residual mountain made up of an outlier of Clarens sandstone, capped by a thin layer of basalt. Here you're as high in the Karoo stratigraphy as you're going to get on the N3. A further 14 km brings you to the start of Van Reenen's Pass, 1 690 m above sea level. A steeply dipping Karoo dolerite sheet, noticeable as a line of dark, rugged, rocky hills at right angles to the road, makes a resistant ridge along the edge of the Highveld, in effect forming the supporting 'spine' of the Great Escarpment in this area (**geosite 1, map 23**). The new N3 takes a less scenic route down the pass, but if you have the time, look out for the Windy Corner turn-off 2 km past the village, and make a short detour on the old tarred road. You will be impressed by the spectacular views,

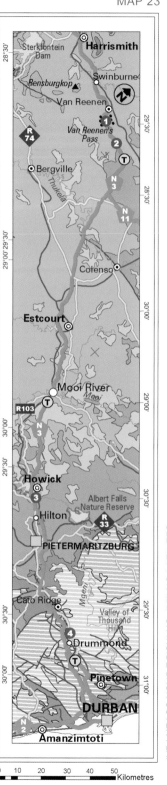

After Van Reenen's Pass there are good exposures of mainly grey mudstone with subordinate layers of paler sandstone of the Beaufort Group, as seen here. This site is close to the bluish shales of the underlying Ecca Group.

178   Geological Journeys

This scenic section of the N3 (part of Van Reenen's Pass is seen on the left) corresponds to the main Drakensberg escarp-ment. A thick northwards-dipping sheet of resistant Karoo dolerite forms the rocky outcrops along the crest of the ridge.

and you will see, at close quarters, part of the crowning dolerite sheet cutting through the shales. Look to the south and, on a clear day, you should be able to make out the high ramparts of the Drakensberg, 60 km away (see ch. 17 for more detail).

Van Reenen's Pass marks your entry into KwaZulu-Natal, and from here the N3 will take you down the stratigraphic column, across older and older formations. A cutting 12 km southeast of Van Reenen reveals alternating sandstone and shales of the lower part of the Beaufort Group and a little further on you will see dark bluish grey shales that are typical of the underlying Ecca Group, and unlike anything in the Beaufort Group **(geosite 2, map 23)**. Some 32 km southeast of Van Reenen, near the Sand River, a road cutting shows sandstone overlain by dark shales, through which a thick dolerite sheet has intruded. You climb slightly as you leave the basin carved by the Thukela River and its tributaries and, around the Ladysmith turn-off, you're back in the Beaufort again until after Mooi River. As before in this unit of generally quite soft sandstones and mudstones, the most conspicuously exposed geology is made up of sills and sheets of Karoo dolerite. Evidence of these is seen in the form of boulder-strewn hills and red soil, and as massive to blocky, dark grey exposures in cuttings and quarries.

The Beaufort Group – window into our colourful past

The geological map of South Africa shows the Beaufort Group as the most extensive single group in the country, with about 200 000 sq km of country underlain by its sediments. They were deposited around 250 million years ago in swampy conditions on a vast Gondwana floodplain, and consist mainly of grey, green and maroon siltstones, mudstones and shales. Interbedded buff and grey sheet-like sandstones reflect the paths of meandering river channels. A wide range of reptiles and mammal-like reptiles lived – and died – in the swamps and along the river banks at this time, as evidenced by their fossilised remains, found particularly in the southern Karoo. South Africa is justifiably famous for the evolutionary developments that such fossils reveal, faithfully recorded in the Beaufort mudstones. On the basis of its fossil reptiles the Beaufort sequence has been divided into eight distinct biozones. The Beaufort Group crosses the divide between the Palaeozoic and Mesozoic Eras, a crossover marked by the cataclysmic extinction of 95 per cent of life on Earth. From the survivors of this event descended the dinosaurs (themselves cataclysmically wiped out in another, later mass extinction some 65 million years ago), as well as all the terrestrial vertebrates we know today (see ch. 5, p. 116).

Shortly past the first Estcourt turn-off, you will see dark bluish grey shale and siltstone of the Beaufort Group in road cuttings; and another series of dolerite intrusions are well shown in the cuttings southeast of the Bushman's River bridge. The big hill starting about 10 km southeast of Estcourt is made entirely of a very big dolerite sheet, which continues for over 10 km. From here the N3 takes you down to Mooi River where, at the tollgate, you should look out for the well-bedded grey shale containing thin layers of pale-weathering sandstone. A look at the geological map will show you that, at Mooi River, you are still in the Beaufort Group, though dolerite is by now the predominant underlying rock, and this continues until Howick.

At Howick, we suggest that you make a short detour off the N3 to see the well-known waterfall on the Mgeni River. Howick was established as a fording place just above the falls, on what was to become the main road to the interior. The 95 m-high waterfall is the result of the river dropping over a thick sill of resistant dolerite **(geosite 3, map 23)**. If you are energetic, take a hike into the forested gorge to get a different view of the waterfall, and a close-up look at the dolerite. The Ecca shales that underlie the dolerite are covered with soil here.

From Howick to Pietermaritzburg the geology is rather poorly exposed, and from Hilton the considerable traffic down Town Hill makes concentrating on driving a priority. There is evidence of dolerite intrusions in some of the road cuttings, and the geological map shows mainly Ecca sediments. As you pass Pietermaritzburg, look for the large abandoned quarry to the north of the road (where a major shopping centre is now located) and you will see the horizontally bedded sediments, predominantly dark grey Ecca shales.

From about 10 km southeast of Pietermaritzburg on the Durban freeway, you see for the first time the very dark blue-grey glacial tillite of the Dwyka Group, the lowest unit in the Karoo sequence. East of Pietermaritzburg there are many good exposures and, although stopping places on the busy N3 freeway are rare, a detour to examine this unusual rock will repay the effort to find one. The geological map shows that the tillite continues as far as Cato Ridge. Brief descriptions of the genesis of this distinctive rock are given in ch. 3 (Durban) and ch. 7 (N2 from Port Elizabeth to Durban).

As you approach Cato Ridge you will become aware of 'table mountains' or mesas in the distance to the north. These are made of flat-lying sandstone of the Natal Group. This is the oldest sedimentary sequence in this area, deposited on the Basement granites around 490 million years ago, and is the time equivalent of the quartzitic sandstones of the Table Mountain Group in the Western Cape, so perhaps the 'table tops' are to be expected. Sand forming the Natal Group was deposited within the coastal stretches of ancient rivers draining long-gone highlands in the northeast. The deposit eventually formed a continuous layer across much of what we know as KwaZulu-Natal today. This was to be covered, in a much later sedimentary event, by Karoo sediments and, finally, by Drakensberg lavas. After the break-up of Gondwana and the erosion that followed, the continuous layer of sandstone was dissected into separate table-lands that we see in this part of KwaZulu-Natal.

At Cato Ridge, look out for the big ferro-manganese smelter to the north of the freeway. Here high-grade manganese ore, railed in from the Northern Cape, is upgraded to metal for export. A short distance northeast of the N3 at Cato Ridge lies the Valley of a Thousand Hills, but to see this scenic terrain – of steep hills and deep valleys, some still wild, others densely populated – you will need to divert to the old Main Road, the R103. Dominating the western side of the valley is 'Table Mountain', a 3 km-long outlier of hard Natal sandstone. The Valley of a Thousand Hills comprises a highly dissected massif of crystalline basement, measuring roughly 30 by 25 km, and now eroded below the level of the surrounding countryside (see more about the Valley of a Thousand Hills in ch. 3, p. 78). The old Durban–Pietermaritzburg Main Road, famous for the annual Comrades Marathon, provides the best access, and will take you into Durban via Pinetown and the M13 freeway.

From Cato Ridge, to the northeast is a long-range view of the spectacular Valley of a Thousand Hills. Here, Natal Group sandstone has largely been removed to expose granite-gneisses of the Natal Metamorphic Complex. Note the flat 'table mountains'.

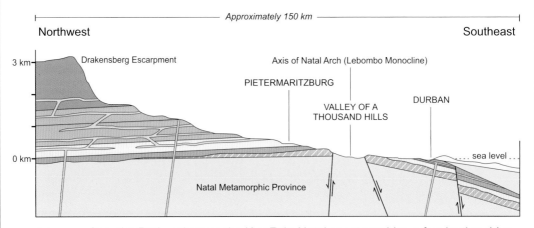

FIGURE 18 — GEOLOGICAL CROSS-SECTION FROM THE DRAKENSBERG TO DURBAN

Approximately 150 km

Northwest | Southeast

3 km — Drakensberg Escarpment | Axis of Natal Arch (Lebombo Monocline)

PIETERMARITZBURG

DURBAN

VALLEY OF A THOUSAND HILLS

0 km — sea level

Natal Metamorphic Province

A journey from the Drakensberg to the KwaZulu-Natal coast provides a fascinating drive back through geological time. Starting at the Escarpment edge, you pass from Drakensberg lava into the full sequence of underlying Karoo sandstones, shales and mudstones, invaded by ubiquitous sills of Karoo dolerite. Past Pietermaritzburg you will see thick resistant beds of flat-lying Natal sandstone of much older age, while the Valley of a Thousand Hills reveals intrusive granites and metamorphic gneisses around 1 100 million years old, but which are more easily eroded.

(Note: The vertical scale is exaggerated for greater clarity)

Young unconsolidated sediments and dunes

Zululand Group sediments (not exposed on section)

Drakensberg Group basalt ⎫

Karoo dolerite intrusions ⎪

Stormberg Group (sandstones and shales) ⎬ KAROO SUPERGROUP

Beaufort-mudstone and sandstone ⎪

Ecca Group shales and sandstones ⎪

Dwyka Group tillite ⎭

Natal Group sandstone

Basement granite and gneiss

Fault with direction of movement

After leaving Midmar Dam the Mgeni River plunges over Howick Falls, a precipitous 95-m drop over a resistant dolerite sill that intruded Ecca shales. It's worth a detour to see the falls and take a short hike to the pool below.

The main players in the formation of this spectacular valley system are the down-cutting Mgeni River, which you will remember seeing at Howick; the softer Basement granite and gneiss underlying the sandstone; and the structural influence of large-scale block faulting. The Mgeni River and its network of tributaries follow a strongly incised and sinuous path across the granitic terrain. The deeply weathered Basement, part of the geologically complex 1 100 million-year-old Natal Metamorphic Province, constitutes rocks that are far more easily eroded than the overlying hard Natal sandstone.

Around Drummond, on the rim of the Valley of a Thousand Hills, you are near the axis of what was known as the Natal, or Lebombo, Monocline. Speaking in very broad terms, the axis stretches from Swaziland in the north, and enters the Indian Ocean at the southern end of KwaZulu-Natal's South Coast. Along it, very ancient Basement rocks are exposed: to the west, at least where you are in central KwaZulu-Natal, are essentially flat-lying Karoo sediments; to the east, the same sediments and volcanics dip shallowly towards the east. A monocline is a fold, though, and normally large-scale folds are reflected by small-scale drag-folds (see text box, pp. 120–121). Instead of drag-folds along this axis, we find an extraordinary amount of faulting, and the currently accepted interpretation of the axis of older rocks flanked by younger rocks is that the structure is a consequence of rifting and drift-related faulting.

East of Drummond, the N3 continues on flat-lying Natal Group sandstone, and exposures are seen in several road cuttings and as scattered, loose boulders. Close to Inchanga, the road follows a gorge in which the sandstones are shown off to advantage, as they are in prominent natural cliffs, easily visible from the road. A short detour onto the R103 will provide excellent close-up exposures **(geosite 4, map 23)**. A few kilometres after the Inchanga turn-off, near Shongweni, the N3 crosses a prominent hill made of upfaulted, weathered biotite gneiss, part of the granite exposed in the

Valley of a Thousand Hills. From east of Hillcrest, the N3 descends, and before and at the Marion Hill Toll Plaza, the Natal Group sandstone is again conspicuous.

After passing Pinetown, a subtle change in the dip of the sandstone may become apparent to the keen observer. It is now dipping shallowly to the east, as a result of the regional block faulting. Now you will be able to see the Indian Ocean in front of you, and the landscape becomes more dissected. From the ridge in Westville you can see Durban, located on the coastal plain, with its very much younger Tertiary dunes. And here the geological map shows that the Dwyka tillite reappears, another effect of rift-related faulting, and dealt with in the section on Durban (ch. 3, p. 74). We hope you have enjoyed this traverse from the Highveld to the coast, from early Precambrian to late Tertiary, and from conglomerate to dune sand.

At Inchanga, the N3 passes through a gorge flanked by steep reddish cliffs of horizontal sandstone, and a detour onto the R103 will allow a close-up look at these pre-Karoo rocks.

10 N4: Pretoria to Skilpadshek

GEOLOGICAL OVERVIEW

The Magaliesberg is a dominant feature of the Gauteng landscape, and this section of the N4 stays in the shadow of this range, both north and south, until well past Rustenburg. Like most elongate, prominent ridges, this one consists of inclined quartzites, not surprisingly called the Magaliesberg Formation. They belong in the Pretoria Group, a main member of the Transvaal Supergroup. The chief reason for their northerly dip here is that they lie just below the Bushveld Complex, whose intrusion was sufficient to depress the floor formations immediately beneath it, causing the edge to tilt.

The route cuts across the floor of the Complex, taking you up through its magmatic stratigraphy as you approach Rustenburg. Headgears, dumps and tall smokestacks tell that you are in mining country as you travel between Brits and Rustenburg: the more southerly workings are for chrome, those further north are the bigger platinum mines, and Rustenburg is the source of a significant proportion of the world's platinum production.

Based on the very extensive platinum-rich reefs found within the Bushveld Complex, the Rustenburg region is at the centre of South Africa's platinum mining industry. Numerous headgears and metallurgical extraction plants dot the landscape. This photo shows one of the Anglo American platinum operations near Rustenburg.

If you're bound for the Pilanesberg, the area is worth spending some time in, not only for its game and birds, but for the remarkable geology of this ancient volcano – and its unusual alkaline rock assemblage.

Even as you draw close to the Kalahari near Zeerust, you are still not beyond the effects of the Bushveld Complex, with its tilting of the Transvaal sediments, and the heat of its intrusion having created andalusite crystals that you can admire in road cuttings as you pass through Herman Charles Bosman country, the Groot Marico.

INSET: *Molten platinum being poured into a ladle at the Waterval smelter at Anglo Platinum's Rustenburg mine.*

Geology of the route

Pretoria to Skilpadshek (Botswana border)

Leaving Pretoria, the N4 follows a broad valley underlain by shales and lavas within the north-dipping Pretoria Group sediments between quartzite ridges to the north and south. The valley continues to near Hartbeespoort Dam, at which point the N4 turns to the north, crossing the Daspoort Range at Saartjiesnek, where conspicuous weathered boulders of intrusive diabase cover the slopes. From the Johannesburg area the best route is on the R511 from Fourways, joining the N4 near Pelindaba. This takes you across the Johannesburg Granite Dome and through almost the entire Transvaal Supergroup, including very good exposures of Malmani dolomite in the Hennops River valley, with its characteristic *olifantsklip* weathering.

Topped by a thick, hard layer of resistant Magliesberg Quartzite, the Magaliesberg Mountains form a spectacular backdrop to Hartbeespoort Dam. The low area in the centre, also the site of the dam wall, was the original Hartbeespoort (gorge) through which flows the Crocodile River, and is the result of down-faulted block.

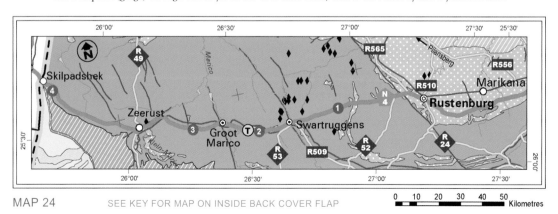

MAP 24   SEE KEY FOR MAP ON INSIDE BACK COVER FLAP

0 10 20 30 40 50 Kilometres

A road cutting 19 km before Swartruggens reveals Dwaalheuwel Formation ironstone, a prominent but thin marker unit consisting of well-bedded siltstone impregnated with fine-grained hematite, overlying the Hekpoort volcanics.

Up ahead, and also running more or less east-west, you will see the main Magaliesberg range, capped by an almost continuous rugged scarp of resistant quartzite of the Magaliesberg Formation. Directly across the Hartbeespoort Dam, the gap in the range is the gorge from which the dam gets its name, where the Crocodile River, which starts on the Witwatersrand, cuts its way northwards through the range, its dissection of the otherwise tough quartzite facilitated by the pulverising action of a major north-trending fault. The gorge was dammed in 1923 to provide irrigation water for fertile soil downstream near Brits, though today its use would generally be perceived as recreational, with its description as the Bushveld Riviera understandable, if a little optimistic. (See also ch. 1, p. 55, for more detail.)

The N4 takes you on a dogleg across the Magaliesberg via Silkaatsnek, named after the Zulu Chief Msilikatsi who once ruled this region, although the slower, alternative road – via Schoemansville, through a short tunnel, and across the dam wall to rejoin the N4 west of Hartbeespoort – is more picturesque. The latter route shows a good cross-section through the glassy, recrystallised Magaliesberg quartzite; here you can marvel at the massive accumulation of sandy sediment laid down in a shallow sea 2 200 million years ago, and with water once again lapping its shores. Note that from Pretoria, the new N4 toll road, the so-called Platinum Highway, will differ somewhat in routing to the N4 described here.

In places the Magaliesberg quartzite has been recrystallised by thermal metamorphism from the intrusion of the nearby Bushveld Complex, accounting for its extremely hard nature. Notice the abnormally coarse-grained quartz crystals seen in this weathered outcrop.

Leaving Hartbeespoort Dam, the most marked geological feature is the ever-present Magaliesberg range that continues along your southern side all the way to Rustenburg. Because of the moderate northeasterly dip of these rocks here, what you see is smooth, rocky dip slope, dissected here and there by well-vegetated ravines. To the north of the Magaliesberg, and in direct contact with the quartzite, lies the Mafic Phase of the Bushveld Complex, the largest layered intrusion in the world, and by far the largest repository of platinum metals and chromium. (See the feature on the geology of the Bushveld Complex in ch. 4, pp. 88–89.) On the N4, you reach the beginning of Bushveld rocks about 7 km west from the dam, although one is hardly aware of it, as outcrops are few and far between, with bedrock being entirely covered by thick scree and the characteristic black turf soil derived from mafic rocks.

But you get a good sense that you're on the richly metal-bearing Bushveld Complex from the many mine workings and tailings dumps, both big and small, seen to the north of your route. Closest to the road are the chrome mines, in the past usually mined by open-cast methods, where a number of narrow, remarkably continuous seams of shiny, black chromite were worked. In places you may see the road sparkling with fine crystals of chromite spilled off passing ore trucks. The Bushveld Complex contains over 70 per cent of world chrome reserves, supplying around 45 per cent of annual global requirements, largely as value-added ferrochrome produced by a number of local smelters.

In the distance further to the north, you will see the infrastructure of major underground mines – headgears, tailings dams and the occasional smelter with tall smoke-stacks. These are some of the platinum – strictly platinum group elements (PGE) – mines of the Bushveld, which in addition to platinum, produce lesser quantities of palladium and rhodium, plus by-product nickel and copper. Two layers of the Complex are mined for their PGEs – the well-known thin Merensky Reef, and the UG2 Reef, the latter geologically akin to the chromite seams. In platinum, too, South Africa is the winning horse by many lengths, with 88 per cent of the world's known PGE resources, and supplying more than 60 per cent of the world's PGE requirements. In 2002 the value of export sales amounted to over R30 billion, almost exceeding that of gold. Like the chrome mines, the giant platinum mines continue well past Rustenburg, making the area from east of Brits to northwest of Rustenburg arguably South Africa's most valuable future mining asset, rivalled only by the same geological units in the eastern and northern limbs of the Bushveld Complex.

About 35 km before Rustenburg, a line of distinctive, dark, boulder-strewn hills make their appearance south of the road, and you will see signs to Buffelspoort Dam, located in these hills. These are formed from a rock locally called Kolobeng Norite, a formation that continues past Rustenburg to the northwest, and represents the marginal phase of the Bushveld Complex. It forms a semi-continuous zone of very early intrusive material at the base of the complex, pre-dating the main phase with all its metals and mysteries.

Near Rustenburg, the Magaliesberg range, which so far has run more or less east-west, now veers off to the northwest, consistent with the structure of the Transvaal Basin, and modified by the intrusion of the Bushveld Complex. At Kroondal, some 12 km before Rustenburg, look out for a small chrome mine to the south of the road. To the east of the town you may also see the smoke-stack and buildings of Anglo Platinum's Waterval smelter. The N4 passes through what is said to be South Africa's fastest growing town, Rustenburg, and then crosses over the hills to the west near the Phokeng and Pilanesberg turn-off, about 6 km west of Rustenburg. Here you traverse a mixed sequence made of Kolobeng Norite and Magaliesberg quartzite, before crossing the last quartzite ridge, conspicuously broken up and locally steeply dipping, some 11 km west of the town.

The Pilanesberg – roots of an ancient volcano

The Pilanesberg Complex, located some 40 km north-northwest of Rustenburg, is geologically interesting in its entirety, as well as including a number of individual sites of geological importance.

The complex consists of a nearly circular dissected mountain massif some 25 km in diameter, and rising over 300 m from the surrounding countryside. It owes its origin to an enormous volcanic eruption, 1 300 million years ago. Around South Africa we see countless examples of acid (granitic) and mafic (dolerite and diabasic) igneous rocks. The Pilanesberg, though, is a rare example of alkaline rocks, and carries the distinction of being the third biggest alkaline ring complex in the world. The once immense volcanic caldera has been largely eroded away but visitors can still see the remains of ancient lava flows and volcanic breccias. The dominant features of the complex are the concentric cone sheets formed by magma that intruded ring fractures created during the inward collapse of the caldera. Old mining sites for fluorite (fluorspar) and a non-diamondiferous kimberlite occur. Some of the rocks are geochemically very unusual, containing higher than normal levels of a number of rare elements. A variety of strange-sounding rock names occur here, such as red syenite, and red and green foyaite. Several sites of geological interest have been demarcated and are described by informative plaques.

You can combine geology with other attractions, as the renowned Pilanesberg National Park, situated within the complex, is regarded as one of the best game reserves in South Africa. Created in 1980, it is a compact, world-class conservation area with considerable ecological diversity, and is assured of a place on tourism itineraries by offering the 'Big Five'. There are always good game-viewing and birding opportunities.

Having crossed the Magaliesberg, and as you make your way west towards Swartruggens, you will see that the countryside is now gently rolling as it drops down to the Koster River. With the exception of plentiful diabase sills, shown by reddish, rounded boulders, the rocks are all northeast-dipping sediments and volcanics of the Pretoria Group. Around 24 km before Swartruggens, almost flat-lying quartzite layers can be seen, and dark, well-bedded, iron-rich sandstone and quartzite; and siltstone beds are well exposed in a road cutting 5 km further on **(geosite 1, map 24)**. Swartruggens is located on khaki-weathering shales of the Timeball Hill Formation. In places, where it is indurated, or 'baked' and tends to split along bedding-planes, this dark shale, or slate, is quarried and sold as 'slasto' for paving and cladding **(geosite 2, map 24)**. Swartruggens is also notable for the narrow but high-grade diamond-bearing kimberlite 'fissures' or dykes 8 km north of the town.

You're entering Herman Charles Bosman country as you approach Groot Marico, still with the hills of Hekpoort volcanics to your right. The soft Timeball Hill shales make up the gently undulating country in

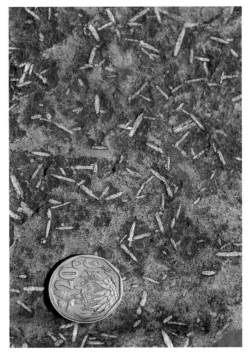

Andalusite crystals in slate in the road cutting west of Groot Marico: a good example of a contact metamorphic mineral (see p. 190).

which you are driving, with sparse cuttings through rock that is mostly quite deeply weathered. About 10 km after Groot Marico, note the turn-off to an old andalusite mine, now closed down. Andalusite, an aluminium-rich contact metamorphic mineral, formed as the shales here were intensely heated by the Bushveld Complex, is used in the manufacture of specialised high-temperature refractories required for industrial furnaces. It may not be worth billions, but South Africa is the world's leading producer of andalusite. About 7 km west of this mine, in cuttings on either side of a small stream running through clearly bedded sediments, the slate shows andalusite crystals up to a centimetre long, which are certainly worth a look (**geosite 3, map 24**).

The hills north of Zeerust are of north-dipping Timeball Hill sediments, including quartzites, which swing from the east-west strike they hold as you approach the town to more northwesterly as you leave it on the last stretch to the Botswana border. From Zeerust to the border this strike trend is followed closely by the road, which stays on, or close to, beds of banded ironstone.

The banded ironstone in the Pretoria Group is frequently associated with an extensive layer of manganese ore, so for geologists, the turn-off to Gopane (a name that has come to be associated with manganese) as you approach the Botswana border comes as no surprise. About 300 m after the turn-off, stop and see the fault breccia cutting slates along which there has been pervasive remobilisation of iron and manganese, giving an outcrop that is not only interesting but extremely handsome (**geosite 4, map 24**). Four kilometres from the Skilpadshek border post, cuttings on both sides of the road show very beautiful 'must see' exposures of Pretoria Group banded ironstone.

Before you know it, you're at the border, the wide Kalahari not far ahead.

It's worth stopping to see this exposure of Pretoria Group banded ironstone in a road cutting as you approach the border.

*The manganese in this fault breccia (**geosite 4, map 24**) is not surprising – there are old manganese mines nearby.*

Manganese oxide, partly as dendrites, adds interest to this jointed shale 9 km east of Swartruggens.

This toll plaza wall is a reminder that the Swartruggens area is widely celebrated for its excellent slate.

11 N4: Pretoria to Komatipoort

GEOLOGICAL OVERVIEW

Maputo and coastal destinations north of it are enjoying growing popularity, and travellers taking this route will find plenty to see geologically.

You stay on sediments of the Pretoria Group to start with and about 25 km east of Pretoria you will be some 15 km south of the celebrated Cullinan diamond pipe. But as you approach Witbank it is carbon in another form that catches your attention, because you are entering one of the country's main coal fields, based on the vast deposits of the Ecca Group. Huge coal-based power stations become a feature of the landscape for a while, and outside Witbank you cannot miss the Highveld Steel and Vanadium smelter. This, too, is located here because of the availability of coal for use in smelting magnetite iron ore from the nearby Bushveld Complex.

Your route will take you across the entire Transvaal Supergroup, and an important feature of the geology is the unusual volcanic sediments and acid lavas exposed. The first of these can be seen around Witbank, where the Precambrian Rooiberg Group

MAIN PICTURE: *About 25 km east of Middelburg, several hundred metres of typical reddish felsite have been exposed in a road cutting.*
INSET: *Close examination shows evidence of volcanic origin, including impressive flow banding.*

comprises a range of felsites. These rocks are essentially similar to rhyolites of the much younger Jozini Formation, at the top of the Karoo Supergroup, which are well exposed in the Lebombo range as you approach the border with Mozambique.

Between these two localities, from the base of the Great Escarpment near Ngodwana to beyond Hectorspruit, you are at the bottom of the geological pile, in the very ancient greenstones and granites that are part of the Kaapvaal Craton. Not far to the south lies the Barberton Mountain Land, celebrated among geologists worldwide for its vivid record of events in Earth's earliest days.

Pretoria to Belfast

From the outskirts of Pretoria, the N4 stays close to the strike of the Pretoria Group, cutting through the Magaliesberg quartzites at Donkerhoek, 15 km from Pretoria **(geosite 1, map 25)**. North and northeast of the now subdued Magaliesberg range, the thick Rayton Formation makes its appearance, consisting of quartzites and shales intruded by numerous diabase sills that form the most prominent, bouldery outcrops.

At Donkerhoek, some 30 km east of central Pretoria, well-bedded, northeast-dipping Magaliesberg quartzites form the easternmost ridge of the Magaliesberg and are evident in the road cutting.

At the Rayton exit, the R64 can take you northwards towards Cullinan, 15 km away. Celebrated in diamond circles as the mine where the world's biggest-ever gem diamond was discovered, Cullinan is worth a visit. (This story is covered in ch. 1, pp. 51–53.) The underlying geology eastwards is the Rayton Formation, but outcrops are generally poor. Past Bronkhorstspruit, the low reddish hills to the north are of the Waterberg Group, another major sedimentary sequence deposited towards the end of Bushveld Complex times. Closer to the road, near the village of Balmoral, a small inlier of pale Bushveld Granite occurs on both sides of the highway and is noticeable in a large quarry **(geosite 2, map 25)**.

MAP 25   SEE KEY FOR MAP ON INSIDE BACK COVER FLAP

0   10   20   30   40   50 Kilometres

To the south, flat-lying sediments of the Karoo Supergroup can be seen: thin glacial tillite of the Dwyka Group at the base, overlain by river-deposited sandstones of the Ecca Group, but good outcrops are few and far between. After passing Balmoral, thick coal-bearing middle Ecca sediments blanket the older formations, and mines of the Witbank coal field make their appearance. Some distance before Witbank you see the massive Highveld Steel and Vanadium smelter on the southern side of the highway. Processing vanadium-bearing magnetite ore that is mined from the eastern Bushveld Complex near Roossenekal, this plant is an important steel producer and a major supplier to world markets of vanadium pentoxide.

Witbank is located on high ground underlain by felsite (acid volcanics) of the Rooiberg Group, the top unit of the Transvaal Supergroup. The high ground is an older inlier surrounded by much younger Karoo sediments. Around 300 million years ago, the vast ice sheets that covered Gondwana, in sculpting the underlying land surface, left this area as an island in a sea of ice. As the ice sheets melted, sediments were deposited in the elongated glacial valleys. Later these became choked – then flooded – with sediment, until the entire region was thickly blanketed, with the vast peat beds already on the way to hard, shiny, black coal (see text box on coal, ch. 13, p. 231).

This granite outcrop, known as Balmoral Granite, occurs as a small inlier on both sides of the freeway, and is exposed as large, rounded boulders. It is medium-grained, slightly pinkish in colour and is part of the Bushveld Complex.

Near the bridge across the Olifants River, some 6 km east of the intersection with the N12, you will be able to see reddish Rooiberg Group felsite, a form of rhyolite typical of the acid volcanics that make up most of this group **(geosite 3, map 25)**. A look at these rocks will show traces of the original flow banding and ejected volcanic fragments. Felsite extends almost to the Middelburg toll plaza, over about 6 km, and forms rounded hills showing good outcrop with scanty vegetation.

Rhyolite is a fine-grained, glassy lava, very rich in silica, and representing granitic magma that erupted on the surface. But this lava did not ooze from great fissures or down the slopes of volcanic cones; rather, it resulted from explosive eruptions, with dense, glowing clouds of very hot volcanic fragments being hurled high into the air. Imagine the still glowing debris falling back to Earth, to become fused and consolidated as beds of welded tuffs and ignimbrites. These seemingly ordinary-looking rocks tell a story of the highest drama.

At the Olifants River bridge just east of Witbank, the Rooiberg felsites are well exposed as hard, reddish outcrops, in places revealing flow banding and incorporating volcanic fragments.

Another excellent exposure can be seen in a road cutting some 15 km east of the Middelburg town turn-off **(geosite 4, map 25)**. Here Rooiberg felsite, ground down by ancient ice sheets, forms the lower ground in the valleys, and you will see fresh, reddish exposures showing volcanic fragments and finer volcanic lapilli. You'll also see rudimentary layering, indicating that the rocks formed by airborne deposition, with the convoluted flow-banding telling of later plastic flow of still semi-molten lava.

To the south of Witbank are the enormous smokestacks and cooling towers of Eskom's Duvha power station, one of the largest in Africa. Why here? you ask. The answer is simple – coal. Duvha has six enormous coal-devouring generating sets and the capacity to produce 3 600 megawatts of electricity. Every year 10 million tons of low-grade coal comes from the adjoining Middelburg Mine directly into the power station. The Witbank coal field, the most important in South Africa, stretches from far west of Witbank to almost as far east as Belfast, and for many kilometres to the south. Coal was known from here as far back as the 1870s and was commercially mined in the 1890s for use on the rapidly developing Witwatersrand gold mines. Today the eastern Highveld region supports scores of mines, producing coal both for export and for domestic use and, equally importantly, for use in Eskom's power stations and Sasol's Secunda plants, making this undeniably the powerhouse of Africa.

South Africa's powerhouse

Coal has always been the main energy source in industrial South Africa. Apart from its role in electricity generation, it forms the primary source material for Sasol's petrochemicals industry, feedstock for steel manufacture and a score of other heavy and light industries, like brick-making and cement production. Without affordable electricity, we would not be able to mine gold and platinum from kilometres below the surface; nor run the major steel, ferro-chrome and vanadium smelters; nor produce titanium or aluminium at Richards Bay. About 77 per cent of the country's primary energy needs are provided by coal, and Eskom is by far the biggest electricity generator in Africa, and ranked seventh in the world. Sasol is the leading coal-to-oil and petrochemicals producer in the world. At present consumption, our coal reserves are estimated to last another 200 years.

It is in this part of Mpumalanga, south of the N4, that most of the coal-fired power stations are found. There are seven big power stations in the region, several of which you will see in passing, with names like Arnot, Camden, Duvha and Kendal.

These operations use gigantic rock-moving equipment called draglines to move thick overburden and expose the coal beds. The coal is then cleaned and graded, and either exported or used in Eskom's mega-sized thermal power stations, seen in the background.

Smart planning and clever design enables these power stations to run on low-grade coal that's unsuitable for export or other industrial purposes, thereby maximising the lives of their dedicated coal mines, and extending the country's coal reserves. These seven power stations have the capacity to produce over 50 per cent of South Africa's electricity.

What of the environmental effects of coal-fired power stations? Yes, the burning of coal does produce air pollution, and the mining does have an impact on the environment. Technology is improving apace, though, providing ever better monitoring, and stricter environmental controls are now in place. Existing and emerging 'clean coal' technology is on the verge of making coal mining and processing more environment-friendly.

As you head eastwards towards Belfast, except for some Rooiberg felsites in the valleys, you travel across flat-lying sediments of the Ecca Group. Close to the Woestalleen turn-off, around 45 km west of Belfast, you may see a small operating coal mine on the northern side of the road – notice the coal washing plant that recovers the better quality coal, and the dumps of low grade 'waste' coal. Strict environmental legislation now requires all open-cast workings to be filled in and topsoil replaced, so that when mining is completed the area will be restored to rolling grassland again.

Close to Wonderfontein, about 25 km west of Belfast, notice a small but well-developed circular pan on the southern side of the road. Pans here – and there are quite a lot of them – are unusual, as they fall outside the arid part of the country where the great majority of such pans are found, far to the west. (For a summary of how pans form, see the text box in ch. 14, p. 237.)

Belfast to Komatipoort

As you head eastwards from the Engen station at the Belfast turn-off, you start your gradual descent off the Highveld, and the route becomes noticeably more scenic. The reason is geological: you are going back through geological time, from the 270 million-year-old Ecca sediments on the high plains, through the entire Transvaal sequence that makes the Great Escarpment, to the 3.5 billion-year-old granites and greenstones of the Lowveld.

Some 5 km from the Engen station is the Bergendal Monument, scene of the last conventional battle of the Anglo-Boer War. Here 20 000 advancing British troops overwhelmed a gallant but outnumbered Boer force in August 1900. A look around the site shows an abundance of large, rounded, weathered boulders, where the Boers made their last stand. They are similar to outcrops west of Bronkhorstspruit, 160 km to the west, and they show diabase sills of Bushveld age, intruded into the sediments of the Pretoria Group that are a dominant feature of this region.

East of Bergendal, where the N4 crosses a railway cutting close to Dalmanutha station turn-off, you'll see the first signs of the characteristic Magaliesberg quartzite, and a short distance further on, look for the ridge of the same quartzite along the south side of the road (**geosite 1, map 26**). While not very imposing here, this formation carries on northwards to form some of the highest mountains in Mpumalanga. The thick sequence of Pretoria sediments and lesser volcanics and sills

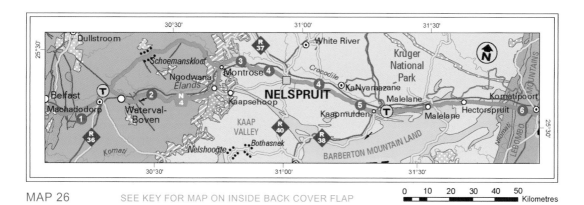

MAP 26   SEE KEY FOR MAP ON INSIDE BACK COVER FLAP

0 10 20 30 40 50
Kilometres

dip shallowly to the west beneath the overlying Karoo sediments. They are well exposed east of here in the panoramic scenery of the Great Escarpment, where the abundance of hard, thick quartzites in this unit has withstood erosion from the east.

After crossing the Magaliesberg quartzite you're on a thick succession of brown- to khaki-weathering shales, stratigraphically below the Magaliesberg Formation, on which the old town of Machadodorp is located, and which continue for the next 25 km to Waterval-Boven. Notice that the instability of the shales in road cuttings necessitates their containment by wire mesh as a safety measure. Just before Machadodorp, off to the south, you will catch a glimpse of another smelter that produces ferro-chrome from chromite mined near

OPPOSITE: *East of Belfast, numerous rounded bouldery outcrops of resistant Bushveld-age diabase sills dot the landscape. The outcrops pictured are on a rocky ridge near the Bergendal Monument.*

LEFT: *Close to Waterval-Boven, this waterfall results from the Elands River plunging over an almost horizontal, resistant ledge of Pretoria Group quartzite.*

BELOW: *Constructed in 1895, the old Waterval-Boven tunnel was driven through hard quartzite of the Daspoort Formation, part of the Pretoria Group.*

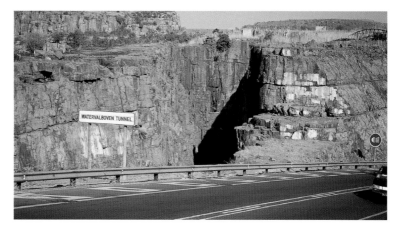

Steelpoort, further north in the Bushveld Complex. About 5 km east of Machadodorp, the N4 splits into two routes, one via Waterval-Onder, and the other via Schoemanspoort; we have taken the former, but the latter will show you much the same geology, while missing the tunnel.

Waterval-Boven, an early railway depot, and Waterval-Onder get their names from their location near the top and bottom of the spectacular 90 m-high Elands River Falls. In 1892–1893 a tunnel – now a national monument – was blasted through the resistant quartzite layer that formed an otherwise unassailable obstacle to the course of the railway line from the coast. This quartzite is clearly visible from the road, and forms the ledge over which the Elands River cascades (**geosite 2, map 26**). The old tunnel is adjacent to the much newer road tunnel.

The road to the Lowveld passes Waterval-Onder and continues down the Elands River valley, providing superb scenery as you descend geologically through Pretoria shales and intrusive diabase, which has formed large, rounded, weathered boulders. You are getting into timber country and soon, near the village of Ngodwana, you will see a massive pulp and paper mill, the largest in the Southern Hemisphere. Some 5 km before Ngodwana, the valley opens up and the ground flattens as you cross, unawares, onto Malmani dolomite. But as you pass the mill, you will see a small hill just off to the south, made of bedded dolomite, with a few old circular lime-burning kilns at its base. And also to the south, as you leave the plant area, you may fleetingly see strangely eroded quartzite of the Black Reef Formation close to the Kaapsehoop turn-off.

Towards the base of the Great Escarpment, at Ngodwana, these historic kilns hint at the changing geology. Limestone for burning (to make lime) came from deposits located within the Malmani dolomite, seen in the background hill.

Kaapsehoop – a detour worth taking

If time permits and you want to see an interesting geological and historic location, we recommend that you turn off the N4 to Kaapsehoop, which provides an alternative, highly scenic route to Nelspruit.

The 12 km-long winding road up to Kaapsehoop sticks close to the contact of the Black Reef quartzite and the overlying Malmani dolomite of the Chuniespoort Group, and you will see outcrops of both as you rise to nearly 1 600 m. Kaapsehoop is located on a narrow plateau at the edge of the Great Escarpment, and the discovery here of alluvial gold in 1882 led to the inevitable gold rush, in this case quite short-lived (see pp. 277–278).

A long period of humid weathering has formed weirdly shaped rock formations in the shallowly dipping quartzites of the Black Reef Formation. A short, labyrinthine walk through the naturally carved sandstone landscape takes you to the view site at the rim of the plateau. Enjoy the panoramic view over a 1 000 m drop into the verdant Kaap Valley below, made of ancient Kaap Valley Granite, and the Barberton Mountain Land beyond. Driving down the Kaapsehoop Pass towards Nelspruit you'll see the sediments of the Godwan Formation underlying the Black Reef quartzites in this area, and resting on Basement granite-gneiss.

At Kaapsehoop the misty weather along the escarpment edge has caused the Black Reef quartzite to weather to a landscape of weirdly shaped sandstone pillars seen here.

If you continue from Ngodwana directly to Nelspruit, the route turns northwards, until you rejoin the other branch of the N4 at the Crocodile River junction at Montrose Falls. But about 4 km west of Montrose, there is a fundamental change in the geology: you are now on Basement granite, clearly seen in the road cuttings as massive, grey, coarse-grained, crystalline rock, conspicuously different from the bedded sedimentary formations seen almost all the way from Pretoria. These are granites of the Nelspruit Suite, a diverse group of 3 100 million-year-old granite-gneisses that make up most of the Basement around here, and extend beneath the sedimentary formations on which you have been travelling, but at great depth. They are exposed here because of the cutting back of the escarpment. You will be able to follow the gneissic granites in road cuttings all the way into Nelspruit and beyond **(geosite 4, map 26)**: notice the dome-shaped hills they form, a characteristic feature of eroding granitic terranes. These are known as exfoliation domes, and they form by a natural mechanical process: layers of granite split off along curved subhorizontal expansion joints that form as the weight of thousands of metres of rocks overlaying the granite is gradually removed by erosion.

Directly after crossing the Crocodile River at Montrose, a large road cutting shows pale, somewhat shiny, greenish grey rocks that are not granites **(geosite 3, map 26)**. They are fine-grained, have well-developed layering, and show a sheared schistose texture – and are commonly called greenstones, the first you will see on this route. For the next few kilometres you will pass over a small greenstone remnant derived from primeval lavas and associated sediments, now surrounded by younger granite. Just 45 km southeast of here lies the rugged 3 200 to 3 500 million-year-old Barberton Mountain Land, one of the best exposed, best preserved and most studied areas of greenstone geology in the world (see text box opposite).

About 20 km east of Nelspruit, a roughly 6 km-wide granite pluton, known as the Mpageni Granite, was intruded through the Nelspruit Granite-gneiss about 2 740 million years ago, and is clearly visible in the Crocodile River gorge **(geosite 5, map 26)**. It does not have gneissic banding, and it's worth stopping at one of the view sites to experience this awe-inspiring setting and see the rock close-up.

A few kilometres east from the gorge lies the village of Kaapmuiden, where the Kaap River enters the Crocodile valley from the south. Now you need to decide whether a visit to the historic gold-mining centre of Barberton, via the R38, is on your agenda.

In the Lowveld region, Basement granite-gneiss is well exposed in numerous bare exfoliation domes, formed by the splitting-off of rock slabs by a process of mechanical weathering. Around Nelspruit the N4 passes a number of these granitic domes. Closer inspection will show a medium- to coarse-grained rock with gneissic texture, often with pegmatitic veins.

The Barberton Mountain Land – a world-renowned greenstone belt

Barberton lies 50 km to the southwest of Kaapmuiden, in the Kaap Valley, at the foot of the Makhonjwa Mountains, and is well worth a visit for those who have time to explore its fascinating geology and gold-mining history. The area is famous for its lode-gold mining that started with the gold rush in 1884 and created a boom town for a few years. Notable events were the discovery of the fabulous Golden Quarry deposit on Sheba Mine and the establishment of legendary Eureka City, now almost completely disappeared. Amazingly, over 120 years later, the gold field is still in production, more than 320 tons of gold having already been recovered. In addition to gold, products mined here have included talc, ornamental stone, verdite, and even, dare we say it, chrysotile asbestos, a fibrous variety of the mineral serpentine.

This is the largest greenstone terrane in southern Africa, and it has revealed the earliest clearly decipherable geological events that took place on Earth from 3 500 million years ago. As to why they are called greenstone belts, the answer is that this is an old field term used for rocks containing abundant greenish minerals such as serpentine, chlorite, amphibole and fuchsite, which characterise the ultramafic and mafic volcanic rocks found in all of these remnants of Earth's early crust around the world.

After passing through the Crocodile River gorge, the northern part of the impressive Barberton Mountain Land is seen in the distance, south of the N4, and is made of a variety of rock types comprising the world-renowned Barberton Greenstone Belt.

The N4 continues from Kaapmuiden to Hectorspruit, for most of the way close to the Crocodile River, passing through farmland. The underlying geology is poorly exposed but a look at the geological map will show that you are driving on the lowermost greenstone formations of the Barberton Supergroup, known as the Onverwacht Group, the mountains to the south being the eastern end of the Barberton Mountain Land. There are few outcrops close to the road in this humid, subtropical terrain, but some of the road cuttings reveal dark ultramafic schists, greenstones of a sort. Close to and east of Kaapmuiden, within the greenstone foothills to the south, you may see the whitish waste dumps from several magnesite (magnesium carbonate) mines, this being one of the country's principal sources of an essential mineral used in making heat-resistant bricks. High-quality talc has also been mined here for use in the cosmetics, paper, paint and plastics industries. Near Hectorspruit, you will see the bare granite boulders of the Salisbury Kop pluton.

The open-pit Strathmore Mine near Kaapmuiden recovers pure magnesite, or magnesium carbonate, which formed by the weathering of ultramafic rocks that are part of the Barberton Greenstone Belt.

At the Strathmore Mine, 'zebra ore' consists of alternating bands of dark brown weathered serpentinite and irregular veins of pure white, very fine-grained magnesite.

Before reaching the Komatipoort village turn-off, you will cross flattish ground underlain mainly by poorly outcropping basaltic lavas, the time-equivalent of the Drakensberg lavas, here known as the Letaba Formation. These rocks once formed a continuous lava field across much of southern Africa and heralded the break-up of Gondwana. The Letaba volcanics overlie typical Karoo sediments, including the equivalent of the cave-forming Clarens sandstone.

Above the basalts lie east-dipping reddish rhyolites of the Jozini Formation, which form the Lebombo Mountains (see ch. 8, pp. 166–167) and which, together with the underlying basalt, make up the Lebombo Group. The rhyolites are well exposed in the Komati River gorge and along the N4 leading to the border post (**geosite 6, map 26**). They include a range of types, including flows, volcanic breccias and bedded pyroclastic rocks. And with that, you are at the border.

A short detour off the N4 towards Komatipoort village will take you to an old low-level bridge across the Komati River where there are excellent water-polished exposures of massive, reddish, fine-grained rhyolitic rocks of the Jozini Formation, part of the Lebombo Group.

Geology of the Kruger National Park

Directly to the north of the Crocodile River lies the Kruger National Park. It is appropriate to comment briefly on the geology of this unique wilderness. The park is underlain mainly by several varieties of Basement granite-gneiss, as well as minor greenstone remnants, and several younger gabbroic and syenite intrusions. In the

far north, Soutpansberg and Karoo sediments occur, and sediments and volcanics of the Karoo Supergroup make up the entire eastern strip. Numerous sites of geological interest have been recognised and are described in the park guidebooks and, at some camps, walking tours with a geological focus can be arranged.

On the basis of the underlying geology, as well as the rainfall, altitude and landform, the Kruger National Park has been divided into 16 distinct ecozones, on the principle that everything in nature is linked. Soil formation is influenced by the underlying parent rocks; trees, shrubs and grasses differ according to soil and climate; and all animal life survives where there is natural protection, enough food and where they can successfully reproduce. Geology – together with climate – thus plays the fundamental role in the development of distinct ecozones, each with its own unique plant and animal communities.

The Kruger Memorial Tablets near Tshokwane in the Kruger National Park commemorate the park's founding in 1898. The tablets are mounted on a group of weathered boulders of Basement granite-gneiss.

GEOLOGICAL OVERVIEW

The irony of the geology of the N7 is that, although it takes you across a number of tightly folded mobile belts for nearly all its length, it starts in the shadow of the horizontally bedded Table Mountain, and finishes, as you approach the border post on the Orange River, with a similar mass of only slightly older, equally flat-lying sedimentary rocks brooding over your departure from South Africa. This route is a tough one, with lots of metamorphism and complicated structure, which we will present as simply and clearly as possible.

The reason for the folding – and different degrees of metamorphism – you will see along the way is that this is one of the few routes that is entirely off the stable craton. It is a vivid illustration of the mobility of the early Earth's crust away from those islands of stability. The first folded and metamorphosed sediments you will see, before you are even out of the metropole, are of the Malmesbury Group, which you cross for the first hour or so. Here you will also see the limestone without which we couldn't build our houses, and manganese and marble.

Then you're into the western branch of the Cape Fold Belt, in range upon range of Cape Supergroup quartzite mountains, the Cedarberg. Out of the hilly country you cross fold belts of the Gariep Supergroup and Vanrhynsdorp Group before getting into the highly metamorphic gneisses and granites of the Namaqua Metamorphic Province. If you take time off in Springbok you will see one of two rare orbicular granites in the country and the oldest copper mines.

You will see geological unconformities aplenty between the Malmesbury Group and the Table Mountain Group at Piekenierskloof, between the Gariep Supergroup and the Table Mountain Group near Klawer, and, near the end of the route, between the Orange River volcanics and the Nama Group near Vioolsdrif.

You could not have asked for a better spectrum of the metamorphism that typifies the mobile belts of the Earth's crust, from the barely changed sandstones of the Table Mountain Group around Clanwilliam to the gneisses at Kamieskroon, where no vestige of the original texture of the rock is left. Small wonder that this is a popular route for geological excursions.

LEFT: *Pink feldspar megacrysts in coarse-grained granite.*
OPPOSITE: *Most of the grey granite is from Concordia, near Springbok. The attractive pink granite is from further afield, mainly around Pofadder.*

MAP 27

Geology of the route

Cape Town to Clanwilliam

Looking northwards as you leave the suburbs, you see the gently sculpted hills of Durbanville ahead. These are made up of sedimentary rocks of the Malmesbury Group, quite different from the Table Mountain Group that makes the rugged, craggy mountains around Cape Town. That's because the Malmesbury sediments consist mainly of shale, made of minerals that break down to clay and are easily mouldable, not the tightly cemented quartz that mostly makes the Table Mountain Group and resists erosion so fiercely.

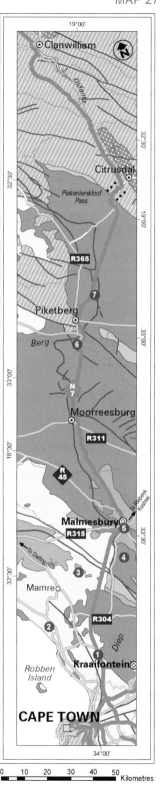

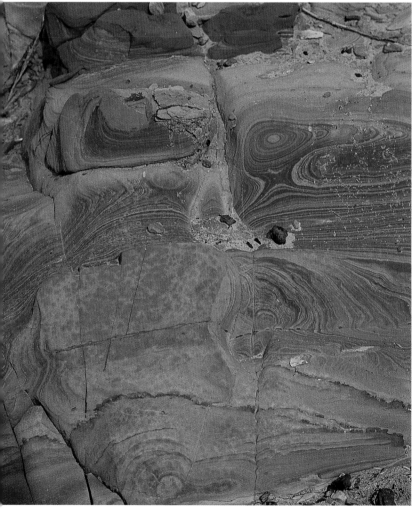

Liesegang banding in Precambrian Malmesbury shales in the road cutting north of the Diep River – worth stopping for if you're not in a hurry.

Soon after you've left the built-up area, you cross a broad vlei and the Diep River, where the road from Durbanville joins the N7. Stop at the cutting just after the bridge for a good look at typical Malmesbury sediments **(geosite 1, map 27)**. They are finely bedded, with some beautiful cross-cutting Liesegang banding (see text box, p. 130), and with quartz veinlets standing out in relief against the very weathered shales.

Not long after this, you'll notice major electricity lines to your left, reminding you that the Koeberg Nuclear Power Station is close – just out of sight, on the Atlantic coast. (The R27, the coast road to Saldanha Bay, goes much closer to it; to read more about this historic utility, see text box, p. 69.) In fact, the next hill you pass, on the right, is the one from which the power station takes its name. As you pass over the rise flanking Koeberg Hill, you'll notice far to the left a couple of areas of exposed dune sand, telling you the wind-whipped west coast is still close **(geosite 2, map 27)**. The string of hills way ahead and to the left **(geosite 3, map 27)** are granite of the Darling Pluton, one of the many bodies of Cape Granite intrusive into the Malmesbury sediments in this part of the world. Then, with these hills still in sight to your left, another two massifs can be seen breaking up the gentle undulations of the coastal plains. Far ahead, the Kasteelberg – after which the village of Riebeek Kasteel is named – is made of Table Mountain Group quartzites, while the high ground off to your right is granite again, this time of the Paardeberg Pluton **(geosite 4, map 27)**.

A potted geological history of the southernmost N7

Deposition of mud, silt and some sand, with some volcanic sediments, or tuffs, occurred between 1 000 and 600 million years ago, followed by folding and low-grade metamorphism. Then, up into the newly formed Malmesbury Group, some 540 million years ago, the Cape Granites came punching through. The landscape was smoothed by erosion, then a prolonged period of sand deposition followed along the coastline of the newly formed Cape Basin. The Table Mountain Group sandstones were forming, pebble-rich in part, with conditions deviating for brief periods to allow finer sediments to be deposited. More sediments were laid down, the whole package was consolidated, and then extended periods of folding followed, starting 280 million years ago. Pure quartz sandstones were hardened to quartzites. The high ranges thus formed were then worn down, over an unimaginable 200 million years, until vestigial stumps like Kasteelberg are all that remain – in these outlying parts, at any rate. Once the resistant quartzites had been stripped off, the softer Malmesbury sediments offered little resistance. Erosion of the massive, hard granites was not so easy, though, and they stood in ever higher relief as the shale and siltstone draped over them were removed. And that, in a nutshell, is what you see today.

Bypassing the centre of Malmesbury, you will see weathered granite of the Paardeberg Pluton in a couple of high cuttings **(geosite 5, map 27)**. There are good exposures of the same rock in a fresh state as you pass Alpha's Rheboksfontein quarry soon after Malmesbury. Here the granite is used mainly for aggregate, though it was from this quarry that the stone used to clad the prestigious Tokara winery and restaurant outside Stellenbosch was mined. Big float blocks of granite and some outcrop are evident on the long descent after the quarry.

From here, for a long way, all you'll see in the cuttings through the gentle scenery are Malmesbury sediments, varying from deeply weathered to fresh and almost slatey-looking. Some elements in the rock, mainly iron, give a pleasing range of hues on the weathered surface: pink, maroon, brown, ochre and

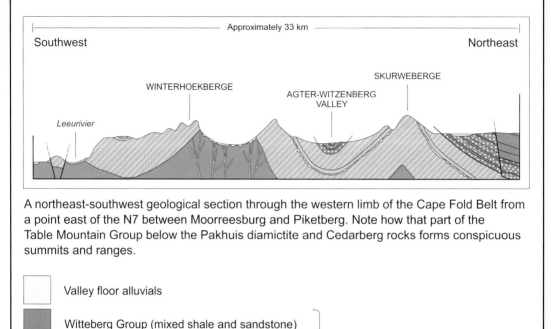

A NORTHEAST-SOUTHWEST GEOLOGICAL CROSS-SECTION THROUGH THE WESTERN CAPE FOLD BELT

Approximately 33 km

Southwest

Northeast

SKURWEBERGE

WINTERHOEKBERGE

AGTER-WITZENBERG VALLEY

Leeurivier

A northeast-southwest geological section through the western limb of the Cape Fold Belt from a point east of the N7 between Moorreesburg and Piketberg. Note how that part of the Table Mountain Group below the Pakhuis diamictite and Cedarberg rocks forms conspicuous summits and ranges.

Valley floor alluvials

Witteberg Group (mixed shale and sandstone)

Bokkeveld Group (mainly shale)

Table Mountain Group (sandstone) except for Cedarberg shale and Pakhuis diamictite

CAPE SUPERGROUP

Malmesbury Group (mainly shale, schist and greywacke, and minor basic intrusives)

Post-Malmesbury Group basic intrusives

FIGURE 19

white; where fresh, it is usually brown to grey. Quartz veining is common, leading to the ground surface being strewn with small, angular fragments of white quartz where the veins are more prevalent.

Soon after passing Moorreesburg, the big Piketberg massif appears in front of you, another of those 'stumps' of Table Mountain sediments mentioned above. This one is particularly extensive, making up a whole environment of its own, with a number of fruit farms on top of the massif benefiting from its microclimate, cooler and wetter than that of the surrounding plains. As you round the corner of the foothills and the town of Piketberg comes into view, you'll see a big industrial installation close on your left **(geosite 6, map 27)**. This is the limeworks of the Pretoria Portland Cement company, which operates lime quarries here, the current source of the limestone feed being the Zoutkloof quarry to the right of the road. This deposit is one of the main sources of limestone for the Western Cape cement industry, and is hosted by the Malmesbury Group. Whether in the Worcester-Ashton valley or in the Little Karoo, or here, the Malmesbury Group and its time-equivalents contain beds and lenses of limestone that, when pure enough, comprise top-quality raw material for cement.

How Rome was built – the story of cement

We all know Rome wasn't built in a day, but what is not widely known is how its architecture and structures have endured so well. We are told that the Romans were the first to use cement. Someone discovered that a naturally occurring rock deposit around the foot of Mount Vesuvius, when crushed up and mixed with water, set hard in a far more effective manner than conventional mud or clay.

It was nearly 2 000 years before someone successfully synthesised cement in the laboratory, and the building industry was revolutionised. In a nutshell, here's the process they developed:

Pure limestone, of which calcium carbonate is the major constituent, is crushed to 25 mm-size particles. Pure silica sand, some iron formation (such as iron oxide) and shale or clay as a source of alumina (aluminium oxide) are added; the total of the iron and aluminium oxides should comprise less than 10 per cent of the mixture, according to a specific formula. The raw mix is then milled to a fine powder and progressively heated. At 900°C the carbon dioxide is driven off, leaving the lime, which is the oxide of calcium, along with the minor components. At 1 500°C a chemical reaction takes place, producing a synthetic mineral called clinker.

If clinker were to be milled again to a powder and mixed with water, it would set in no time at all, but not with very strong bonding. To slow down the uptake of water during the hydration and curing process, gypsum (calcium sulphate) is added to the clinker before final milling to cement. The gypsum initially coats the tiny clinker particles, slowing their reaction with the water that is added to make concrete, and leading to a finer crystalline structure and a more stable, stronger bond.

The old pit of the Piketberg limestone works of Pretoria Portland Cement: a good example of the top-grade limestone found in the Malmesbury Group and other units of this age in the Cape.

As you drive up the Piekenierskloof Pass, notice the pebble runs in the quartzites of the Piekenierskloof Formation at the base of the Table Mountain Group.

As you drive on past the town, have a good look at the Piketberg massif and note that the beds of quartzite are dipping away from you, in other words to the west, at about 20°. Further north, you'll see that the dips flatten, and by the time you get into the sediments of the Table Mountain Group in the Piekenierskloof Pass near Citrusdal, the dips are to the east, so you will have cut across a broad gentle anticline, entirely underlain by Malmesbury rocks.

At closer range, you are going through white to off-white, highly kaolinised, feldspathic sandstones with interbedded grits and conglomerates, cross-cut by the ubiquitous, wavy Liesegang banding (**geosite 7, map 27**). These sediments are quite different from anything you've seen so far in the Malmesbury Group.

The last exposure of Malmesbury shales you'll see here is in the cutting for a culvert under the road at the beginning of the Piekenierskloof Pass, just before the Eendekuil turn-off, where you are back into rocks reminiscent of the first cutting outside Cape Town: finely laminated shales or phyllites in a variety of pinks, maroons and ochry yellow.

With the road too narrow for you to be able to stop safely, you'll have to take in the Piekenierskloof Formation at the base of the Table Mountain Group as you drive slowly up the pass. The pale quartzites commonly carry small, beautifully rounded pebbles of vein quartz, and are interbedded with thin beds of conglomerate as well as red mudstones which, in a few cases, themselves carry small pebbles. By the time you get to the top of the pass, you have gone into the equigranular quartzites more typical of the Table Mountain Group. Note the beds through which the pass cuts dipping into the Olifants River valley. If you look carefully, you will find the beds on the opposite slope also dipping down towards the river, telling you that you're coming into a syncline. In the middle of the syncline, around Citrusdal, are sediments of the overlying Bokkeveld Group. Once you get into the valley you drive along the western limb of the syncline, parallel to its axis, which is never far from the Olifants River, until well past Clanwilliam. Some distance to the east lies the impressive Cedarberg range, composed of several Table Mountain Group Formations that are gently folded, and showing magnificent exposures.

After signboards to Silwerstroom and Die Poort, Cedarberg shale appears in the cuttings, seen wherever the Table Mountain Group is extensively developed. This thin (maximum 150 m-thick) unit divides the group into its upper and lower formations and is a key marker. From here, you travel close to it for a while. With lowish hills to your right and a big valley to your left, you cross over from the Cedarberg shale into the Skurweberg Formation of the upper Table Mountain Group opposite a neat-looking farmstead in the valley below. The sandstone is well exposed from here for a few kilometres and is riddled with very clear cross-bedding, and attractive Liesegang banding.

MAP 28

Clanwilliam to Kamieskroon

The next stop we recommend is a weathering surface shown by the concentration of manganese nearly 20 km further on. You've gone past the second big dam on the Olifants River, with a small resort, the Onderberg Oord, on its edge, and down a long slope towards the low country you were on before Piekenierskloof. The escarpment is again prominent on your right. For a while you will notice the red mudstones, reminiscent of those near the foot of Piekenierskloof, or just above the Cape Granite on Chapman's Peak Drive. Just beyond the 26 km beacon, you can't miss the black-stained rocks on both sides of the road, below the basal contact of the Table Mountain Group **(geosite 1, map 28)**. These rocks belong in the Gariep Supergroup. Now you're into a section of structureless and very weathered rock with a pitted surface, with black manganese oxide impregnating anything that was permeable and coating whatever was not. This is a zone of fossil soil and weathered rock, on which the basal Table Mountain Group sediments were deposited after the underlying Gariep rocks had been exposed to the atmosphere, probably for many millions of years.

The intense manganese concentration at the top of the Gariep sediments, below the contact with the Cape Supergroup sediments, is probably the result of several cycles of enrichment. You cannot miss these exposures in the road cutting as you descend into the Olifants River valley.

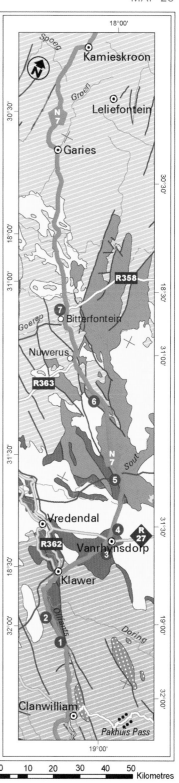

In the next cutting, you find yourself opposite harder schist, unlike anything you've seen on this route. Now you're well and truly into the Gariep Supergroup, another package of schists of late Precambrian age. These rocks are a little older than the Malmesbury sediments, and were subjected to even greater tectonism and metamorphism, which explains their schistose and contorted appearance. They are mostly deeply weathered, but close scrutiny will show that they are different from the almost horizontal sandstones and mudstones of the Table Mountain Group just above them. This contact, for the most part marked by a thin bed of angular white quartz pebbles, can be seen at a few places around the 38 and 39 km beacons **(geosite 2, map 28)**.

After the turn-off to Klawer you've climbed somewhat, and are out of the Olifants River valley and through the Gariep Supergroup. You cross a few Table Mountain Group ridges leading westwards off the escarpment and then the road cuttings are through sediments of the Vanrhynsdorp Group, ochry iron formation and limestone, largely reconstituted to marble, as well as phyllites that are weakly to strongly kaolinised. To summarise: you've crossed the Malmesbury Group first, then the Gariep Supergroup, and now the Vanrhynsdorp Group. They are all of the same broad age – about 800 to 550 million years old – and were all deposited in different parts of a mobile belt, a complex elongate basin varying from very deep water to shallow shelf, and subjected to folding and the accompanying metamorphism.

The last cutting just before Vanrhynsdorp is worth stopping for, to see some beautiful recrystallised limestone or marble, as well as very weathered, ochry iron formation, with some concretions of heavy, black, high-grade manganese oxide **(geosite 3, map 28)**. You will have seen the turn-off to Jumaqua Marble Mine and have discovered that, like its Malmesbury equivalent, the slightly younger Vanrhynsdorp Group is quite lime-rich.

By the time you reach Vanrhynsdorp you are back on the 'low country', with the escarpment wall off to the east, running on and on as far as you can see. Verdant citrus orchards and potato fields are a thing of the past. Dry Namaqualand lies not far ahead; to its west is the sandy coastal plain, to its east the plains of Bushmanland, and to your right now, above the escarpment, the Karoo.

After Vanrhynsdorp the cuttings show fresh to very weathered, fine-grained to gritty sediments of the Vanrhynsdorp Group, partly overlain by red, wind-blown sand, partly by white surface limestone or calcrete, which is also diagnostic of a dry climate. Where the underlying rock has permitted, this calcrete is rich in gypsum, or sulphate of calcium, which is used in the manufacture of cement (see text box, p. 211). Note the Maskam gypsum mine, not far off the road to the right and 5 km past Vanrhynsdorp **(geosite 4, map 28)**.

Intricately patterned recrystallised limestone, or marble, of the Vanrhynsdorp Group can be seen in the cutting just as you enter the town of the same name.

About 5 km north of Vanrhynsdorp, the Maskam gypsum mine exploits gypsum-rich calcrete for processing and use in the cement industry. In the background is the Great Escarpment.

The last river you cross for a long way is the Sout River, where you also pass under the railway line that links the Sishen iron ore and Aggeneys base metal mines, far off to the northeast, with the port at Saldanha Bay. Drive slowly as you approach, because on the left-hand side next to the road is a fine unconformity, where steeply dipping basement sediments are covered by flat-lying muds of an earlier, much higher level of the river **(geosite 5, map 28)**. After you've crossed the river, look to the left again and see another river terrace that is even older and higher than the railway line.

There are many cuttings where you'll see the same Vanrhynsdorp sediments, varying from intensely weathered to very fresh. Keep an eye on the kilometre beacons: soon after the 48 km beacon and the road off to Kliprand, to the right, you're in for a change. So far on this route, the most highly metamorphosed rocks you've seen are schists, still recognisable, more or less, as sedimentary rocks.

The first outcrop after the Kliprand road is of much more metamorphosed rock, namely augen gneiss, a dark, banded, coarsely crystalline rock with big augen (the German word for 'eyes') of plagioclase feldspar **(geosite 6, map 28)**. This is fairly typical Nababeep-type gneiss. And from here on until you are close to the Orange River, gneiss of one kind or another, and granite, are practically all you'll see in road cuttings. Like the schist you've seen until now, the degree of weathering – and kaolinisation – varies enormously. In addition, until you're past Nuwerus, you'll continue to see the better stratified Vanrhynsdorp metasediments making the higher ground. They stand higher because they are younger than the gneisses, which are somewhat older than 1 000 million years. So although not nearly as venerable as the Archaean Basement around Johannesburg, these gneisses are the oldest rocks seen since leaving Cape Town.

An older, higher terrace of the Sout River, with the extremely leached palaeosurface below it, seen from just north of the Sout River.

One of several unconformities on this route, between deeply weathered and highly contorted schist of the Precambrian Vanrhynsdorp Group and the overlying horizontal terrace muds deposited by an earlier stage of the Sout River.

Namaqualand – more than just flowers in the spring

Much has been written about the rocks you're starting to cross, which form part of the Namaqua Metamorphic Province. It's a geological entity that takes up most of the northwestern corner of South Africa, stretching from Nuwerus into Namibia, and from the West Coast to the edge of the Kaapvaal Craton in the east, beyond Upington. It is a vast and complex geological terrane, that only in recent years has become reasonably well understood. It consists mostly of gneisses – both paragneisses formed from sediments, and orthogneisses, metamorphosed intrusive and extrusive igneous rocks. It contains minor amounts of other metasediments, like quartzites, iron formation and schist, the mineralogy of which did not permit them to form gneisses.

It's not only man's curiosity that has resulted in the profound geological interest in this area: it is its mining potential, mainly of base metal mines, with millions of tons of copper, lead, zinc and silver having been won from the ground. During the 1970s and 1980s, Namaqualand and Bushmanland saw many geologists and geophysicists passing through, seeking mineral riches, and deposits such as Black Mountain and Gams were discovered (see ch. 15, p. 272). The Okiep copper mining district was already well known, having been the focus of a hyped-up copper mania in the mid-1850s. Back in 1685 the governor of the Cape, Simon van der Stel, led an expedition to Namaqualand to look for copper, and prospected the showings in what he named the Koperbergen, near present-day Springbok. And even before that, the indigenous Namas were producing the red copper metal.

Pass Nuwerus and head on, but slow down as you come to Bitterfontein. This town owes its existence mainly to its being the extreme northwestern railway terminal in the country and has, accordingly, a very big marshalling yard (**geosite 7, map 28**). Close to the N7 and at the northern end of the yard, you'll see a mass of mammoth blocks of grey stone. Some of it comes all the way from the Pofadder area; most, though, is from Concordia, just east of Springbok. In the dimension stone business it's all called 'granite', and is destined for Cape Town, where it will be loaded for overseas, to be used as ornamental stone, tombstones and such like.

In the cuttings, most of what you see is true gneiss, conspicuously banded with pale minerals – feldspar and quartz – and others that are dark, mostly biotite and hornblende, alternating in swirling patterns. The sinuosity and segregation of minerals tell of a long and turbulent history of tectonism and high temperatures. Lenticular bodies of pale, very coarse-grained pegmatite are testimony to partial melting, 'sweating out' and remobilisation of the lower temperature minerals, mainly feldspar and quartz. Where deeply weathered, the more quartzo-feldspathic gneiss may be largely to completely kaolinised until it is snow white; otherwise, it retains its original texture to a greater or lesser degree, and is always an attractive rock.

The banding you see usually doesn't express itself in the weathering and, over time, more or less cubic blocks, formed by the roughly orthogonal joints that occur in any massive rock like granite or gneiss, have had the corners and edges weathered off them to become more spheroidal. The tendency of such blocks to rest one on top of the other, sometimes in columns of three or four, has led to this being described as 'woolsack weathering'. As you go northwards, you'll see more and more of the smooth exfoliation domes (also called 'whale backs') that characterise granite-gneiss country in tropical latitudes, reminiscent of the Matopos in Matabeleland or Rio de Janeiro's Sugarloaf or, closer to home, Paarl Rock.

As you travel north from Vanrhynsdorp, you climb imperceptibly for most of the time, and the country changes from very gently undulating to hilly. By the time you are opposite Karkams, between

Even in a poor year, when rainfall has been low, the gneiss country of southern Namaqualand blazes with colour. The smooth bare slopes are typical of this kind of geological terrain.

MAP 29

Garies and Kamieskroon, you catch glimpses of the lowlands in the west that you've left behind, the only indication of how much you have climbed. You'll be around the 800 m above sea-level contour until you reach Kamieskroon.

Kamieskroon to Vioolsdrif

After Kamieskroon, the country becomes even hillier than it has been as you drop into the Buffels River valley, with cuttings in a wide variety of gneisses. You stay in this valley for a while, then climb slowly again until, with the smallholdings south of Springbok in view, the road levels off and the countryside is slightly flatter. You now see the first signs of human habitation for a while and, as you approach Springbok, the flat-topped, grey slimes dam tucked into the hills east of the town comes into view, the first indication that you're in mining territory. This is the treatment residue from Carolusberg, one of the bigger of the 23 scattered copper mines that once made up the mining complex, now virtually all mined out.

North of Kamieskroon the country is more rugged than it has been as you drop down into the valley of the Buffels River, a major and very ancient drainage system.

A ONE-DAY DETOUR IN AND AROUND SPRINGBOK

If you have the time, it's worth spending a day in and around Springbok, the oldest mining district in South Africa. But before donning your historian's hat, have a look at the famous, rare orbicular granite west of the village of Concordia **(geosite 1, map 29)**. It's a national monument, and one of just two known occurrences in South Africa, and of only a handful of such rocks around the world. The small koppie of orbicules, which are something of an enigma in geology, is quite unusual – and decorative enough to merit a visit.

If you were to continue your tour chronologically, you would start with Van der Stel's Koperberg prospecting shaft, reached via the well-signposted village of Carolusberg just east of Springbok. It is also a national monument, and the year, 1685, is carved out above the portal of the mine, undoubtedly lending it an air of authenticity **(geosite 2, map 29)**.

The mining geology of the district is fascinating – all the copper deposits are hosted in unusual, coarse-grained, mafic intrusives, known as the Koperberg Suite, a discontinuous swarm of over 1 500 relatively small 'mafic bodies' that are confined within highest metamorphic grade gneisses. More than 105 million tons of copper ore have been mined and treated here, from which over 2 million tons of copper metal have been produced.

The small Blue Mine in Springbok was reputedly the first mine in South Africa to achieve commercial production, shipping 11 tons of copper ore from Hondeklip Bay in 1852, although it was never a producer of any consequence. Of the numerous small mining companies that formed, only The Cape Copper Company (1863), and the Nababeep Copper Company (1888) continued for any length of time. Early mines were at O'okiep, Nababeep, Concordia and Spectakel. At first, copper ore was transported by road to the coast at Hondeklip Bay for export and, later, a narrow-gauge railway was constructed to Port Nolloth. Later still, smelting took place on site – as you will learn in the Nababeep Mining Museum. And some mine names and historic constructions will tell you that Cornish miners brought their experience here.

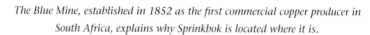

The Blue Mine, established in 1852 as the first commercial copper producer in South Africa, explains why Sprinkbok is located where it is.

The historic pump-house at the O'okiep mine recalls the days when the mines were called 'Wheal'. Some historic family names and a sprinkling of fine old buildings are all that remain of the Cornish legacy.

Started in the 1860s, the O'okiep Mine, north of Springbok, was the main operation from 1892 until 1918, and was, for a time, the world's richest copper mine **(geosite 3, map 29)**. Another of the early mines was Nababeep South, where the smelter and refinery were later established. Evidence of mining is everywhere, and visits to both the towns of Okiep (as it is now spelled) and Nababeep offer a fascinating glimpse into the past – including seeing the old Cornish pump-house and the historic smelter smokestack.

In 1937, the mines were acquired by the O'okiep Copper Company (OCC), with Newmont Mining Corporation, an American company and one of the early 'multinational' mining companies, as principal shareholder. First concentrate was produced in 1940, initiating the use of the revolutionary sulphide flotation process South Africa. An aggressive exploration programme showed a large number of hidden ore bodies, which sustained the extraction of metal until recently. Newmont withdrew in 1984, selling to Gold Fields of South Africa, who in turn sold the mines to Metorex. With reserves dwindling, mines are now in the process of being closed down. The plant at Nababeep has stopped operating and, with little prospect of finding new bodies of ore, it's the end of an era that has lasted more than 150 years.

ABOVE: *The coarse crystallinity of pegmatites is exemplified in the Swartkop mine, where feldspar, muscovite and a little beryl are mined.*
INSET: *This shows a radial arrangement of very coarse muscovite crystals.*

North of Springbok, it's a while before the scenery changes, and then the change is quite drastic. After crossing some slightly lower – but still hilly – country north of Okiep, you are back at about the elevation of Springbok by the time you see the Steinkopf 20 km signboard, where the country opens out into rolling plains dotted with hills. Ahead and to the left is the first flat-topped ridge you've seen since you passed Vanrhynsdorp, with conspicuous terracing by harder units on the slope up to the crest. This feature is significantly different from the gneissic topography you've left behind. It's made up of subhorizontal sediments – sandstone, shale and limestone – of the Nama Group, which, although the same age as the Vanrhynsdorp Group, are barely tectonised and not metamorphosed. The eastern, more broken part of the ridge ahead, the part that you'll drive through, is the same gneiss you've been on, older than and stratigraphically below the Nama sediments.

Look back and to your left after you're well through the ridge north of Steinkopf. From this perspective you get a good idea of the flatness of the ridge – actually a narrow plateau. You are crossing the same hill-peppered plains as before Steinkopf, dropping slowly towards the rugged topography of the Orange River valley proper. Notice that some of the koppies on the plains, and parts of the ridges, are of very dark material, which are mafic dykes that intruded after the gneisses had formed. Note, too, that there are a couple of pegmatites in this stretch that have been worked for their minerals: to the west of the road, just after you have passed the 92.8 km beacon, is the road to Blesberg, where feldspar, beryl and mica have been extracted, with pockets reported of high-grade tantalite; and at Swartkop, reached by a turn-off at the 95.6 km beacon, mica and feldspar have been extracted.

As you pass the board showing that you are entering Vyfmylpoort, you see the flat Nama sediments ahead of you, with a high mass of conspicuously jointed dark grey-green rocks much closer. These are the Orange River Group volcanics; the andesites here have been dated at almost 2 000 million years old, which would make these volcanics the oldest rocks you've seen on this route. The Vyfmylpoort narrows until the course of the river – generally dry now – that carved it out approaches the road from the left. The steep andesite slopes follow the river up to the road where you cross this sandy bed for the first time. You may want to stop to break off a piece of essentially unmetamorphosed rock, something you haven't seen for a long time, and to get a good look at an

Towards the end of this route, the horizontal Nama sediments seen above overlie the much older formations at road level, in the same way that the Cape Supergroup sediments around Cape Town overlie the Malmesbury Group sediments on the flats.

andesite. Remembering that Chile's Andes mountains – whence the name 'andesite' – and their foothills produce a good proportion of the world's copper, it makes sense that one of southern Africa's biggest 'porphyry copper' prospects, called the Haib, lies in an extension of these volcanics north of the Orange River in Namibia, not far from here. Stop at the end of the next cutting, again to the left of the road after you've crossed a bend in the river twice. Look very carefully, and you will see some of the minerals you might well see if you were prospecting in Chile – bright green and blue secondary copper minerals **(geosite 4, map 29)**.

There is a dilemma here, though, and it's nothing to do with the copper. You have just crossed 300 km of gneisses, which are dated at 100 to 800 million years *younger* than the Orange River volcanics towering over you. The gneisses have been deformed and metamorphosed time and time again, yet these supposedly older andesites – now at a level slightly lower than the gneisses – have, to all intents and purposes, escaped that treatment, for reasons about which we can only speculate.

These Haib Formation andesites in Vyfmylpoort show traces of the copper mineralisation that is more conspicuous north of the Orange River.

Rounding the leftward bend in the road and river after this, you see massive volcanic rocks covered by well-bedded Nama sediments that you've seen only at a distance until now **(geosite 5, map 29)**. Here they are not very high above the road and, as you cover the last few kilometres to the Vioolsdrif border post, you see the sediments step lower and lower until the lowermost beds are right at your side, and you can see that they consist of buff sandstones interbedded with pale siltstones. Ahead – west of the border post – you see the full section of the Nama succession towering above the valley. And there, across the Orange River, is Namibia.

13 N12: Johannesburg to Witbank

GEOLOGICAL OVERVIEW

This route, the shortest (in terms of kilometres) described in this book, is also one of the busiest, being the main freeway east from Johannesburg. The underlying geology, although not spectacular, is some of the most economically important in the country. South and east of Johannesburg, the N12 traverses almost the entire width of the Witwatersrand Supergroup, and you will see good outcrops and the remains of gold mining on a large scale. Turning eastwards, the route passes one of the world's greatest gold fields, the East Rand, in its heyday a prolific producer, but now largely worked out; the towns and numerous scattered tailings dumps tell

that story. East from Delmas, surrounded by Highveld farmland, there is little to tell that you are crossing the Witbank coal field, South Africa's largest and most productive coal field, and the powerhouse of the country. Only when you see the massive thermal power stations does it become a reality, and it brings into focus the fact that the thick underlying coal beds were formed on a temperate coastal lowland fringing the Karoo sea 260 million years ago.

Seen from the suburb of Ridgeway in Johannesburg, Mondeor conglomerates are abundant and spectacular, and are composed almost entirely of well-rounded quartz pebbles. In contrast to conglomerate 'reefs' lower in the Witwatersrand sequence, however, these conglomerates lack pyrite and contain very little gold.

Geology of the route

Johannesburg to Witbank

South of Johannesburg, the N12 from Potchefstroom forms part of the Southern and Eastern Bypass. (For a more detailed look at the local geology, see ch. 1, p. 34.) Initially, as you go eastwards through attractive, hilly suburbia, you will be driving more or less along the uppermost part of the Witwatersrand Supergroup, the Mondeor and Elsburg Formations, made up of around 1 000 m of reddish-weathering, south-dipping quartzites and conglomerates, none of them significantly gold-bearing **(geosite 1, map 30)**. To the south of the N12 is a line of prominent bushy ridges and koppies, which are dark basal lavas of the overlying Ventersdorp Supergroup **(geosite 2, map 30)**.

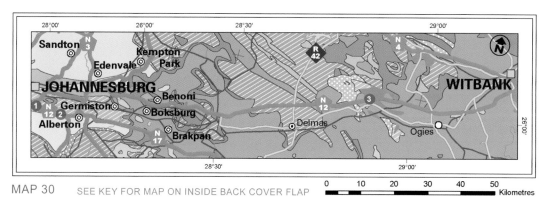

MAP 30   SEE KEY FOR MAP ON INSIDE BACK COVER FLAP

0   10   20   30   40   50
Kilometres

These have been dated at 2 700 million years old, and were erupted as thick, widespread 'floods' of basalt, entirely covering all older formations over a large part of central South Africa (see ch. 15, p. 256).

Passing Alberton, and now heading northwards through south-dipping quartzite ridges, you may see the Simmer & Jack headgear east of the road, and you will notice that this area has been environmentally degraded by past gold-mining operations; slimes dams are a common sight, and retreatment of the tailings and rehabilitation is in progress (see text box on mine dumps, p. 48). Immediately after you cross the M2 freeway at the Geldenhuis Interchange, the largely unoccupied ground tells you that you are driving over the east-west strike of the now mined-out Main Reef conglomerates, which also marks the stratigraphic break between the upper and lower divisions of the Witwatersrand geology, the Central Rand and West Rand Groups (see Witwatersrand stratigraphy, p. 39).

Some 4 km further on, and to the left, is the rocky eastern end of Linksfield Ridge, made of the lowermost formation of the Witwatersrand, the Orange Grove quartzite; north of this ridge are the ancient granites of the Basement. So, in a matter of less than 10 km, you have geologically traversed almost the entire Witwatersrand, a sequence that took around 250 million years to deposit in the Archaean Witwatersrand sea.

At Gillooly's Interchange, the N12 branches off eastwards again, and after crossing another quartzite ridge, thin horizontal Karoo sediments largely blanket the older Witwatersrand formations, and there is little geology to be seen as you pass through Boksburg and Benoni. The yellowish sand dumps and paler slimes dams remain a conspicuous feature of the landscape to the south; you are passing through one of the great mining areas of all time, the East Rand gold field. Over 1 000 million tons of gold-bearing ore have been mined here, from which nearly 10 000 tons of gold have been produced, and this activity gave rise to the surrounding urban development. After passing Daveyton, the countryside opens up into gently rolling farmland of the eastern Highveld.

South of Johannesburg the N12 cuts through a thick sedimentary package of orange-weathering quartzites that dip to the south, and contain numerous layers of quartz-pebble conglomerate. This Mondeor Formation is uppermost of the Witwatersrand Supergroup.

In the middle distance the prominent, bush-covered hills south of the N12 form part of the Klipriviersberg Nature Reserve, and are made of thick outpourings of Ventersdorp lava that erupted around 2 700 million years ago and covered the Witwatersrand Basin. Weathered Witwatersrand quartzites outcrop in the foreground.

East of Johannesburg, a lone surviving headgear at the old Simmer & Jack mine stands sentinel near the N12 freeway, a reminder of days of golden glory. This mine produced over 450 tons of gold during its life.

ABOVE LEFT: *Rounded boulders of volcanic agglomerate of the Loskop Formation, made of coarse, angular lava fragments set in a matrix of fine-grained tuff, occur alongside the road, reflecting a time of explosive eruption.*
ABOVE RIGHT: *When broken open, the fresh rocks are dark greenish grey.*

The geological map shows that much of the underlying geology is of the Transvaal Supergroup, but it is mostly thickly blanketed by soil. Eastwards, these older formations are covered by flat-lying sediments of the Karoo Supergroup; at the base, the thin glacial sediments of the Dwyka Group are overlain by thicker shales and sandstones of the coal-bearing Ecca Group, and these thicken both to the east and to the south.

It was the early Boer settlers who first used coal in this area, having discovered black outcrops in stream valleys. Now known as the Witbank coal field, it stretches from Delmas in the west to Belfast in the east, and further than the eye can see to the south. You won't see any coal in the road cuttings along the freeway, though, just occasional weathered shale and bedded sandstone. But there are some outcrops of the underlying rocks; one, 45 km west of Witbank just after crossing the Wilge River, is worth a closer look. A spread of dark boulders occurs on both sides of the freeway, and some have been blasted out to make way for the road. The outcrops and loose boulders reveal angular pinkish volcanic rock fragments of widely ranging size and very poorly sorted, set in a finer dark greenish matrix. You are looking at a fine example of agglomerate, a volcanic breccia formed by the rapid deposition of erupted volcanic debris close to a once-active volcano; this is part of the Loskop Formation, the very topmost part of the Transvaal sequence **(geosite 3, map 30)**.

Large areas of the N12 freeway along which you are driving are underlain by thick layers of coal. The clue to this comes from the massive Eskom thermal power stations seen from the road, which are based on the continuous supply of coal from dedicated collieries, making this region the powerhouse of the country (see the text box on page 197).

The thick layers of coal just below the surface are suited to open-cast mining, using colossal equipment and all the economies of scale, or, where the overlying sediments are too thick, to shallow underground mining. The expert rehabilitation now being done returns the land virtually to its original state. Where the coal quality is low, it is upgraded by 'washing' to remove poor-grade coal and unwanted rock. Most of the high-grade coal is sent by dedicated railway line to Richards Bay for export. In 2003, coal was South Africa's third most valuable mineral commodity, truly 'black gold'. Vast tonnages are also used directly in the massive power stations in the region, as well as in Sasol's unique fuel- and chemicals-from-coal processes (see ch. 5, pp. 108–109).

TOP: *Numerous coal mines, both underground and open-cast, are found in the Witbank coal field. This mine, Leeuwpan Colliery near Delmas, is mined on a relatively small scale for coal beds that lie near the surface.*
INSET: *Export quality coal is sent by dedicated railway line to the Richards Bay Coal Terminal, from where it is exported worldwide.*

You will see signs of numerous coal mines in the distance, and as you get nearer to Witbank the evidence is hard to miss, such as the massive black mine dump on the northern side of the freeway, consisting of accumulated waste from the Landau colliery. Closer to Witbank, on the southern side of the freeway, another big dump, now terraced and grassed, is a tribute to the environmental sensitivity of mining companies today. Better late than never, we might say.

Witbank is located on higher ground, and from the geological map you will see that a new formation has made its appearance: the reddish volcanic rocks of the Rooiberg Group (see ch. 11, p. 196).

Coal beds – fossilised forests of the past

During a period of temperate climate around 260 million years ago, after the Great Ice Age, extensive river floodplains developed and large deltas were created along the northern coastline of the inland Karoo sea. Accumulated sediments formed the shales and sandstones of the Ecca Group, host to all South Africa's producing coal beds. Coal, defined as readily combustible rock containing more than 50 per cent carbonaceous material, is the metamorphosed remains of plant matter that accumulated and was compacted on a large scale. Later, this organic material was subjected to increased temperatures and pressures as a result of being buried within the sedimentary Karoo sequence that hosts all of South Africa's coal deposits.

During Ecca times rivers flowed southwards along valleys carved out by the earlier Dwyka-age glaciers and ice sheets. Sand and clay filled the valleys, abundant Glossopteris flora lined the river banks and, over considerable time, the sediment-choked lakes became transformed into thick swamps, and peat bogs formed on the wide floodplains. The temperate climate resulted in seasonal deposition of vegetation, shown by South African coals generally containing more inorganic material (and therefore more residual ash) than Northern Hemisphere coals. In South Africa, these coal beds are now preserved mainly on the Mpumalanga Highveld, extending into KwaZulu-Natal, Gauteng and the Free State. Isolated outliers of the same age occur in other parts of southern Africa, like the Springbok Flats, north of the Soutpansberg and the Waterberg, as well as in Botswana and Zimbabwe.

Have a look at the artist's recreation of the environment at the time when these temperate forests and swamps existed – it's hard to believe that the shiny black rock called coal originated in this way.

The Ecca coal environment: an artist's reconstruction of a temperate southern African coal forest, some 260 million years ago during the Permian Period, when warming caused the Dwyka ice sheets to recede.

14 N12: Johannesburg to George

GEOLOGICAL OVERVIEW

Though quite close to the more direct and popular N1, this southwesterly route from Johannesburg differs dramatically from it in several respects.

Both routes cross, for most of their length, the Karoo, a stretch of country that might be construed as boring if you were to disregard what you see in the road cuttings, and close your mind to how it all happened and what it means. Both start in Johannesburg and end at the coast, but that's where the similarity ends. The N12 takes you, for all intents and purposes, along the northwestern edge of the Witwatersrand Basin for well over 100 km, past mine after mega-gold mine. This is followed, for over 200 km, by gently rolling countryside underlain by both volcanic and sedimentary formations of the Ventersdorp Supergroup, which closely followed the Witwatersrand sequence in time. As you leave behind the image of hard, blue-grey conglomerates and the gold in them, you start to see gravels of a much younger generation being dug over, this time for their diamonds. And while Wolmaransstad may be no more than a name on a map to most South Africans, hard deals are struck there over diamonds, and fistfuls of banknotes change hands. No one, though, needs to be reminded of why Kimberley, not far down the road, is a name that resounds through the annals of the diamond business, and why kimberlite is sought on every continent.

LEFT: *The name 'kimberlite', the rock from which almost all diamonds originate, immortalises the town of Kimberley. However, finding a diamond like this in kimberlite is a rare event.*
OPPOSITE: *The present-day city of Kimberley from the air showing the Kimberley Mine 'Big Hole' in the foreground, together with the Kimberley Mine museum, while in the background is the open-pit of the De Beers Mine.*

Victoria West has a geological museum of which it can be justifiably proud, and the fossils on display in the Karoo National Park at Beaufort West are a good reason for overnighting here. But it is the trip southwards from here, passing through the Swartberg range in the breathtaking Meiringspoort, and down the Outeniqua Pass to George, that makes the whole of the N12 to the coast worthwhile, as the wonders of the Cape Fold Belt are laid bare. It is an unforgettable experience.

Geology of the route

Johannesburg to Wolmaransstad

For the first 70 km of the drive you are never very far from dumps, slimes dams and shaft headgears. You will pass boards that echo activity on the Johannesburg Stock Exchange more than any geography lesson, with names like Randfontein, Western Areas, Kloof, Driefontein, Blyvooruitsig, Deelkraal and others, all part of the Carletonville gold field. You will find mine names, too, that speak of the new South Africa, like Savuka and Mponeng and Tau Tona. The reefs are mostly kilometres beneath the surface, tilted and covered by rocks many millions of years younger.

Twenty kilometres west of Potchefstroom, as you pass the R502 to Orkney, you'll see the mines of Stilfontein and Klerksdorp ahead of you **(geosite 1, map 31)**. Almost as far as you can see, off to the left as you approach Stilfontein, there's ample evidence of the large-scale mining that took place here in the second half of last century and continues today: this is the Klerksdorp gold field. And although the quartzites and shales – and minor conglomerate – of formations well known on the Witwatersrand can be found practically within the suburbs of Klerksdorp, it is the fabulous Vaal Reef that still produces the great majority of this important field's gold. Nor did the Klerksdorp gold field, apparently so far out on a limb, lag behind the Witwatersrand. In 1885, the first samples from the district, already a well-established farming area, assayed high values of gold, and the 'reefs' were being prospected just months later. By 1888, the Klerksdorp Stock Exchange and Chamber of Mines were established.

From Klerksdorp to Warrenton you will be travelling over rocks of the Ventersdorp Supergroup. Some 200 000 sq km in extent, this great sedimentary and volcanic basin formed on the Kaapvaal

The West Wits No. 1 metallurgical plant shown here, looking from behind the plant towards the road, serves the AngloGold Ashanti Mponeng Mine, on your right soon after passing the turn-off to Carletonville. These surface installations give no clue to what lies below: massive warren-like operations, mining narrow seams of gold in such low concentrations that it is scarcely ever visible to the naked eye; and all this more than 3 km beneath the surface, where the temperatures are so high that work would be impossible without the steady supply of cooled air.

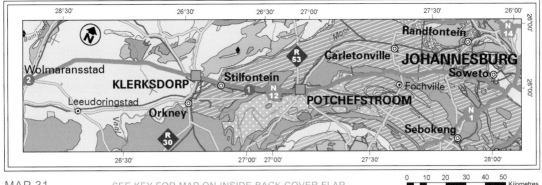

0   10   20   30   40   50

Kilometres

Craton shortly after the Witwatersrand Basin took shape. Although largely covered by younger formations, here and there you will see reddish, weathered outcrops which, if broken open, will reveal dark grey-green andesite or basalt. Around Makwassie, outcrops of maroon to pink acid (silica-rich) lava called the Makwassie Porphyry can be seen.

As you pass through the town of Wolmaransstad, note the collection of diamond diggers' equipment for sale in a yard prominently fronting on the main street. If you were a registered diamond buyer in times gone by, you might have had an office here, where the diggers would bring you their week's sortings for weighing and scrutinising through a loupe, or magnifying glass; then you would establish whether your valuation and that of the man across the desk from you could be reconciled **(geosite 2, map 31)**.

MAP 32

Wolmaransstad to Kimberley

Not far to the west of the town the 'runs' begin – wide valleys carved over the ages by rivers bound for the Vaal River not far to the south **(geosite 1, map 32)**. Though these rivers are now almost extinct, in their time they carried their diamonds from pipes and fissures far to the north to deposit them in the Vaal. From there, some of the gems were carried westwards to the Orange River at Douglas and on to the West Coast. Others, according to geological circumstances, were deposited in these parts. There are some quite big mining operations as you head westwards, tailing off before the turn-offs to Soutpan and Boskuil.

About 15 km before Bloemhof, where the road climbs to cross the railway line, look to your left for the Bloemhof Dam. The Vaal River, which swings away from the road near Klerksdorp, is now near the road again. It will stay close for nearly 100 km until you cross it just north of Warrenton, and you'll find that there are diggings along it from place to place, revealed by the piles of turned-over earth and pebbles **(geosite 2, map 32)**. You will see further dumps from diamond workings far off to the right as you pass the 14 km beacon next to the road. This run, and another converging from the west – the last two in these parts – reach the Vaal in and just west of Bloemhof. West of this, the diggings are confined to the Vaal River and its old courses.

Between Wolmaransstad and Bloemhof, you have probably noticed a plethora of anthills, or termitaria, peppering the landscape, and may have wondered about them. Why such intense activity here and not elsewhere? The answer relates to the termite-friendliness of the soil itself, which contains non-swelling clay that doesn't stay wet for prolonged periods. Termitaria are something of an enigma. As with icebergs, by far the majority of the termite colony lies below the surface – though after soaking rains, when pools on the surface tell of a saturated soil profile, the above-ground portion undoubtedly comes into full use. The tall towers that termites build in tropical and equatorial latitudes have been shown to be degrees cooler than ground temperatures, and even lower mounds may help ventilation and cooling.

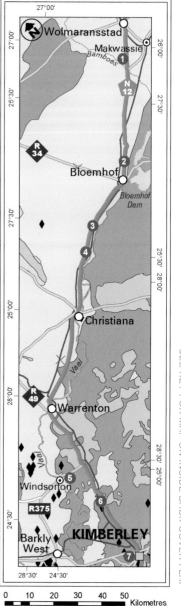

Just after the 'Christiana 40 km' signboard next to the road on the right is the first of a number of pans **(geosite 3, map 32)** – more than likely dry – that tell another part of the evolutionary story of South Africa.

You will quite likely see well-developed, white, powdery calcrete in the vicinity of these dry pans, either at or near the surface in the surrounding countryside. You'll see plenty of it from here onwards along the N12, though it is before Christiana that it is best developed as a thick layer of relatively pure calcium carbonate, in contrast to the thin white coatings in joint-planes of dolerite

Pans: why, and how, do they form?

In the South African context, pans are shallow depressions that may contain water, but are generally dry, broad floors of muddy and salty accumulation. Knowing where pans form has been crucial in understanding how they form.

First and foremost, they form in arid climates around the world. Bear in mind, however, that climates change. Dry today doesn't mean it was dry when the pans started to form, and areas where pans are found that are not currently arid may have been much drier in the recent geological past. Where the aridity is extreme, though, and the wind regime such that sand will be blown into depressions, pans will not form.

Topography is another important factor: flattish terrain not reached by river networks is a basic prerequisite. If these two criteria – one climatic, the other geomorphological – are met, the likelihood of pans forming is good. A less easily quantifiable requirement is that there should be a 'susceptible surface', which relates to the rock, or unconsolidated sediment, that is found at the surface.

Two main processes are required for the large, flat-floored, hard-surfaced, unvegetated depressions to form: salt weathering and wind-borne erosion or deflation.

Although a variety of rock types lie beneath the pans, salt weathering depends on the presence of unconsolidated Kalahari sediments, or shales of the Dwyka and Ecca Groups. These are not only more susceptible to salt weathering, but are a source of salt. The salt that most effectively accelerates breakdown of the bedrock is sodium sulphate, which is present in high concentrations in the Karoo sediments, in particular. In some cases, sodium chloride, the chemical name for table salt, is the predominant salt and can be commercially recovered.

With rapid breakdown of bedrock, the wind removes the products of weathering, which are particularly fine and easily moved when the bedrock is shale. The sediment is generally not removed very far and, with a particular wind direction predominating in most arid climates, tends to accumulate in crescent-shaped lunette dunes.

Pans may also occur in palaeo-drainage features, broad valleys that have been abandoned by the rivers that formed them, usually following river capture. Ancient courses of the Orange-Vaal system, and the Koa, Sak and Hartebeest valleys of the Northern Cape, are examples of this, with some very big pans occupying these valleys, such as Grootvloer and Verneukpan near Brandvlei.

Saltpans – this one between Bloemhof and Christiana – are a familiar sight to anyone who journeys across the drier western parts of South Africa.

You definitely do not want to live downwind of a calcrete-crushing operation.
This plant, just south of Britten, is producing lime mainly for agriculture.

and some of the sediments seen further south. Very soon after the turn-off to Britten siding, a plant producing agricultural lime from this calcrete is made conspicuous by the clouds of white dust that envelop the operation. The quarries where the calcrete is being excavated can be seen a little beyond the plant, also on the left-hand side, and opposite a big pan across the road **(geosite 4, map 32)**.

Soon after you pass the first prominent ridge you've seen for a long time, capped with Karoo dolerite, and past the road off to Windsorton, keep a lookout for the mine dumps far off to the west **(geosite 5, map 32)**. These are from a cluster of diggings around Windsorton, an area whose history goes back almost to the beginning of diamond mining in South Africa in the 1870s. Celebrated doyen of early diamond geologists, Percy A Wagner, writing in 1914 about the alluvial fields of Griqualand West – mainly centred on Barkly West and Windsorton – noted that they were *'producing quite as many diamonds as during any previous period of their history, and give every assurance of continued vitality'*. Dr Wagner's prognosis has been amply vindicated, with no end in sight. What is remarkable, too, is the quality of the stones from these parts: taken as a whole, their dollar-per-carat value handsomely competes with diamonds from any other field or mine in the world.

Headgear at the Riverton (or Pole) Mine, one of numerous small mines set up on a diamond-bearing kimberlite pipe.
Although it has ceased operation, some intrepid investor might yet take a chance and buy the rights to resume mining.

About 20 km after leaving the distant dumps of Windsorton behind, you will see more dumps ahead of you, close to the road this time. With the river by now far to the west of your line of travel, you have probably concluded that these are not from alluvial workings. Before spotting the dumps, you might have seen the iron structures of an extraction plant, unlike anything you saw on the river diggings, and decided this must be a kimberlite mine **(geosite 6, map 32)**. This is the old Riverton or Pole Mine, on a kimberlite pipe, and one of scores of small mines in the Northern Cape and North West Provinces that have exploited small pipes and fissures. Like many of them, this one has ceased operation, though it is by no means impossible that some entrepreneurial group will buy the rights and see if they can turn to account what remains in the ground.

Within minutes of passing Riverton, Kimberley is in sight ahead. If you have time to spare, it's worth planning to overnight here, or at least stopping for a visit, particularly if you have never seen the Big Hole and its museum before.

Kimberley, the Big Hole and other attractions

Kimberley resonates throughout the world as the home of diamonds, and visitors come from afar to view the historic scene. A first visit should start at the Kimberley Mine Museum and the awesome Big Hole **(geosite 7, map 32)**, the void that was left in place of Colesburg Koppie, so-named in 1871, and flattened by hordes of diggers by 1872. By 1914, the excavation was 215 m deep (read about the history of the Big Hole in the text box on pp. 240–241). This, the largest hand-dug hole on Earth, shows a number of layers. The brown rock at the surface, about 30 m thick, is a Karoo dolerite sill. Where the walls start sloping, to a depth of about 100 m, is black Karoo shale, followed by a thick zone of competent Ventersdorp lava

The 'Big Hole' in Kimberley is the largest hand-dug hole in the world. From the surface downwards is a layer of brown dolerite, followed by soft blackish Karoo shale overlying resistant Ventersdorp lava that forms the vertical walls.

revealing the outline of the kimberlite pipe. Well below the water level is Basement granite, at around 400 m below the surface, the deeper part of the pipe having been mined from underground down to 1 040 m. Some 22.5 million tons of kimberlite were removed to produce 14.5 million carats of diamonds before the mine was closed in 1914. The open-air village is an authentic recreation of Kimberley life as it was in the hectic days of the diamond rush, from the 1870s to the 1900s. The De Beers Diamond Room, with its unique collection of uncut diamonds and famous replicas, and the Mining Hall are of special interest. De Beers also arranges daily underground tours (by appointment, mornings only) and twice-daily surface mine tours at the Bultfontein Mine.

THE GLITTERING DIAMOND DEPOSITS OF KIMBERLEY

While diamonds occur naturally in many shapes, this is the classic shape of an octahedral gem diamond.

In 1869, after the discovery of the 89½-carat 'Star of South Africa' on the farm De Kalk, situated on the Orange River just before its confluence with the Vaal, the colonial secretary of the Cape, Sir Richard Southey, prophetically said: *'This is the rock on which the future success of South Africa will be built.'* The news soon spread, and from far and wide South Africa attracted hordes of prospectors, diggers and entrepreneurs to focus on the search for diamonds; the great South African diamond rush had started.

In early 1870, alluvial diamonds were found in river gravels at Pniel on the Vaal River, and soon the 'wet diggings' around Klipdrift (Barkly West today) became the most famous alluvial diggings in the world.

Later in 1870, a farmer found a 50-carat diamond in a dry stream bed on his farm, Jagersfontein (see ch. 5, pp. 114–115), from a 'dry digging'. Not knowing that this was the primary source, diggers fanned out across the countryside to look for more so-called dry diggings. Soon diamonds were found near a vlei called Dutoitspan, another dry digging about 30 km to the south of the Vaal River, and in 1871, more diamonds were found in dry diggings on the farm Bultfontein. Prospectors continued finding diamonds below the hard white calcrete layer, and a mining camp was set up, which became known as Beaconsfield, today a suburb of Kimberley. The De Beers and Kimberley pipes were discovered soon after this, the latter by the so-called Red Cap Party, manifesting as a small hill called Colesberg Koppie, which is now the site of the Big Hole. The centre of Kimberley developed between these two pipes. The nearby Wesselton pipe was only discovered 19 years later, in 1890.

The diggers worked claims 30 x 30 Cape feet in size on a grid system. As mining progressed, and deeper, harder levels of kimberlite were accessed, considerable practical difficulties arose, and accidents must have been common. Photographs show an almost unbelievable web of ropeways and cables entering the Kimberley Mine. Claim syndicates were formed, which eventually became consolidated into larger, more manageable holdings. In due course, mining conditions became untenable, and consolidation of small operations was the only way forward. The diamond magnates manoeuvred and negotiated, buying up claims and syndicates, and taking control of mining and diamond production. In

A variety of cut gems.

1889 Cecil John Rhodes of De Beers Consolidated Mines purchased the Kimberley Mine from Barney Barnato for £5 338 650. Under De Beers' management, the Kimberley mines quickly became the most important primary diamond producers in the world, at the centre of the De Beers empire.

There were five famous large mines, namely: Kimberley (with an original surface area of 3.7 ha) and De Beers (5.1 ha) within the town centre; Dutoitspan (10.6 ha) and Bultfontein (9.7 ha) some 4 km to the southeast near Beaconsfield; and Wesselton (8.7 ha) a further 2 km away. A number of smaller, lesser-known kimberlite intrusions also exist. Diamond production has been vast, amounting to over 171 million carats up to 1993. The twin towns of Kimberley and Beaconsfield grew up alongside the open workings, and amalgamated in 1913.

But perhaps the most far-reaching contribution made by the fabulous Kimberley diamond field was to provide much of the capital, the know-how and the entrepreneurial spirit for the development of the Witwatersrand gold fields.

TOP: *This picture, probably taken from Colesberg Koppie before it disappeared, shows the rapidly growing settlement of Kimberley in the 1870s.*
RIGHT: *An almost unbelievable web of ropeways and cables entered the Kimberley Mine, making conditions almost untenable. As a result, claim syndicates were formed, which eventually became consolidated into larger, more manageable holdings.*

THE ORIGIN OF DIAMONDS

Diamond, nature's hardest substance by far, is the high-pressure mineral form of carbon, and only forms at depths greater than 150 km below the surface and at temperatures of more than 1 000°C; that is, below the thickest crust and within the upper mantle (see p. 19). They are formed in patches of upper-mantle rocks that are called peridotites and eclogites, samples of which are found in kimberlites as well-rounded 'boulders' or xenoliths, which may, on rare occasions, be studded with diamonds.

Kimberlite is the name for rock formed by eruption of magma derived from the upper mantle, the result of deep geological processes that cause the upper mantle to melt partially, and for the molten rock to intrude through the Earth's crust. The name almost certainly comes from the city of Kimberley, where this rock-type was first described in 1887, although diamonds had unknowingly been recovered from pipes since 1871. In South Africa, over 1 500 kimberlite intrusions are known, but only a few carry diamonds in commercially recoverable quantities, and even then the richest kimberlite contains only an infinitesimally small volume of stones.

Kimberlite magma, containing an abundance of superheated water and carbon dioxide, rushes up from the depths to cause extremely violent eruptions. Explosive penetration of the strata they burst through forms steep, carrot-shaped pipes, called diatremes. The explosive blowing of a large hole on the land surface results in a volcanic crater, while in the deeper root zone, the diatreme narrows into a dyke. Kimberlites incorporate fragments of all the rocks they pass through – pieces of the upper mantle, deep crustal rocks and shallow wall rock.

Diamonds are not formed in kimberlite, but are liberated from shattered diamond-bearing mantle rocks during ascent of kimberlite magma. Scientists have shown that diamonds are ancient, ranging from 1 000 to 3 300 million years old, and very much older than the host kimberlite pipes and dykes in which they are carried to the surface as accidental fragments, called xenocrysts, from depths of at least 150 km. Diamonds are found at all levels within a kimberlite pipe or fissure, but most kimberlites do not contain diamonds, presumably because diamond-bearing material in the upper mantle is rare. The kimberlites most likely to contain diamonds are those that intruded very old, thick, cool continental crust overlying relatively cool mantle – such are the conditions under the Kaapvaal Craton of South Africa.

The Kimberley eruptions took place around 90 million years ago; since then, erosion of the land has removed more than 1 km of rock, so that original volcanic craters have disappeared. This erosion, and movement of liberated diamonds into ancient river courses over millions of years, provided the wealth of alluvial diamonds that exist in South Africa and off the West Coast.

An artist's impression of the eruption of a kimberlite volcano. This geological cross-section and reconstruction shows what the landscape around Kimberley may have looked like 90 million years ago. The eruptions were extremely violent and formed large craters, which have been completely removed by erosion.

MAP 33

While in Kimberley it's worth taking the N31 to Barkly West on the Vaal River, where the alluvial diamond story began in 1870, and to the museum and historic diggers' village there. You can also visit the nearby Nooitgedacht glaciated pavement, a national monument. Here, Dwyka glaciation polished and striated underlying Ventersdorp lava, visible testimony to the presence and power of the ice sheets. Late Stone Age Khoisan artists used the smooth surfaces to make their rock engravings or petroglyphs, which can also be viewed here.

Back in Kimberley, among the historic buildings and monuments in the centre of town, a modern one stands out – Harry Oppenheimer House, the De Beers diamond sorting office. All southern African diamond production is sent here and, under high security, with windows designed for optimum natural light conditions, are sorted into a wide range of different grades before being marketed. Millions of carats pass through here annually, so don't expect to be able to visit.

Kimberley to Three Sisters

About 39 km south of Kimberley you cross the Riet River, another important diamond-bearing river **(geosite 1, map 33)**. The Riet has not left the rich legacy of the Vaal gravels, but its course has taken it within a stone's long throw of the Jagersfontein and Koffiefontein pipes, both major producers in their day, and its gravels have seen action and produced good stones. Soon after crossing the Riet River, note the turn-off to Koffiefontein; this was one of the big diamond producers of bygone times, now into a new lease of life, albeit it on a small scale compared to its heyday, as the very sizable dumps are reprocessed.

Even as far south as Hopetown, on the south bank of the Orange River, you are still in diamond country. In fact, you are where it all started. For it was in the Hopetown district, in 1866, where it was first speculated that the little yellow stone acquired by Schalk van Niekerk from the farm De Kalk might have value beyond that of a child's shiny plaything. The gem was sent to Dr Atherstone, medical doctor and pioneer geologist working in Grahamstown in the Cape Colony, to be identified. Atherstone's affirmation that this was a diamond – the first to be recognised as such in South Africa – was to set in motion a trickle of interest that would swell to a rush and change the course of history. It weighed 21¼ carats, and became known as the 'Eureka'. Two years later, Van Niekerk bought a fingertip-sized stone from a Griqua shepherd for 500 sheep, 10 oxen and a horse. The 83½ carat 'Star of Africa' was traded, not long afterwards, for £30 000, which would have replaced Van Niekerk's stock payment a hundredfold. The building where Van Niekerk sold

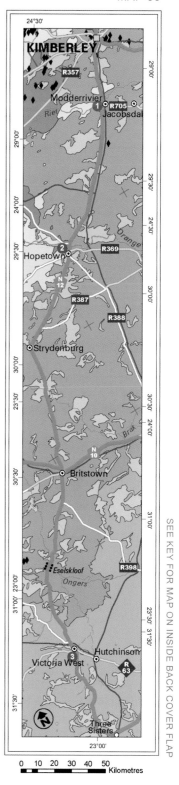

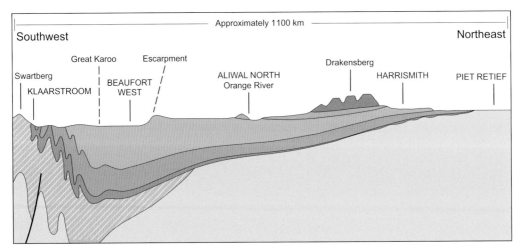

GENERALISED CROSS-SECTION ACROSS THE MAIN KAROO BASIN FROM MPUMALANGA TO THE SWARTBERG

This conceptual and vertically exaggerated cross-section covers a distance of about 1 100 km from Piet Retief in the northeast to Klaarstroom in the southwest. The Karoo Basin developed north of the Cape Fold Belt, where it is deepest, and sediments thin to the north. Most of the sediment-fill was derived from the tectonically active southern mountains and from highlands to the east. Over time the basin became a stable, shallow depository for continental sediments and also decreased in size. Eventually much of the basin was flooded by the Drakensberg lavas of which only remnants now exist.

Drakensberg Group
Molteno, Elliot and Clarens Formations
Beaufort Group
Ecca Group
Dwyka Group
} KAROO SUPERGROUP

CAPE SUPERGROUP

PRE-CAPE ROCKS AND BASEMENT

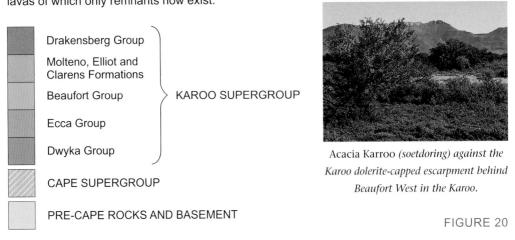

Acacia Karroo *(soetdoring) against the Karoo dolerite-capped escarpment behind Beaufort West in the Karoo.*

FIGURE 20

this stone, for a third of the final price, still stands, and if you go into the Noordkaap Landboudiens in the main commercial street (Kerkstraat), you will be shown the pane of glass scratched to prove the diamond's authenticity. They are historical scratches indeed **(geosite 2, map 33)**.

With Hopetown behind you, you have said goodbye to the diamond fields. Ahead lies the Karoo, unparalleled source of fossils, and criss-crossed by fossil-hunters from earliest times. A hundred and thirty odd years ago, Dr Atherstone frequented these plains rich in fossilised specimens. If you want

ABOVE: *The well-known Three Sisters koppies typify the way that alternating hard and soft sedimentary rocks – or, in other cases, sediments and dolerite – express themselves in the Karoo landscape.*

BELOW: *Dolerites in a variety of climates exhibit this kind of spheroidal, or onion-skin, weathering.*

to know more about the family of Permian fish, a specimen of which was brought to his office, and which ultimately took its name from the good doctor, *Atherstoniidae*, go to the museum in Kerkstraat in Victoria West **(geosite 3, map 33)**. It's worth a visit anyway, as one of the best small museums in the country, with beautiful recreations of earlier Karoo times, and some fascinating and beautiful displays. There is a recreated skeleton of the fossil reptile *Bradysaurus seeleyi*, too.

Shortly after leaving Victoria West, you start to drive through country that is increasingly broken up. This is because you are descending the Great Escarpment, separating the 'high Karoo' from the 'low Karoo'. And quite soon you will find yourself joining the N1 at Three Sisters. From here to Beaufort West, the N12 and the N1 are one and the same route (for geological descriptions, see ch. 5, p. 118). You'll pick up the N12 again, if that's your route, just west of Beaufort West.

MAP 34

Beaufort West to George

From where the N12 leaves the N1 and you head southwards again, you're going to cross Karoo sediments that are horizontal to start with, and become more and more conspicuously folded as you approach the Swartberg range. Then you get into the Cape Fold Belt and Cape Supergroup sediments.

Just after you pass the 25 km beacon on the N12, with the dry Tarka River immediately to the west, in a cutting on your left are some good exposures of tillite of the Dwyka Group **(geosite 1, map 34)**. This is the glacial rock at the base of the Karoo Supergroup, described – together with its genesis – in ch. 5, p. 148). It's worth stopping to see the range of sizes and characters of the material that makes up this rock, from quite big boulders, through cobbles and pebbles, all of a wide variety of rock types, to the fine blue-grey 'rock-flour' that makes up the binding matrix. There is some crude bedding just discernible and it is generally accepted that, in the south, the ice sheets that were transporting the sediment were floating, rather than grinding over the land,

The folding starts even before you get into the mountains. This anticline-syncline pair is in shale and greywacke of the Ecca Group near the crossing called Droekloof 1, north of Klaarstroom.

0   10   20   30   40   50
Kilometres

as they were further north, where they scoured the pavements they rode over. The tillite here is in the southern of two anticlines, with synclines flanking it on either side. This means that, as you travel southwards – towards the older Cape sediments that make the mountain range – instead of moving down in the stratigraphic succession, you move up, first crossing over the younger Ecca shales and sandstones that overlie the tillite, before crossing them again for the last time. Only then do you start to move down in the succession again.

These Ecca sediments occupy a 10 km-wide synclinorium, and you will see lots of quite 'tight' smaller parasitic folds. The sort of cleavage that normally accompanies quite intense folding of fine-grained sediments is widespread in the area; note that the more competent sandstones are generally uncleaved, or at least not cleaved to nearly the same extent as the shales and mudstones. As you travel southwards, this synclinorium is the last structure seen in Karoo Supergroup sediments. Soon you will be seeing folding of quartzites of the Cape Supergroup on a much grander scale.

Watch for signboards along the road, as well as the kilometre beacons. About 10 km after passing the high cuttings with the Dwyka tillite, just after the 12 km beacon, you're back in a low cutting with

There are several extremely handsome cutting exposures of glacial Dwyka tillite as you approach the rampart of the Swartberge.

tillite, and the foothills of the Swartberg range are not far ahead. This time, when you've crossed the Dwyka tillite, you're off Karoo sediments and onto the top unit of the underlying Cape Supergroup, known as the Witteberg Group. The road keeps to the shales, mostly strongly cleaved, but you are soon in a valley in the quartzite foothills. You can't miss the bare slopes of quartzite dipping down towards you off the first ridge, and you'll soon be cutting through an even higher ridge of the same quartzites, where, if you look carefully as you enter the cutting, you'll see some nice drag-folding of the quartzites.

Keep your eyes open for the signboard for Droëkloof 1 a couple of kilometres after this. The next cutting after this shows beautifully folded sandstones and siltstones, especially on the western side of the cutting, though across the stream course to the east there's good folding in the river bank. It's certainly worth stopping for a good look at all of this (**geosite 2, map 34**).

Cape Fold Belt or Cape Thrust Belt?

Near the turn-off to the west to Prince Albert and before you get to Klaarstroom, you are into one of the shaly formations of the Bokkeveld Group, and will see how extremely cleaved the rocks are, now that you're approaching the core zone of the fold belt. After Klaarstroom, and as you are virtually at the portal of Meiringspoort and about to cross the river at Bloupuntdrift, look to your left and see the first really clear example of thrusting on this route, in this case of Bokkeveld sandstones **(geosite 3, map 34)**. *It should be mentioned that, though not always as manifest as this, the thrusting in this belt is such an important part of the deformation that it is sometimes called the Cape Thrust Belt. Together with the inclined axial planes you can see in the folding in the mountains, this thrusting is a good indication of the asymmetric style of deformation in the entire belt. (For a summary of the structural evolution of the Cape Fold Belt, see p. 300.)*

Look for the roughly horizontal line at the base of this beautiful folding: it is the decollement or plane of dislocation (indicated by the dashed line), which is why we might, more accurately, talk about the 'Cape Fold and Thrust Belt'.

Try to pass through Meiringspoort in the middle of the day when the sunlight best reveals the magnificent folding, truly one of the most impressive and accessible sights of South African geology. At about the middle of Meiringspoort is a well-signposted rest and information spot at Watervalkloof **(geosite 4, map 34)**. Stop there and have a look at the exhibits on the history of the gorge and, if you have the time, cross the road and the river, so you're as far west as you can get at this spot. Have a good look at the slope behind the waterfall, in other words on the eastern side of the gorge. Let your eye travel towards the top of the slope and see the strong and sudden contrast between conspicuously folded sediments lower down the slope, and almost horizontal unfolded quartzites making the skyline. If you look hard you will see the thin Cedarberg shale marking the base of the upper, undisturbed beds. Close inspection of the shale here has shown that its own base is highly fractured, and there is no doubt that the northward-directed compression has used the soft shale as a lubricant, thereby freeing, as it were, the quartzites above the shale from folding. So, in contrast to the last spot, there has been no ripping of the quartzite; just large-scale gliding in the lowest part of the Cedarberg shale.

From Nooiensboomdrift you see the lower Table Mountain quartzites dipping very steeply to the south for the first time, from top to bottom of the slopes. A short distance further on, you are out of the poort and into the lower hills of the Kansa Group, with their strongly cleaved rocks

Red slopes like this one between De Rust and Oudtshoorn, carved from north-dipping Enon conglomerate,
are a common sight in the Little Karoo. These sediments formed rapidly in confined rift troughs as the
African coastline was being formed for the first time.

conspicuously veined with quartz. If you are stopping in Oudtshoorn and will be visiting the caves, you'll see much more of the Kansa Group, in copious fresh outcrop. (See ch. 18, p. 304.) These sediments are 50 million years younger than those of the Kango Group. They are both older than the Table Mountain Group, though, and were folded before that group was laid down. As you leave the protective mountain rampart, the hills lose their altitude and, as you enter De Rust, though you don't see it, you cross the fault contact between the Kansa Group and the Jurassic Enon Formation. (For more on the depositional environment of the Enon Formation, see ch. 18, p. 302.)

Soon after leaving De Rust, you will see off to your right the strangely shaped red hills that are typical of the erosion of Enon conglomerate in the Little Karoo **(geosite 5, map 34)**. Approaching Oudtshoorn, you get a good impression of them at close quarters. The red coloration is typical of Enon conglomerate anywhere, telling firstly of a generous quota of iron oxide supplied during its deposition, and secondly, and more importantly, of the rapid deposition of the conglomerates, there having been insufficient time to winnow the iron minerals, much finer than the boulders and cobbles, out of the rock. You can be sure that any bare red slopes you see in these parts have been cut in Enon conglomerate.

Though you cannot bypass Oudtshoorn, you may not choose to stop there now. For more on the Little Karoo, with some background to the town's stone buildings and the geology of the region, see ch. 18, pp. 300-311.

For 50 km after you've left Oudtshoorn, you will see on both sides of the road scattered remnants of a very well-developed, beautifully planed land surface, in places giving way to the slopes below in a vertical scarp. These are remnants of the very ancient African Erosion Surface, and the rock making the resistant capping is silcrete of the Grahamstown Formation. Imagine a time 20 million years ago when the whole of the wide Little Karoo valley, between the Outeniqua mountains to the

This Grahamstown Formation 'conglomerate' could be mistaken for the Enon Formation, but its clasts are quite angular, suggesting minimal transport, and contrasting with the river-worn Enon clasts.

One of several recumbent folds of quartzites of the Table Mountain Group in the Outeniqua Pass.
Such flat fold axial planes tell of a strong component of shearing in the compression that caused the folding.
The dashed line indicates the approximate position of the fold axial plane (see illustration on p. 121).

south and the Swartberg range to the north, was a vast unbroken peneplain sloping imperceptibly towards the meandering Olifants River. During a period of considerable stability, and over millions of years, silica was removed by groundwater from sand grains and carried towards the surface by capillary action in the weathered soil. Eventually, with changing climatic conditions, it formed a hard cement at the surface around everything in the upper soil, including big blocks of broken bedrock. That, in a nutshell, is how the silcrete of the Grahamstown Formation was created. There are a couple of good examples of it just before and after the turn-off to Uniondale along the N9 **(geosite 6, map 34)**. Although this rock looks a lot like Enon conglomerate, close scrutiny will show that it's not as conspicuously red as the Enon, and the clasts are not as well rounded, having travelled no appreciable distance.

By the time you reach the point where the N9 turns off from the N12, you have just crossed back onto the Table Mountain Group, having been on shales and sandstones of the Bokkeveld for most of the way since leaving the Enon conglomerate near Oudtshoorn. Now you're on the quartzites which you saw so spectacularly folded in Meiringspoort. Stop at the view site near the top of the Outeniqua Pass and have a look at the cuttings to your right as you descend. You will see a couple of recumbent isoclinal folds, in other words with limbs parallel to each other, the fold axis having been tilted through about 90° from the vertical **(geosite 7, map 34)**.

From the foot of the pass to George on the N2 you're on the pre-Table Mountain Group basement, with minimal exposure. Remember, this coastal plain is extremely ancient, having been flooded and exposed more than once – there has been more than enough time to leach the surface, and leach it again (for more on the evolution of the southern Cape coastal plain, see p. 139). So that, although the southern Cape between Mossel Bay and Humansdorp may enjoy one of the most agreeable climates anywhere, it is not known for its fertile soil – ask any farmer.

15 N14: Pretoria to Springbok

GEOLOGICAL OVERVIEW

This chapter vividly unfolds one of the ironies of historical geology. Unlike fruit, or people, rock formations aren't necessarily more crumpled the older they are. There are the remains of tiny fossil algae, and 'pillow structures' in submarine lavas that are as perfectly preserved in Archaean formations over three billion years old as they are in rocks a thousand times younger, while rocks far less ancient may have been changed beyond recognition. That's what can happen, as this route illustrates, when you move off and away from the craton.

Near the beginning of your journey, you see sediments of the Witwatersrand and Transvaal Supergroups and lavas of the Ventersdorp Supergroup, all deep into the almost lifeless Precambrian, relatively undeformed and almost unmetamorphosed. As you head westwards over the wide plains of the southern Kalahari, you cross the edge of the Kaapvaal Craton around Olifantshoek, and start to see sediments dipping quite steeply, although their sedimentary character is still clearly recognisable. This is not the case as you leave Upington, heading west, where high-grade metamorphic rocks – biotite gneisses with pegmatite veins cutting them – bear no resemblance to the much older rocks you left behind many hours ago. You are now well and truly into the Namaqua Metamorphic Province and, though the age of these rocks is only just over a billion years, their origin, and the events that have changed them so, challenge geologists as few others do.

On your way to Springbok, you pass signboards to the appropriately named Hotazel, site of the world's biggest manganese deposits; you see signs of the massive Sishen iron ore mine, and hurry past the Asbestos Hills; and you may wonder how such troublesome rocks turned to magical tiger's eye. Further west, you travel past the Aggeneys base metal mine and the vast, as yet untapped, zinc deposit of Gamsberg, and, just outside Springbok, the copper mine visited by Simon van der Stel in 1685. The journey is long; it's anything but boring.

LEFT: *In the Augrabies area the earlier granites were intruded by mafic rocks, probably dolerite or diabase. During the strong metamorphism that was experienced, these rocks were changed to ridges of black-weathering amphibolite.*
OPPOSITE: *Below the Augrabies Falls, the erosive power of the Orange River has carved out one of the most spectacular gorges in Africa within the Augrabies Granite.*

Geology of the route

Pretoria to Delareyville

The N14 starts in Pretoria as the N1, and then heads westwards towards Krugersdorp. To begin with, you cross sediments of the Pretoria Group, followed by Malmani dolomite of the Chuniespoort Group, which, like the Pretoria Group, belongs to the Transvaal Supergroup, all dipping gently to the north. The dolomite – magnesium-rich limestones – forms the flattish terrain around Centurion. About 17 km from Pretoria, after the route has turned to the southwest, you pass over the inconspicuous Black Reef Formation, the basal unit of the Transvaal Supergroup, after which road cuttings show that you are crossing the ancient granites of the Johannesburg Dome.

Some 50 km from Pretoria, at Muldersdrift, you cross the headwaters of the Crocodile River and, at nearby Pinehaven junction, the N14 makes a sharp right turn. Here you are on the even older ultramafic rocks of a greenstone remnant known as the Muldersdrift Complex, which decomposes to the fertile, reddish soil that supports the flower and fruit farms flanking the road. The prominent quartzite ridge to the south of the Orange Grove Formation is the start of the south-dipping Witwatersrand Supergroup that overlies the granites and greenstones. Proceeding westwards, you will notice this ridge becoming lower, until at Oaktree, some 10 km from Pinehaven, it has disappeared.

The gold-bearing Black Reef reappears near Oaktree, making a low ridge trending off to the north. For the rest, you are on Malmani dolomite, only occasionally seen in dark grey to chocolate-brown outcrop, and with you for most of the next 75 km.

Continuing via Tarlton, you may notice the slight rise to the southeast. This marks the position of the Black Reef quartzites and the underlying Witwatersrand sediments, while the big mine tailings dams near Krugersdorp point to the existence of the West Rand gold field not far off. The geological map shows a significant geological structure here, the Klerkskraal Anticline, with the Black Reef continuing westwards in the crest of this structure, more or less parallel to the N14, for some 30 km. It has marginally younger dolomite present on both sides, dipping gently away from it.

The small, scattered heaps of dark rocks that can be seen from the road tell of old manganese workings, where black manganese oxide derived from the underlying dolomite was concentrated near the surface. The process leading to manganese concentration occurs when dolomite contains fairly high levels of manganese, perhaps exceeding 2 per cent in places. As it weathers, manganese is released and, under favourable conditions, accumulates in the soil and in small solution cavities in the dolomite as residual manganese 'wad', comprising mainly the manganese oxide, psilomelane.

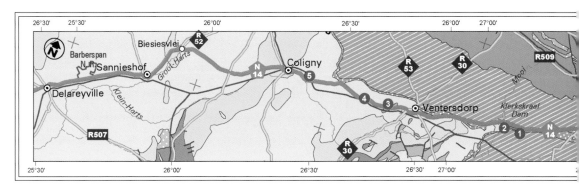

MAP 35   SEE KEY FOR MAP ON INSIDE BACK COVER FLAP

Over the Malmani dolomite west of Tarlton, there are numerous small old mining workings from which cobble-sized nodules of secondary black manganese oxides (or manganese wad) are piled.

About 25 km from Tarlton, and very close to the road, gold was mined on the farm Drylands between 1987 and 1991 **(geosite 1, map 35)**. Nearly one and a half tons of the metal was recovered by the chemical heap leach process from surface manganese wad, and you can still see the gold recovery plant, as well as conspicuous black waste dumps; it's possible that mining will resume here again on a small scale.

A few kilometres further on, the Klerkskraal Dam appears north of the road. In the small valley on its southern side are good exposures of the Black Reef and its basal contact with the Basement granite. Several poorly sorted conglomerate beds are separated by quartzite, and there is evidence of historical gold prospecting of the conglomerate reef, which is virtually flat-lying **(geosite 2, map 35)**.

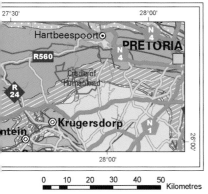

After another 17 km, note the subtle change in the vegetation as the N14 makes its way onto the Ventersdorp Supergroup. This major geological unit underlies, and so is older than, the Malmani dolomites you've been travelling on. At its thickest it reaches nearly 8 000 m, and was deposited on a supercontinent being stretched out by convection currents deep in the mantle. At the end of Witwatersrand sedimentation, deep fissures, conduits for molten lava, opened up and the Ventersdorp lavas flooded out onto the surface. South of Ventersdorp, an unusual fragmental volcanic rock known as agglomerate is found close to the N14.

The Ventersdorp Supergroup

The small North-West Province farming town of Ventersdorp has given its name to this remarkable geological sequence that now occupies a northeast-trending elliptical basin more than 200 000 sq km in extent. It is found from near Strydenburg in the southwest to Thabazimbi in the north and Balfour in the northeast, with most of the sequence covered by younger formations (see text box on sedimentary basins, p. 42). It was deposited over a relatively short period, a little more than 2 700 million years ago, at the end of Witwatersrand Supergroup deposition and before the start of Transvaal Supergroup sedimentation. Detailed knowledge of this sequence has been obtained from the hundreds of boreholes drilled through it to reach the underlying, but unrelated, gold-bearing Witwatersrand formations.

Ventersdorp sediments and widespread flood basalts and andesites accumulated on the Kaapvaal Craton in fault-bounded troughs, or grabens, which developed under tensional conditions in the crust. Despite its thickness and extent, the only economic importance lies at its base in a conglomerate, developed in the Carletonville and Klerksdorp gold fields, and in places very rich in gold. Resting unconformably on older and inclined gold-bearing Witwatersrand formations, the Ventersdorp Contact Reef contains gold particles that were eroded from the gold-bearing Witwatersrand conglomerates and reconcentrated in residual gravels close to the surface. These gravels were soon covered by outpourings of Ventersdorp lava, preserving their fabulous wealth for today's mining.

From Ventersdorp to Vryburg (see also map 36, p. 258), you are mostly on rocks of the Ventersdorp Supergroup. About 6 km west of Ventersdorp, though, you see low, north-striking quartzite ridges and, in a road cutting between the ridges, a thick sequence of reddish shale and banded ironstone. The latter is the probable equivalent of the Contorted Bed (see p. 43), and this formation is a small inlier of West Rand Group sediments of the lower Witwatersrand, exposed through the Ventersdorp Supergroup **(geosite 3, map 35)**. Here, about 130 km from the typical Witwatersrand geological locality in Johannesburg, the rocks are very similar; this marks the westernmost edge of the Witwatersrand Basin. The nearest big gold mines are at Klerksdorp, 55 km to the south (see pp. 234–235).

Close to Ventersdorp, an exposure of dark pyroclastic rock containing a variety of fragments of variable size is the result of an explosive volcanic eruption around 2 700 million years ago.

West of Ventersdorp a thick bed of conglomerate made of boulders and cobbles of diverse rock types reflects a time of rapid erosion and deposition within a river system, when a thick sandbar was also deposited, around 2 650 million years ago.

Shortly past Ventersdorp, this well-bedded, iron-rich rock, part of the West Rand Group (lower Witwatersrand stratigraphy), is remarkably similar to the Contorted Bed seen in Braamfontein, Johannesburg, and is probably the equivalent formation.

At the Bodenstein rail crossing, blocks of dark basaltic volcanic rock of the Ventersdorp Supergroup's Allanridge Formation are exposed, some showing amygdales, originally steam cavities in the lava, now filled by silica.

About 14 km west of Ventersdorp, shortly before Makokskraal, a text-book deposit of boulder conglomerate and channel sandstone is exposed in a road cutting (**geosite 4, map 35**). Well-rounded pebbles and boulders of a variety of rock types form an impressive thickness of very coarse sediment, undoubtedly of fluvial origin, interbedded with and underlain by cross-bedded, braided river channel sands. They belong in the Platberg Group of the Ventersdorp Supergroup (see the text box, opposite page, on the Ventersdorp Supergroup), and reflect bulk erosion off nearby areas of strong relief, analogous with the much younger Enon Formation in the southern Cape, also deposited in grabens. If you are lucky, you may even find small boulders of typical Witwatersrand conglomerate in the debris, probably from the formation not far to the east.

From Makokskraal to Coligny, the area is underlain by Ventersdorp lava, occurring as dark, bouldery outcrops. At the Bodenstein railway crossing east of the grain elevators, you can see hard, dark grey-green basalt containing mineral-filled amygdales that were once steam cavities in the cooling lava **(geosite 5, map 35)**. Close to the Coligny town dam, the basalts give way to a short stretch of quartzite, though Coligny itself is situated on Basement granite, shown by the light-coloured sandy soil. It forms an elongated 'window' reflecting a north-south-trending basement swell. Beyond Coligny, the N14 crosses back onto Ventersdorp rocks and stays on them almost all the way to Vryburg. At Biesiesvlei, on the junction with the R52 to Lichtenburg, you will cross the inconspicuous and seasonal Harts River, where another small window of Basement granite is shown on the geological maps.

Delareyville to Kuruman

About 15 km west of Delareyville, Soutpan, the big saltpan to the south of the road, is also located on a window of Basement granite, and once produced common salt on a small scale **(geosite 1, map 36)**. About 20 km from Vryburg, O'Reilly's Pan is situated on an outlier of the Dwyka Group (Karoo Supergroup), overlying the Ventersdorp lavas. (Read more about how pans form in ch. 14, p. 237). The bustling town of Vryburg, some 20 km to the west, is built partly on Dwyka tillite (see p. 148 for more on Dwyka tillite) and partly on Ventersdorp lavas.

In the small watercourse that crosses the N14 on the western side of Vryburg, close to the nature reserve's entrance gate, there are low outcrops of almost flat-lying quartzite of the Vryburg Formation. This unit forms the base of the Transvaal Supergroup here, and is correlated with the Black Reef Formation further east. You are moving onto the Ghaap Plateau, a flat, monotonous triangle of mainly dolomitic limestone, extending to Kuruman in the west and to Campbell and Griquatown in the south, and this quartzite marks the edge of the Griqualand West basin of the Transvaal Supergroup.

The underlying Campbell Rand dolomite here, the same rock formation as the Malmani dolomite seen in the Transvaal Basin, is flat-lying and without prominent outcrops, showing itself occasionally as small exposures of grey-weathering 'olifantsklip' dolomite in culverts and as boulders along fences. Much of the surface is covered by shallow soil and whitish calcrete, or surface limestone. Some 40 km east of Kuruman, the monotony of the plateau is relieved when you see in the far distance the Kuruman Hills, a range that extends north-south more or less continuously for over 400 km, from Prieska in the south into Botswana in the north.

MAP 36   SEE KEY FOR MAP ON INSIDE BACK COVER FLAP

0 10 20 30 40 50 Kilometres

TOP: *West of Delareyville is Soutpan, a large saltpan located on Basement granite that once produced salt on a small scale, and is one of several in the district.*

INSET: *The 'Eye of Kuruman' provides crystal-clear water into a pool, an oasis of the southern Kalahari, and is the source of the Kuruman River. Robert Moffat's Kuruman Mission, established in 1824, was founded on this abundant water source.*

Kuruman, described as the 'Oasis of the Kalahari', is a town of considerable historical importance, where a mission station was established in the early nineteenth century by the Scotsman Robert Moffat. Located on the upper part of the Campbell Rand dolomite, close to the Kuruman Hills, it is best known for its natural geological wonder, the 'Eye of Kuruman', a spring that is said to deliver over 20 million litres of crystal-clear water every day **(geosite 2, map 36)**. Stop at the oasis garden on Main Street and see for yourself the endless stream of artesian water pouring out of the dolomite. It is the source of the north-flowing Kuruman River and is said to be the biggest natural fountain in the Southern Hemisphere. The spring is supplied by water that flows through a system of interconnected solution channels in the dolomite, which is dammed up by a diabase dyke and forced to the surface.

Kuruman to Kakamas

Continuing west, you cross the Kuruman Hills, which become the Asbesberge (Asbestos Hills) further south. These hills are well known for their large deposits of blue asbestos, or crocidolite, material now recognised as a health risk of the worst kind, and for which mining is a thing of the past. Blue asbestos is believed to have formed by low-temperature regional metamorphism of sediments rich in sodium, iron and silica, and under conditions of stress. The rock package of finely bedded, iron-rich Transvaal Supergroup sediments that make up the Kuruman Hills dips very shallowly to the west, and constitutes a vast resource of low-grade iron ore. Excellent exposures of somewhat weathered, finely layered rocks are seen in road cuttings some 12 to 15 km west of Kuruman (**geosite 1, map 37**). Unique to these iron formation hills is tiger's-eye, which forms near the surface when fibrous asbestos is completely replaced by iron-rich silica, changing colour in the process from blue-grey to golden brown.

To the west of Kuruman, the Kuruman Hills (called the Asbestos Hills further south) are made up of well-laminated, fine-grained rocks including shaly layers, reddish chert (jasper) and hematitic iron oxide.

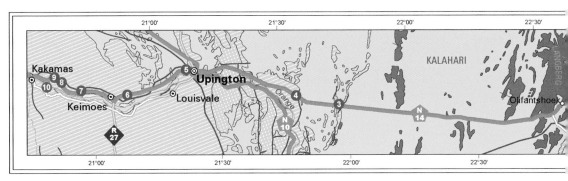

MAP 37 SEE KEY FOR MAP ON INSIDE BACK COVER FLAP

After passing the Kuruman Hills, the countryside opens up into typical Kalahari thornveld dominated by camel-thorn trees, an indication of the thick cover of Kalahari sand that blankets most outcrops.

While to the north lies Hotazel and the vast Kalahari manganese field, the N14 turns southwest, and passes the mining town of Kathu and the Sishen Mine, South Africa's world-class open-cast iron ore mine. From the road, the mine is indicated by the benched, planed-off hills, and large dumps of mining waste. The origin of the high-grade iron ore is geologically complex and still debated. At a grade of more than 60 per cent of iron, proven reserves at Sishen are in excess of 2 300 million tons, making it one of the biggest iron ore deposits in the world. At present, 25 million tons are produced annually, mainly for export via Saldanha Bay, as well as for local steel plants. An excellent example of high-grade breccia-type iron ore is exposed in a road cutting on the N14 close to the main mine operations **(geosite 2, map 37)**. But if you have time and can arrange it ahead, a mine visit is well worth the time.

This gravel pit west of Kuruman shows a typical blanket of reddish, wind-blown sand of the Kalahari that obscures most outcrop, but provides good soil for certain trees, notably the camel-thorn.

About 10 km south of Sishen, the N14 turns west again towards Olifantshoek and Upington. A few kilometres past the turn-off to Upington, you will cross over the dedicated 800 km-long railway line from the mine to the deep-water docking and loading facility

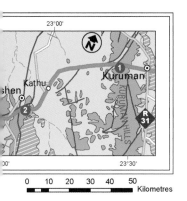

at Saldanha Bay on the West Coast. Underlying the wide, featureless plain ahead of you are basaltic and andestic volcanic rocks of the Transvaal Supergroup, but outcrops are few. Far ahead lie the massifs of the Langberg range, made of a geological sequence you've not seen before on this route. The Olifantshoek Supergroup is dated around 1 900 million years old, making it younger than the Transvaal Supergroup that you have been travelling over since Vryburg. The village of Olifantshoek nestles at the foot of the Langberg range, with dark volcanic andesite of the Hartley Formation forming the hill on which the cellphone mast stands. Massive, moderately to steeply dipping quartzites make up the hills west and north of the village.

The Langberg, north and south of Olifantshoek, is made of the thick Olifantshoek Supergroup, composed of quartzites and shales dipping shallowly to the east. Further west it is largely covered by wind-blown Kalahari sand.

These formations continue at least 100 km north as the Korannaberg, before disappearing under Kalahari sediments, while to the south they stretch for 140 km to near the Boegoeberg Dam on the Orange River. In contrast to the horizontal formations you've been on, these rocks show conspicuous dips and folding. You are leaving the stability of the Kaapvaal Craton behind you and approaching the Namaqua Metamorphic Province, a zone of mobile belts. The Olifantshoek Supergroup was laid down in a basin on the edge of the Kaapvaal Craton and is not classified as part of the Namaqua Metamorphic Province. The folding in it was much earlier than in the Namaqua Province, and it appears to have been only slightly affected by the Namaqua metamorphism.

West of Olifantshoek, the road to Upington forms what is arguably the most desolate and empty stretch of highway in South Africa, traversing over 100 km of wide Kalahari plain broken only by isolated hills and massifs, or inselbergs, of Olifantshoek quartzite. The plains are covered by thick Kalahari deposits, including numerous stabilised red sand dunes; thick calcrete is invariably seen in roadside borrow pits, and makes up the undercourse of the highway.

The vast Namaqua Metamorphic Province is a geologically complex region of crystalline basement, exposed for over 500 km from east of Upington to west of Springbok. In the south it is hidden under a thick cover of much younger Karoo formations, although geologists believe it ties up with similar metamorphic rocks that re-appear some 900 km to the east, known there as the Natal Metamorphic Province (see ch. 3, p. 76).

After widely scattered outcrops of Olifantshoek quartzites across the plains, it is worth stopping in the cutting close to the signboard showing 'Upington 60 km'. Sheared, vertically bedded quartzite and schist of the 1 290 million-year-old Wilgenhoutsdrif Group have been stretched out and dismembered in a process known as boudinage, indicating the great strain suffered during deformation **(geosite 3, map 37)**.

Surprisingly, between 45 and 30 km east of Upington, undeformed and almost horizontal, purplish red conglomerate and gritty reddish sandstone beds are well exposed in several road cuttings **(geosite 4, map 37)**. These are the uppermost part of the 1 123 million-year-old Koras Group, which was deposited in small basins on top of rocks of the Namaqua Province during the waning stage of the Namaqua events.

The Wilgenhoutsdrif quartzite forms prominent sheared outcrops. Within this steep fault zone, notice the break-up of hard quartzite into slivers and boudins, surrounded by highly schistose, brownish fault gouge.

East of Upington, flat-lying and undeformed, these 1 100 million-year-old Koras sediments, including beds of pebbly conglomerate, overlie the highly deformed rocks of the complex Namaqua Metamorphic Province.

ABOVE: *The orange-red sand dunes in the Upington area are the youngest geological formation in the region. Blown in from the north, they are generally aligned northwest and are often well covered by grass. Their porosity allows them to store considerable moisture.*

LEFT: *Around Upington, strongly deformed, banded amphibolite, often with a gneissic texture, is common and consists entirely of recrystallised metamorphic minerals – amphibole, biotite and plagioclase feldspar. Note the thin pegmatite vein.*

You will see prominent ridges of north-trending hills made of sheared, glassy white quartzites between 25 and 13 km east of Upington. They extend far to the south, roughly parallel to the Orange River, and are thought to be the oldest formations of the Namaqua Metamorphic Province, called the Vaalkoppies Group.

The plains you drive across here are part of the peneplain called the Post-African Surface. It is cut by the Orange River drainage system, which, over the eons, has removed the Karoo sediments that formerly covered the Basement formations. As you drop down towards Upington, the increasingly complex Basement geology becomes better exposed.

The Namaqua Metamorphic Province that you are now well into consists of intensely folded, highly sheared and strongly metamorphosed and granitised sediments and volcanics that have been intruded by numerous plutons of mainly granitic composition. The province evolved on relatively thin continental crust over a lengthy period, ending around 1 100 million years ago. What you now see are the roots of a major mountain chain, once of Himalayan proportions. With no Archaean crustal plate in Namaqualand, it is conjectured that the long-lived period of mountain-building – driven by convection in the hot mantle – resulted from the collision of the Kaapvaal Craton to the east with a fragment of continental crust from the west, which subsequently parted company with it again.

Upington is built on a river terrace some 15 m above the Orange River flood plain, and water-worn pebbles are common on the surface. Heading westwards through the vineyards on the north bank of the river, you will see complex geology dominated by coarse-grained gneisses and dark rocks called amphibolites. About 5 km out of town, there is fresh grey biotite-amphibole gneiss in a road cutting, through which thin pegmatite veins have been intruded **(geosite 5, map 37)**. The red sand dunes that reach the road some 10 km southwest of Upington are linear, northwest-trending seif dunes within a permanent dune field, and they represent the youngest formation of the Kalahari Group. As elsewhere in this area, calcrete is conspicuous, and is used extensively for road-making.

West of Keimoes, calcrete is shown developing from an underlying, partly weathered, calcium-rich mafic rock containing calcrete veins, and changing to massive compact 'hardebank' calcrete at the top.

This coarse-grained, megacrystic (or augen) Currie's Camp Gneiss consists mainly of massive (whitish) feldspar crystals formed by metamorphic growth, surrounded by glassy quartz and dark biotite mica.

At Currie's Camp, about 12 km northeast of Keimoes, notice the extremely coarse-grained gneiss that comprises three minerals – very large crystals of whitish feldspar, called megacrysts (some up to 8 cm in length), flattened masses of almost black biotite that's prominent on the rock foliation, and lesser glassy quartz. Called the Currie's Camp Gneiss, it's an excellent example of intrusive granitic gneiss **(geosite 6, map 37)**. The rocks in Keimoes are also granite-gneiss, known as the Vaalputs Granite, and at least 13 different types of gneissic granite have been recognised during geological mapping around here.

We have already mentioned calcrete or surface limestone, and noted its abundance around Upington and elsewhere. About 3 km west of Keimoes, an excellent exposure in a cutting shows its formation from an underlying dark, mafic to ultramafic intrusive rock.

The road to Kakamas continues alongside the river and, over the next 15 km or so, the underlying rock-type, a dark gneiss, is known as the Friersdale Charnockite. Stop near the Friersdale church to see the peculiar weathered outcrops of this rare type of granite **(geosite 7, map 37)**. The rock name 'charnockite' comes from India, where it was named after Job Charnock, the founder of Calcutta, whose tombstone (dated 1695) was made of a similar rock – the first described specimen of this unusual rock type.

At Friersdale, this dark weathering rock is a peculiar variety of granite, containing the unusual mineral hypersthene (an orthopyroxene). It is widespread in the Keimoes area and reflects a complex igneous-metamorphic origin.

East of Kakamas, near Warmsand, lies this prominent northwest-trending hill, known as Neusberg, through which the Orange River has carved a poort. Directly to the west of the hills is a major zone of shearing and a change in geology.

Schistose, mica-rich quartzite, highly sheared and glistening white when it catches the light, is well exposed in the Neuspoort road cutting and is known as the Goedehoop Formation.

At Warmsand, the route moves away from the river into more mountainous country known as the Neusberg, where, some 11 km before Kakamas, a cutting through the mountain range reveals steeply northeast-dipping, glistening quartzites. A close look at these will show that they are made of sheared, completely recrystallised, sericitic (finely micaceous), flaggy quartzite **(geosite 8, map 37)**.

Nine kilometres from Kakamas, you will cross a rugged range of hills known as Bobbejaanskrans, composed of pinkish to orange-weathering quartz-feldspar gneisses **(geosite 9, map 37)**. These formations represent original 'supracrustal' formations, sedimentary or volcanic rocks that were deposited on an early basement, and which were deformed and metamorphosed during the Namaqualand event.

A kilometre further on, with the green Kakamas valley ahead of you, close by on the southern side of the road is a large white pegmatite koppie known as Baviaans Krans, where feldspar and beryl were extracted during the 1960s **(geosite 10, map 37)**. If you are feeling adventurous, drive in on the gravel road and take the track up to the old mine site, and you may be rewarded with a variety of interesting pegmatite minerals, including rose quartz, amazonite and topaz.

The Augrabies Falls, 35 km northwest of Kakamas, are a 'must-see' for anyone interested in geology, or simply in wonderful scenery. From Kakamas, continue on the N14 for 8 km and, after crossing the Hartebeest River, turn right; from here, the park rest-camp is about 28 km further on.

The defunct workings of the Baviaans Krans pegmatite occur south of the road, on extremely coarse-grained quartz, feldspar, white mica and a variety of less common minerals, including rose quartz, amazonite, topaz and beryl.

THE AUGRABIES FALLS NATIONAL PARK – A GEOLOGIST'S PARADISE

This is one of South Africa's premier geological attractions, only a short distance off the N14, and on a sweltering Northern Cape summer's day is an ideal oasis. On the northern side of the Orange River lies the vast Riemvasmaak desert wilderness area and hot spring, another ideal destination for geological and 4x4 enthusiasts.

ABOVE: *The spectacular 65-m plunge of the Orange River into the gorge. The unweathered rock formation, eroded and polished by the river, is called the Augrabies Gneiss.*

INSET: *The Augrabies Granite is a medium-grained rock of granitic composition and magmatic origin, showing a gneissic texture. The main minerals are large crystals of pinkish-white feldspar, glassy quartz and shiny black mica.*

In the Augrabies Falls National Park, the hot, dry desert climate and the texture of the massive gneisses combine to produce unusual 'moonscape' formations, such as large exfoliating granitic domes and bizarrely weathered boulders.

Augrabies, a Khoi word meaning 'the place of great noise', is a unique desert park where the wide Orange River narrows and plunges a total of 145 m through a granitic ravine into the vertically sided, zigzagging Augrabies Gorge. Higher than the Victoria Falls, Augrabies is ranked the sixth highest major waterfall in the world. If you are here during the seasonal floods, a spectacular view of multiple waterfalls awaits you as the brown Orange River cascades into the seething canyon. Considering that most of the rain falling on the South African interior takes this route to the sea, you will start to understand how the river has gouged out such a canyon. During past millennia and periods of wetter climate, it must have been an even more dramatic sight. Nowadays the river has been tamed by major dams upstream, such as the Vanderkloof (formerly PK le Roux) and Gariep (formerly Hendrik Verwoerd) Dams.

The underlying geology is fairly simple – almost the entire area is made up of two varieties of granite-gneiss, known as the Augrabies Granite in the central part of the park, and surrounded by the Riemvasmaak Gneiss. At the rest-camp, have a look at the fresh granite, a slightly pinkish, medium-grained, mildly gneissic rock consisting of feldspar, quartz and black biotite flakes, one of a suite of intrusive rocks of the Namaqua Province. Above the falls, this rock forms the water-worn outcrops and massive free boulders of an ancient river flood plain. Lowering of the river's base level, combined with a probable zone of weakness in the bedrock, resulted in rapid incision of the gneissic granite below the nick-point at the falls. A drive or hike downstream will reveal pink-orange, amazingly shaped, weathered granite-gneiss outcrops, including spectacular dome-shaped masses of exfoliating granite, bands of black-weathering amphibolite and patches of quartz-rich pegmatite debris. Views from several accessible vantage points into the canyon are superb.

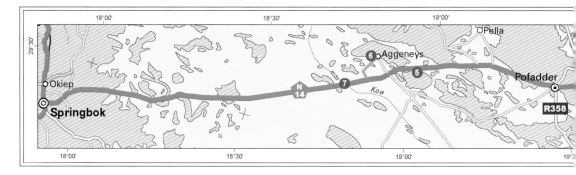

MAP 38 SEE KEY FOR MAP ON INSIDE BACK COVER FLAP

Kakamas to Springbok

The N14 to Springbok takes you via Pofadder, across the wide open spaces of the vast Bushmanland peneplain, punctured by occasional inselberg-type mountains. You are on gneissic terrain of the Namaqua Metamorphic Province all the way.

Even while you're still in Kakamas, there is a good example of fresh augen gneiss as you pass the 'Arrive Alive' board on the western edge of town **(geosite 1, map 38)**, and while still driving through vineyards, you will see veins of quartz and pegmatite, which characteristically leave their rubble strewn over the surface.

You're barely aware of rising away from the Orange River, and as you look out to the right, you'll see the fall is barely perceptible. You're on a gently sloping peneplain, carved by the present cycle of erosion, with the river as its base level. The scattered inselbergs, ridges and plateaus dotted about it are remnants from earlier cycles, still in the process of being worn down. From the 105 km beacon (east of Pofadder), notice a number of conspicuously flat-topped massifs ahead: the tops of these are parts of the peneplain of the last cycle of erosion, when the wide plains were a couple of hundred metres higher than now **(geosite 2, map 38)**. Then, 100 million years ago, with the sea level receding, and new base levels forming, the sculpting of a new set of valleys began. First the valleys deepened as they widened, then, when the new base level had been reached, they just widened and widened until, in an endless cyclical progression, plains became mesas, and valleys became plains – the new generation. Remember, the gneisses of which those plateaus are made are folded into every conceivable attitude, and the flat tops you see are nothing to do with any bedding in the rocks.

From about the 95 km beacon you'll start to see koppies and ridges off to your right which are far darker than any of the other hills. These are remnants of mafic to ultramafic intrusives, much younger than the gneisses they cut: in time you'll pass quite close to them and may want to stop at various points for a closer look **(geosite 3, map 38)**.

There's not much outcrop here, and cuttings are few and far between and quite low. The most conspicuous rock you see at the surface is pegmatite, which, being rather coarsely crystalline and usually quartz-rich, resists weathering more than the gneiss. Close to the 57 km beacon is a pegmatite where the quartz is pink in places, to the point where it would almost qualify as rose quartz **(geosite 4, map 38)**. As is often the case, the rock this pegmatite cuts through is amphibolite, in part at least.

At the 35 km beacon, you'll notice that you're travelling into a wide valley, dotted with red sand dunes. Over to the right, you may notice that the hills stand above a base level of the landscape that is dropping away imperceptibly but steadily. This suggests that the Orange River valley is not far off; the river itself is just over 30 km away. The hills ahead are clearly unrelated to the Orange River,

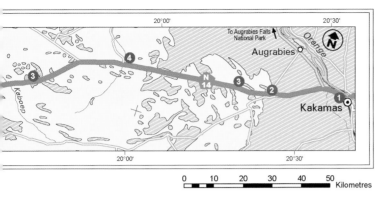

BOTTOM: *You will notice the red dune sand piling up against dark intrusive rocks in the Koa valley.*
INSET: *Much pinker than this and the rock would be mined as rose quartz: an outcrop near the road sign showing Pofadder is 57 km away.*

though. You're coming into hilly country around Pofadder, which will persist, particularly to your right, until after Aggeneys. The whole geological environment is changing dramatically, with important quartzite and iron formation layers entering the stratigraphy, exactly the sort of rocks you have come to expect in hilly terrain. As you proceed westwards, the ridges behind Pofadder take on the stature of an imposing mountain range: the ridge peaks are getting higher to the northwest, reaching a maximum of over 1 200 m, while the valley floor is dropping, so that the differential between valley base and mountain peak – climbed in under 3 km – is more than 700 m. It's rugged country, especially compared to the gentle plains you've just left behind.

The discoveries at Aggeneys

In 1968, a big copper-zinc 'massive sulphide' deposit was discovered near Prieska and, by 1969, a base metal exploration boom such as had never before been seen in South Africa was in progress in the Northern Cape. For the most part, except for the copper deposits around Springbok, this corner of South Africa was terra incognita. But soon a major North American copper producer, Phelps Dodge Corporation, became aware of the potential that this region offered. In 1970 Phelps Dodge heard, for the first time, the name that would soon be on every South African exploration geologist's lips: Aggeneys. A 15 m-deep copper-stained shaft on the slopes of Swartberg, on the farm Aggeneys, had been brought to their attention. Although, since its excavation 40 years earlier and abandonment soon after, it had been investigated by at least four mining companies, none had recognised the signs hidden in the rocks.

A visit to Aggeneys in early 1971 confirmed the favourability of the geological setting. A sulphide gossan along the flank of the mountain – such as most exploration geologists dream of but never see – led to protracted negotiations and, ultimately, a prospecting and option-to-purchase agreement.

By mid-1971, the first borehole sited at Black Mountain – a translation more easily bandied in New York offices than Swartberg – had intersected a wide zone of sulphide ore, rich in base metals and silver. A major campaign of drilling followed, and soon Black Mountain was eclipsed by another find, 6 km to the southeast and hitherto unknown – the Broken Hill deposit. Considerably richer in base metals than Black Mountain, it was estimated to hold 38 million tons of rich sulphide ore, containing lead, zinc, copper and silver – a world-class metal deposit by any standards.

In 1977, Phelps Dodge took on a South African partner, Gold Fields of South Africa, which was quick to establish an underground mine and concentrator at the Broken Hill deposit. These are still in full operation today and are what you see from the road. Ownership has changed again, this time to Anglo American PLC, whose exploration continues to add to ore reserves. And what of the original Swartberg deposit? Detailed exploration has shown its grade to be too low for profitable mining, vindicating, in an ironic twist, the old-timers who abandoned it.

The Aggeneys discoveries turned the Northern Cape into a crucible of intrigue and excitement and, for many, disappointment. Now, 30 years later, peace has returned to Bushmanland, while in big cities a world away, hundreds of man-years of detailed geological maps gather dust.

A view of the head gear, associated offices and workshops of the new Deeps Project.

Closer to the road, the flat tops are becoming a feature again as you pass the 'Aggeneys 40 km' signboard, especially the big plateau ahead and to your left (**geosite 5, map 38**). This is Gamsberg, a slightly stretched-out, flattened 'doughnut' rather than a true plateau, and famous in the world of mineral exploration for the very big zinc deposit it contains. Ten kilometres on, you can see the roadways up its northern slope, with dark grey rock below two portals into the hill. These are prospecting adits (horizontal tunnels), made as part of the evaluation of the deposit. The Gamsberg orebody is low-grade but large, and its mining awaits a zinc price projection sufficiently positive to assure profitability. There's no doubt it will happen – it's just a question of when.

The verdant mine village of Aggeneys, clearly visible just north of the road, bears testimony to what can be grown in the wastes of Bushmanland if you just add water (**geosite 6, map 38**). Before you leave, though, note the flat-topped ridges behind the front foothills and the mine. The headgears and slimes dam are soon behind you as you proceed westwards across the ancient peneplain of which you've seen other remnants, quite a way back and at Gamsberg.

You may have noticed that you've been entering another broad valley

The Simon van der Stel copper mine, dating back over 300 years (as the date engraved over the entrance testifies), was named for the governor of the Cape, who visited the area in a quest for geological riches.

since passing Gamsberg and, as you pass Aggeneys, you'll see the low dunes again. This is the Koa valley, along which, many millions of years ago, the waters of the Orange River flowed, leaving their calling cards of sparkling stones before moving on from the bed already carved out, across the plains to where geological circumstances direct that they should now flow (**geosite 7, map 38**).

By the time you see the 87 km beacon (from Springbok) you're out of the Koa valley and on the plains again, though not for long. Quite soon the hills are not so widely scattered, and 40 km from Springbok you're into the broken country that makes most of central Namaqualand. Not much further on you start to see the granite-gneiss domes that are so much a feature of these parts, and before you know it, you're in Springbok.

16 The Great Escarpment

GEOLOGICAL OVERVIEW

In this chapter we'll travel along – and close to – the Great Escarpment from Kaapsehoop in the south to the Olifants River in the north. Deeply incised by active rivers and streams, the underlying rock formations are mostly well exposed; there is no better example of geology shaping magnificent scenery. More than 100 million years of steady uplift of the land surface in the east of the country has been countered by a process of down-cutting erosion. This, in turn, has been helped by the consistently high rainfall over much of that time, as moisture-laden tropical air off the warm Indian Ocean condenses along the escarpment.

BELOW: *This classic view across the Blyde River canyon provides another real geological cross-section. The 'Three Rondawels' are 'roofed' by softer-weathering shale, while the 'walls' are of more competent quartzite, both of the Wolkberg Group.*
INSET: *The view northwards showing the Blydepoort Dam and the almost flat-lying capping of Black Reef quartzite in the distance.*

This is a region of great geological antiquity, the oldest Basement granite-gneisses ranging from 3 500 to 3 100 million years, and the youngest – intrusive sills related to the Bushveld Complex – a still venerable 2 000 million years. There are two geologically distinct terranes: the crystalline granite-gneiss Basement in the east, which forms the Lowveld, and, overlying this, the mainly sedimentary formations of the Transvaal Supergroup, forming the high ground west of the north-south-trending escarpment.

The reason the landscape is so strongly controlled by the underlying geology is mainly one of the passage of time. The quartzites that comprise an important part of the Transvaal Supergroup, which are significantly more resistant to erosion than the Basement granite-gneiss of the Lowveld, tend to stand high above it. It is the platform-like quartzite of the Black Reef Formation that particularly dominates the topography throughout the region, as you'll see.

The region's recent history is influenced by South Africa's first major gold rushes around Sabie and at Pilgrim's Rest in 1873, and at Kaapsehoop in 1882. Today gold mining has all but ceased at these sites and tourists abound, with the historic museum-village of Pilgrim's Rest giving vivid insight into the mining legacy of an area immortalised by the pen of Sir Percy Fitzpatrick.

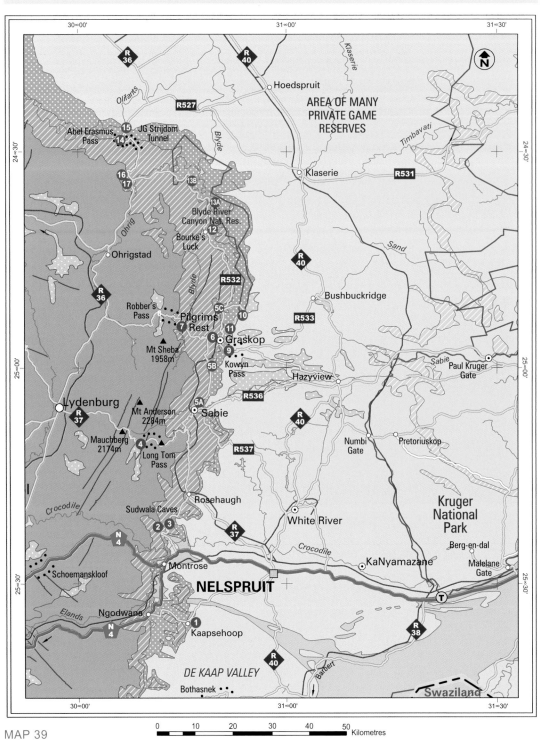

MAP 39

276 Geological Journeys

In a general treatment like this we have to confine ourselves to the most impressive sites, with others mentioned in passing only. Depending on the roads you follow, you will see more or less of these sites: from the descriptions and pictures, and with the use of the geological map, we hope you will be able to recognise and interpret other features on your own. Our roughly linear route will take us from Kaapsehoop, just south of the N4 west of Nelspruit, north to the Abel Erasmus Pass, with short branches to east and west.

Kaapsehoop Escarpment

If you are travelling east along the N4 to Nelspruit and don't have time for a full Great Escarpment tour, try the less-travelled, scenic route via Kaapsehoop **(geosite 1, map 39)**, on a 'back road' 12 km from Ngodwana and 28 km west of Nelspruit. At Kaapsehoop, gold was discovered in a small creek in 1882 and the resulting diggers' village, named 'Duiwels Kantoor', soon became the centre not only of

FIGURE 21

EAST-WEST GEOLOGICAL CROSS-SECTION
OF THE GREAT ESCARPMENT THROUGH PILGRIM'S REST

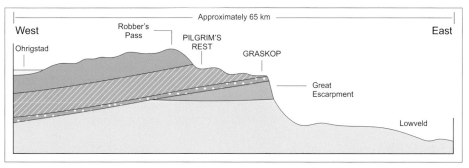

This region of panoramic scenery owes its existence to a fortuitous combination of geology and climate. At the escarpment edge hard, resistant and almost flat-lying quartzites of the Transvaal sequence overlie more easily weathered Archaean Basement granites and gneisses of the Lowveld. Millions of years of rain from moisture-laden air coming off the Indian Ocean have rapidly eroded the Basement rocks, leaving a spectacular retreating scarp. West of Pilgrim's Rest, gently west-dipping resistant quartzite beds of the Pretoria Group have acted in a similar manner, forming the elevated terrain.

River alluvium

Pretoria Group

Malmani dolomite

Black Reef Formation

Wolkberg Group

TRANSVAAL
SUPERGROUP

Basement granite-gneiss

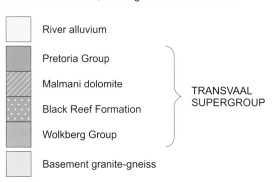

*From God's Window looking south along the edge
of the Great Escarpment, the flat-lying quartzite
formation is part of the Wolkberg Group.*

a local gold rush in and around the creek but, more notably, as a base for prospecting the fever-ridden Lowveld valleys below. Sited in the mist belt on the brink of the Great Escarpment, this might have struck outsiders as a mysterious place, with its weirdly shaped rock formations looming up in the fog. Today, we know these strangely weathered rocks as shallow-dipping quartzites of the Black Reef Formation. Small amounts of gold were mined here from the basal conglomerate of the Black Reef.

From the village, take a 15-minute walk through the labyrinthine carved sandstone landscape to the view site at the edge of the Godwan Plateau and look over the 1 000-m drop into the lush De Kaap Valley below. On a clear day you will see the Barberton Mountains and Swaziland nearly 40 km to the south and east, with the low country between underlain by the softer Kaap Valley Granite Pluton. Lying under the Black Reef quartzite is the older Godwan Formation, which, in turn, rests on Basement granite-gneiss, clearly visible on the Kaapsehoop Pass. On the Ngodwana road you will see typical outcrops of the Malmani dolomite that overlies the Black Reef.

These pillars of Black Reef quartzite gave rise to the original name of this area, 'Duiwels Kantoor'.
This area was once the scene of hectic gold prospecting.

At the Kaapsehoop escarpment, almost horizontal Black Reef Formation quartzite forms a hard, resistant layer over older Godwan Formation. Far below, to the east, lies the De Kaap Valley, underlain by easily weathered granite.

Sudwala Caves and Dinosaur Park

To get to the caves **(geosite 2, map 39)**, you need to return to the N4. Just east of Montrose and near Rivulets siding, you have crossed Basement granite and passed through an impressive road cutting in greenstone (see p. 206): at this point you should take the R359 towards Rosehaugh. Another 8 km along the Houtbosloop valley brings you to the Sudwala Caves turn-off. The caves are located high on the slopes of a mountain made of Malmani dolomite, and not far below the overlying Pretoria Group shales and quartzites. A cave tour is recommended, during which you will see enormous underground caverns, bizarre cave formations, and clear evidence of Earth's early life (see text boxes, pp. 280–1 and 283). The caves are known to extend for several kilometres into the mountain and several caverns containing spectacular cave formations have been found, but these are not open to the public. The adjoining park shows large, life-like representations of a variety of dinosaurs that may have roamed this same terrain millions of years ago.

Located within stromatolitic Malmani dolomite, the extensive Sudwala Caves system contains numerous stalactites and stalagmites. This bizarre formation is known as the 'Screaming Monster'.

The origin of caves

The Malmani dolomite (and, to a lesser extent, its Campbell Rand equivalent) is well known for its limestone caves in different parts of South Africa, including those at Sudwala, Makapan's Valley, and the Cradle of Humankind around Sterkfontein. As a shelter from storms and a safe refuge in times of flight, they have played an important role in man's history over millions of years.

But how do these caves form? Fairly close to the surface but beneath the water table, slightly acidic rainwater selectively and slowly dissolves and removes carbonate rock (limestone or dolomite) from pre-existing cracks and fractures in the rocks. As shown in the illustration, over a period of many millions of years, and probably under much higher rainfall conditions than we have today, rainwater constantly percolates through cracks, joints and fractures in the chemically reactive limestone, slowly widening the cracks. Eventually, streams that run across these formations disappear underground, to charge the natural subterranean aquifers. Slowly but surely, narrow interconnected fissures and passages form, which over time slowly join to form larger subterranean, water-filled chambers. Occasionally, natural springs may issue forth large volumes of artesian water, such as at the 'Eye of Kuruman' (see p. 259).

With climatic change and lowering of river valleys, the water table falls, emptying the upper caves of their water, and leaving them air-filled, ready for stalactites and stalagmites to start forming; rainwater continues to dissolve away the limestone, to be re-deposited as dripstone when a suitable open space is reached. Narrow shafts, or avens, may eventually find their way to the surface. At the same time, below the water table, deeper caves may be forming. Needless to say, it all takes millions of years. Cave breccias form when washed-in surface debris, plus internal collapsed material, accumulates within a cavern and becomes cemented hard by lime in groundwater. Such breccia, forming as cones, often contains fossil material of great scientific value. Ultimately the cave roof may collapse, exposing the cave to the surface as a sinkhole or doline.

Makapan's caves (see also p. 92) were formed, as illustrated, in Malmani dolomite in the rugged country northeast of Mokopane.

FIGURE 22

 Soil

 Calcified cave breccia including soil, rocks, fossilised animal and plant debris

 Cave formations (stalactites, stalagmites and flowstone)

 Original dolomite, bedded and fractured

 Dolomite below the water table

 Water-filled cavities

W/T Water table, lowering over time

 Vegetation

 Grass

STAGES OF HOW A SOLUTION CAVE IS FORMED IN DOLOMITE

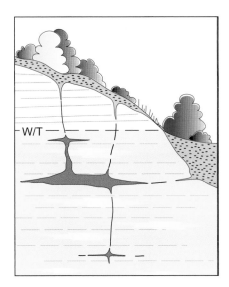

Stage 1: Small caverns begin to form by the dissolution of dolomite beneath the water table. Dissolution is focused along zones of weakness and fractures.

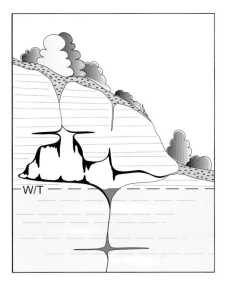

Stage 2: The water table drops as a result of deepening valleys and changing climate, and the enlarged caverns are filled with air. Calcite cave formations start to form.

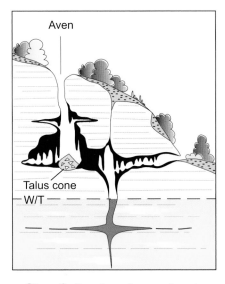

Stage 3: Cave formations continue to develop while below, ongoing dissolution may continue. Shafts reach the surface and debris is washed into the cave, forming a talus cone.

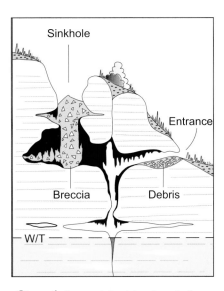

Stage 4: Accumulating talus deposits form cave breccias of different ages by percolating lime-rich water. The cave may collapse to form a sinkhole, and erosion expose cave breccia.

Sudwala Pass and its stromatolites

If you continue north on the R539 up the Sudwala Pass **(geosite 3, map 39)** towards Rosehaugh, a few kilometres after crossing the Houtbosloop, you will see excellent exposures of Malmani dolomite, including a well-banded variety, and giant domed fossil algal structures called stromatolites (see text box opposite). The large road exposure shows fresh, pale dolomite, with interbedded layers of black chert. Note the striking uniformity of the dolomite. Not to be missed are the mega-domal stromatolites, several metres across, best exposed in the road cutting at the top of the pass.

More than just interesting for the evidence they present of early Precambrian life, these stromatolitic dolomites represent a milestone in Earth's history that is as easily overlooked as it is fundamentally important. The early life forms that helped build these very dolomites also provided the Earth's first oxygen, without which the higher forms of life would not have evolved.

The upper part of Sudwala Pass is well known for its intriguing and enormous algal stromatolitic domes in the Malmani dolomite. These well-layered, elongated mega-domes are thought to reflect carbonate deposition in a deeper subtidal environment (but less than about 100 m water depth), where algal sedimentation took place under fairly calm conditions.

Dolomite – Earth's first oxygen generator

The Malmani dolomite (and its equivalent Campbell Rand dolomite in the Northern Cape) is part of the Transvaal Supergroup that was deposited in a vast inland sea on the Kaapvaal Craton. It makes up a 2 000 m-thick carbonate sequence over large parts of central South Africa. Now occurring in two well-defined structural basins, these were connected during the time of their formation 2 600 to 2 400 million years ago. Have a look at the geological map to see the modern-day distribution of the dolomite.

Dolomite is a fine-grained, calcium-magnesium carbonate rock, originally formed by the slow accumulation of microscopic grains of calcium carbonate in a warm tropical sea. This process was intimately involved with the production of layers of sticky algal growth, called algal mats, in the very shallow intertidal to subtidal zone. If you look closely at the well-etched, weathered outcrops, you will see several diagnostic clues to the organic origin of the dolomite. Notice a fine crinkly lamination that reflects the original sticky algal mats or layers that formed on the sea floor and trapped or precipitated fine carbonate material. Look, on a slightly larger scale, for small to large rounded or elongated dome-like structures, called stromatolites, that clustered in coral-like reefs in the shallow sea, and were Earth's prolific life-form at the time. These mound-like features are the fossilised remains of large masses of algal mat build-up that were shaped by tidal currents. And if you could look through a high-powered microscope, you might also see traces of minute, single-cell micro-organisms preserved in the rock. These are the remains of 2.5 billion-year-old blue-green algae, not very different from those existing today. Modern-day algal mats are rare, but are known from Shark Bay in Australia, where living stromatolites can still be found in a strongly saline, shallow sea.

But rock was not the only thing that the blue-green algae, or cyanobacteria, gave rise to. By the process of photosynthesis – active even in matter as primitive as algae – the cyanobacteria were busy converting primeval carbon dioxide into oxygen on a vast scale, and slowly releasing it into the sea. There the oxygen first combined with iron to form vast sedimentary, layered formations rich in iron; later, it was released into the atmosphere, hitherto dominated by carbon dioxide and nitrogen. Photosynthesis continued over a very long time, and oxygen continued to be 'pumped' into the atmosphere. Slowly, the protective ozone layer built up, increasingly shielding the Earth from deadly ultra-violet radiation. This paved the way for the evolution of multi-cellular organisms, and then the emergence of life from primeval oceans onto land. And the rest, as they say, is history.

This algal-laminated dolomite was formed by the slow accumulation of countless layers of minute, single-cell organisms, forming 'algal mats' on a shallow, tropical sea floor. The sticky algae trapped or precipitated fine carbonate particles to form 'crinkly' limestone layers that were later altered to dolomite.

Long Tom Pass

From Sabie, situated on a small plateau underlain by the Black Reef Formation, take the Lydenburg road to the southwest; after about 8 km you will meet the R37 from Nelspruit. Until now you have been travelling over dark, brown-weathering dolomite, but near the intersection you will clearly see the overlying quartzite and pale-weathering shales that form the base of the Pretoria Group. This sequence continues for the next 20 km, dipping gently to the west, and revealing occasional thin quartzite bands sandwiched between the predominant shales, as well as rounded boulders of intrusive diabase. The views across the Sabie Valley and beyond are magnificent, and it is certainly worth stopping to have a look. Marvel, as you admire the scenery, at the endurance of the early traders who, in 1871, pioneered this arduous route to Lydenburg from faraway Delagoa Bay (later Lourenço Marques and now Maputo). Near the top of the Long Tom Pass **(geosite 4, map 39)**, at 2 149 m, in a section called Mauchberg (after German geologist-explorer Karl Mauch), the dominant quartzite and diabase sills provide resistant cap rocks. Over the top of the pass, the road more or less follows the shallow dip slopes of the Pretoria Group down into Lydenburg.

Near the top of the Long Tom Pass, the Mauchberg provides impressive views. Here the shale-rich Pretoria Group is capped by resistant, shallowly west-dipping quartzite and lavas, making up the high ground.

Waterfalls around Sabie and Graskop

If it's waterfalls you're after, then there is no better place than in the vicinity of these towns on the R532. It shouldn't surprise you to know they are all due to some or other geological barrier. Sabie Falls (73 m high) **(geosite 5A, map 39)** in the town plunges over a ledge of flat-lying Black Reef quartzite into Sabie gorge on its way to the Lowveld. In the mountains behind Sabie, there are the scenic Horseshoe Falls, Lone Creek Falls (68 m) and Bridal Veil Falls (70 m), all worth a visit. All owe their existence to rapidly eroding streams in the Sabie valley meeting with hard quartzites at the upper contact of the Malmani dolomite and the overlying Pretoria Group. In the background, you will see 2 284 m-high Mount Anderson, highest point in the Great Escarpment region. North of Sabie, close to the R532 to Graskop, is the 56 m-high Mac-Mac Falls **(geosite 5B, map 39)**,

ABOVE LEFT: *The Sabie Falls tumble over a thick ledge of Black Reef quartzite and have eroded a spectacular gorge.* **ABOVE RIGHT:** *Resistant Black Reef quartzite forms a thick ledge over which the 56 m-high Mac-Mac Falls tumble, cutting back a deep gorge into the escarpment. When the flow is strong, twin waterfalls are formed.* **INSET:** *Close to Graskop, this very unusual rock formation shows how a small stream has eroded an underground pathway through the Malmani dolomite.*

said to have been split into two streams as a result of blasting by over-zealous prospectors. North of Graskop are the Lisbon Falls (92 m) and Berlin Falls (150 m) **(geosite 5C, map 39)**, both resulting from streams falling off platform-like Black Reef quartzites. Close to Graskop you will see a sign marked 'Natural Bridge' **(geosite 6, map 39)**. A short walk off the road reveals a small stream that has found its way through a cave-like hole in dolomite, with the 'bridge' thus formed used in bygone times to cross the stream.

Pilgrim's Rest and Robber's Pass

Early in 1873, gold was discovered in a small tributary of the Blyde River, and the area was soon the scene of the biggest gold rush yet seen in South Africa, with 1 500 diggers recovering gold from hill-slope soil and stream sediment alike. Nuggets were a regular feature of the diggings, with the prize specimen weighing 6.6 kg. By 1881, most of the claims had been worked out and the diggers had moved on, leaving the heavyweights to move in with their underground operations. When the last Pilgrim's Rest mine was closed down a year short of the centenary year – 1972 – over 100 tons of gold had been recovered. The mine village **(geosite 7, map 39)** was declared a national

ABOVE: *The almost dry Pilgrims Creek was once the scene of feverish alluvial gold mining as prospectors tried their luck, and sometimes struck it rich, in 1873. Pilgrims Rest is now a 'living museum' and home to the annual gold-panning championships.*

INSET: *Robber's Pass gets its name from a Zeederberg coach robbery that took place at the summit in 1899, with the loss of £10 000 in gold. The plaque in the picture, mounted on Timeball Hill Formation quartzite, commemorates the route taken by Sir Percy Fitzpatrick and his dog Jock.*

monument and today is preserved as a working museum. The information centre provides an excellent idea of the mining history, and a visit to the Diggings Site Museum takes you back to the heady days of alluvial mining.

The source of the alluvial gold was interconnected, concordant, flat-lying quartz-carbonate-sulphide 'reefs' – actually veins – and discordant or cross-cutting veins of the same mineral composition close to the top of the Malmani dolomite. These gold-bearing veins are of hydrothermal origin and the hot, mineral-rich fluids are thought to have been associated with the Bushveld Complex. A scenic drive up Robber's Pass **(geosite 8, map 39)** provides a good look at the overlying Pretoria Group shales and quartzites, all dipping shallowly to the west.

Kowyn Pass and Panorama Falls

From Graskop, also located on a plateau of Black Reef quartzite, the R533 to Hazyview and Bushbuck Ridge takes you down the Escarpment via the scenically magnificent Kowyn Pass. Just east of Graskop is the spectacular Panorama Gorge, where at Panorama (or Graskop) Falls **(geosite 9, map 39)** a stream plunges off a Black Reef quartzite ledge. Within 5 km east of Graskop, you are on granite-gneiss of the Nelspruit Suite, having passed down through the resistant quartzite and the underlying sediments of the Wolkberg Group, deposited in an early or proto-basin of the Transvaal sequence, and including layers of conglomerate (see Blyde River Canyon, p. 288).

God's Window and The Pinnacle

You should plan to visit God's Window **(geosite 10, map 39)**, 9 km north of Graskop, and reached via a short turn-off from the R532. From the lip of the escarpment, the views east and south across the Lowveld are breathtaking, showing an almost sheer drop of 750 m. Here the almost horizontal capping formation, also consisting of weathered and eroded quartzite, is the upper part of the Wolkberg Group, which is slightly older than the Black Reef. Closer to Graskop, in nearby Driekop Gorge, The Pinnacle **(geosite 11, map 39)** provides an unusual geological phenomenon – an isolated 30 m-high quartzite tower severed from the escarpment edge by erosion of the rocks that linked them. Eons ago, this rock column was part of the rocky plateau.

ABOVE: *From 'God's Window', looking south along the escarpment edge, the flat-lying quartzite formation is upper Wolkberg Group underlying the Black Reef Formation, but here indistinguishable from it.*
BELOW: *Bourke's Luck Potholes in the Treur River were formed by the swirling, erosive action of water and pebbles acting on Black Reef quartzite. Rich alluvial gold is said to have been recovered from these potholes by gold prospector Tom Bourke.*

Bourke's Luck Potholes

About 35 km north of Graskop, on the R532, lies the village of Bourke's Luck. The recreational area set aside along the Treur River is part of the Blyderivierspoort Nature Reserve, and the 'potholes' **(geosite 12, map 39)** mark the start of the Blyde River Canyon. The potholes were formed by swirling water-erosion, over countless thousands of years, of the Black Reef quartzite that makes the river bedrock. First, river-borne pebbles and boulders carve out small depressions, which soon entrap the abrading river debris. The hollows grow by constant abrasion and, over time, deepen to cylindrical potholes up to several metres deep. The reason this is not a more common sight is because of the delicate equilibrium that needs to be maintained between river current, the shaping pebbles and the bedrock itself, in order to keep the rock clasts in place for long enough to effect their entrapment. Gold prospector Tom Bourke is rumoured to have found considerable gold in the potholes.

In this three-dimensional view across the Blyde River Canyon, the background massif is capped by a continuous layer of Black Reef quartzite, which overlies a thick, brownish sequence of Wolkberg quartzites and shales.

Blyde River Canyon

You can view this 25 km-long canyon – certainly one of the largest on Earth – from either the top or the bottom. At the top, Black Reef quartzite forms the plateau, below which you see the quartzites and shales of the slightly older Wolkberg Group, with granite-gneiss at the base. The Wolkberg Group marks the start of sedimentation in the northeastern part of the developing Transvaal proto-basin around 2 600 million years ago. For a bottom-up perspective of the canyon, drive around to the eastern side of the mountain range, via the JG Strijdom Tunnel and Klaserie, and visit the Blyderivierspoort Dam.

For views from the top, travel further north from Bourke's Luck and take the well-marked turn-offs to the view sites. The first lookout provides awe-inspiring views of the entire rock succession, a life-size geological cross-section **(geosite 13A, map 39)**. You will be standing on bare outcrops of Black Reef quartzite, looking east across the deeply incised canyon, with the Blyde River at the bottom, and the plateau surface across the gorge of the same resistant Black Reef quartzite. The mountain you can see to the southeast still has a thin residual capping of the Malmani dolomite that once covered the entire area. Brightly coloured cliffs, hundreds of metres high, are formed of resistant Wolkberg quartzites. The eroded gap forming a valley directly to the east, cutting through the almost horizontal sedimentary formations, is underlain by basement granite-gneiss. The second lookout is at the well-known Three Rondawels view site, overlooking the Blyderivierspoort Dam, nearly 800 m below, and shows similar geology **(geosite 13B, map 39)**. The Rondawels are crowned by comparatively soft Wolkberg shale, and to the east is the flat-topped mountain called Marepe, capped by Black Reef quartzite.

Abel Erasmus Pass and the Wolkberg

Another scenic drive on the R532 takes you via the alluvium-filled Ohrigstad River valley, and then north on the R36 over the Abel Erasmus Pass. As you cross the whole thickness of Malmani dolomite sequence, you'll see various forms of laminated and stromatolitic dolomite, dipping gently to the southwest. Safe places to stop for a good look at outcrops are regrettably few, but look out for the chocolate-brown soils and the typical olifantsklip weathering. To the north, the impressive Wolkberg range tracks your progress, the shallow dip slopes being made of Black Reef quartzite. To the west, the hills are of the shale-rich Pretoria Group.

Soon you are in a shaded gorge, cutting your way down through thick Black Reef quartzite and the underlying Wolkberg shales and quartzites. Around you are rock cliffs and buttresses of southwest-dipping strata, coloured in places by brilliant yellow lichen. The road skirts past an enormous outcrop of calcareous tufa (one of several in the area), known as the Devil's Pulpit, a cavernous secondary carbonate deposit formed at what was once a large waterfall. Carbonate minerals, dissolved out of the dolomites further south, were carried here by the river and redeposited at the waterfall **(geosite 14, map 39)**.

The JG Strijdom Tunnel brings you to another world, the tropical Lowveld. In front of you is the major Olifants River, which, in getting here, has drained a large part of the eastern Highveld before emerging through the escarpment. Disappearing away to the northwest is the Wolkberg range **(geosite 15, map 39)**, made of the formations through which you have just passed. If you continue on eastwards towards Klaserie, the same geological formations continue to the south – the impressive ramparts of the Great Escarpment, previously seen from the other side, above the Blyde River Canyon. The highest peak, Mariepskop (1 944 m), is made of Wolkberg formations.

Echo Caves and the Museum of Man

At the T-junction of the R532 from the Blyde River Canyon view sites and the R36, turn south towards Ohrigstad, away from the Abel Erasmus Pass. A kilometre south of the junction is a turn-off west to Echo Caves, some 4 km up a branch of the Molapong valley, and located within the Malmani dolomite. On privately owned land, they are open for hour-long public tours, with spectacular cave formations to be seen **(geosite 16, map 39)**. In the distant past, tribes used the caves as a refuge; and tools, pottery and human bones have been recovered from the site. Closer to the R36 the Museum of Man makes an interesting educational stop **(geosite 17, map 39)**. Here, in the dolomitic hillside, a large rock overhang has been excavated by archaeologists to reveal evidence of Middle and Late Stone Age cultures, as well as more recent Voortrekker habitation.

Near the Echo Caves, this cave-like overhang in Malmani dolomite provides the location for a small cultural and archaeological museum, the Museum of Man.

17 KwaZulu-Natal Drakensberg

GEOLOGICAL OVERVIEW

Peaking at nearly 3 500 m above sea level, and giddily precipitous, the Drakensberg-Maluti range is one of the finest examples on the planet of erosional mountains. It is the last remnant of the vast basalt plain that covered the centre of Gondwana, an ancient relic, shrinking inexorably as rivers eat into it on all sides. The breathtaking grandeur of the range has earned the 200 km-long uKhahlamba-Drakensberg Park World Heritage Site status (uKhahlamba is a Zulu word meaning 'Barrier of Spears').

The high ground consists of basaltic lava, piled over 1 500 m thick, which erupted over the desert sands of the Clarens Formation and heralded the break-up of the Gondwana supercontinent (see text box, p. 294). It is this basalt, called the Drakensberg Formation, that forms the precipitous cliffs and rugged peaks known as the 'High Berg', while the Clarens sandstone forms lesser heights and smaller plateaus known as the 'Little Berg'.

RIGHT: *The 'Amphitheatre' in the Royal Natal National Park is probably the best known view of the Drakensberg. The 'High Berg' is made of basalt lavas of the Drakensberg Formation, while the lower 'Little Berg' is composed mainly of Clarens Formation sandstone. In the foreground is the boulder-filled Thukela River.*

INSET: *A cross-section of the front lobe or 'nose' of a now-solidified basalt lava flow. Notice the development of filled-in stream cavities (amygdales) on the margins, with elongated pipe amygdales at the base, bending in the direction of flow, and round amygdales near the upper surface.*

Before the break-up of Gondwana, the Lesotho mountain plateau at the top of the Drakensberg was part of a peneplain of continental dimensions, standing much lower than it is now. After the eruption of the Drakensberg lavas around 180 million years ago, deep forces stirred within the Earth; the supercontinent became uplifted, and a major rift valley system developed along what is now the east coast of South Africa. Over eons, the rifts widened, new oceans formed, new coastlines and, behind them, new continents. Uplift of the southern African continent, particularly the eastern portion, continued and new east-draining rivers eroded the wet coastal highlands. A new major cycle of erosion was at hand, the consequence being that the high ground was cut back to form the ever-retreating Great Escarpment, creating the present-day coastal plain as it did so. This escarpment has withdrawn over 150 km from the present coastline, and the rate of erosion of the Drakensberg is said to average 1.5 m per 1 000 years or 1.5 mm per year.

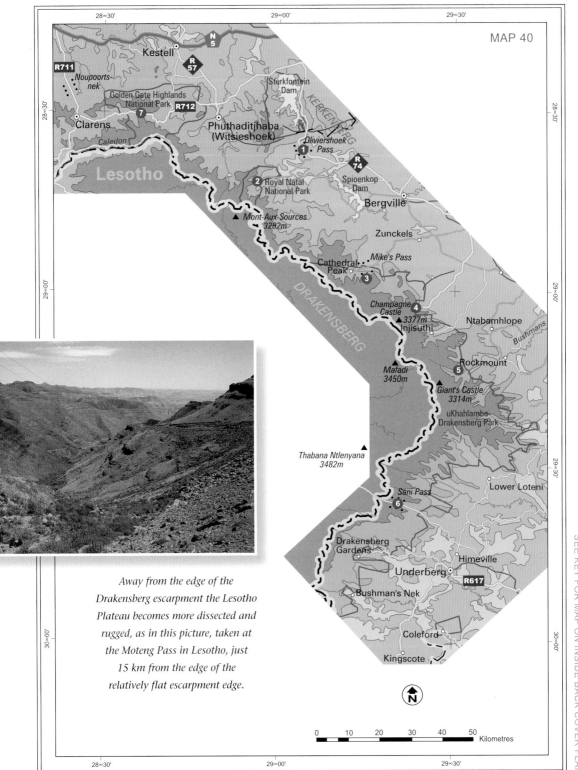

MAP 40

*Away from the edge of the
Drakensberg escarpment the Lesotho
Plateau becomes more dissected and
rugged, as in this picture, taken at
the Moteng Pass in Lesotho, just
15 km from the edge of the
relatively flat escarpment edge.*

0 10 20 30 40 50
Kilometres

FIGURE 23

ROCK FORMATIONS SEEN IN THE DRAKENSBERG AND ITS FOOTHILLS

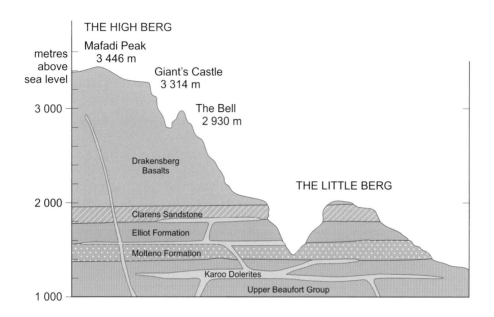

DRAKENSBERG BASALTS
Thin basalt flows built up a lava pile around 2 000 m thick. Abundant whitish amygdales represent small steam cavities trapped in the cooling lava. The Drakensberg is a remnant of the once vast lava field that covered much of southern Africa.

CLARENS SANDSTONE FORMATION
Forms characteristic cliffs made of yellowish to pinkish fine-grained sandstone and siltstone, about 100 m thick. This sandstone was deposited by wind under desert-like conditions, prior to the eruption of the lavas. Notable for many cave-like overhangs.

ELLIOT FORMATION
Around 200 m thick, it consists mainly of multi-coloured mudstones and lesser sand-stones, deposited on an arid to semi-arid flood plain. It has produced dinosaur fossils, the earliest known tortoise in Gondwana, and small, early mammals.

MOLTENO FORMATION
Consists of alternating sandstone and shale beds, and is rich in plant and insect fossils, reflecting a long period of lush riverine and flood plain vegetation. Dinosaur fossil trackways have been found.

UPPER BEAUFORT GROUP
Called the Tarkastad Formation, these beds comprise alternating fine- to medium-grained sandstones, and maroon, green and bluish mudstones. Deposited after the major 250-million-year extinction, they contain fossils of mammal-like reptiles.

KAROO DOLERITES
Widespread sills and dikes are identical in composition to the Drakensberg lavas. Best developed in the Beaufort Group, they can be traced upwards into the lavas, and provided the 'plumbing' system that fed the basalt flows far above.

The emplacement and origin of the Karoo Igneous Rocks

The thick pile of Drakensberg lava is only a small remnant of the eruption of 'flood' basalt on a continental scale, which extended as far as western Zambia, southern Mozambique and eastern Namibia. The lavas form part of what geologists call the Karoo Igneous Province; the other, deeper part, the widespread Karoo dolerite sills and dykes, are chemically identical to the basalts.

It is estimated that a volume of up to 2 000 000 cubic km of lava was erupted within 1 million years, about 183 million years ago. This represents an area of 1 000 km by 1 000 km, covered by lava 2 000 m thick. These volcanics occupy a critical niche in our geological history, closing a 130 million-year period of practically continuous Karoo sedimentation, and foreshadowing the break-up of Gondwana. Closely related volcanic rocks are found in South America, Antarctica and Tasmania, eloquent confirmation of the hypothesis of Continental Drift.

The Drakensberg and the adjacent Lesotho plateau now preserve a 1 800 m-thick sequence of superimposed flows of basalt of essentially similar composition, lying directly above the Clarens sandstone. Individual flows, extruded as hot, very fluid magma called pahoehoe (or 'ropey' lava), welled upwards through long fissures and flowed out over the surface; the complex lava flows, or layers, range from less than one metre to tens of metres in thickness. The ubiquitous Karoo dolerite dykes are considered to represent the feeder channels, although finding a direct link between a dyke and a flow is exceptional. It is not difficult, though, to imagine the sills, sheets and dykes, so common in the surrounding lower country, as a complex and interconnected plumbing system to lava-erupting fissures.

Careful observation of an exposed lava face will more than likely reveal several basalt flows, defined by more or less horizontal zones of white to greenish amygdales. These are original steam bubbles within the lava, called vesicles, that were later filled by silica, calcite and zeolite minerals. They occur in two forms: elongated pipe amygdales at the base of the flow, often bent in the direction of flow; and rounded amygdales at the top. That there was relatively little time between lava flows is shown by the lack of weathering or erosion.

The Drakensberg Formation is made up of many superimposed individual flows of basaltic lava that erupted through fissures in the Earth's crust as hot, very fluid magma called pahoehoe. *The picture clearly shows the still well-preserved, flow-like nature of the lava, seen here on Moteng Pass, Lesotho.*

The emplacement of the Drakensberg lavas over a short period must have had a major impact on Earth's climate at the time, with the vast quantities of gases emitted into the atmosphere resulting in global die-back of vegetation and starvation for millions of species.

Geology of the route

Oliviershoek Pass

This mountain pass (1 740 m) **(geosite 1, map 40)** provides an attractive alternative route from the Free State into KwaZulu-Natal, via the R74 from Harrismith, and passes the Sterkfontein Dam. Before descending the pass you will see major outliers of Clarens sandstone on both sides of the R74: historic Kerkenberg to the northeast, and Babangibone (2 328 m) and Mount Lebanon to the southwest. It's worth visiting the site at the base of Kerkenberg, where Voortrekker leader Piet Retief and his party made camp before some of them entered Natal in 1837 down nearby Retief's Pass, on their ultimately ill-fated journey. Proceeding down the pass, you will see flat-lying mudstones and sandstones of the Molteno and Elliot Formations, informally known as the 'Stormberg' Group, and the upper Beaufort Group.

At the top of Oliviershoek Pass in the Free State, and beyond Driekloof Dam, look out for this flat-topped mountain, Mount Lebanon, made of Clarens Sandstone.

There are a number of extensive Karoo dolerite sills in the Drakensberg foothills, shown here, near Zwelisha, by dark bouldery outcrops and the dark red soil that they produce.

Royal Natal National Park

At the base of Oliviershoek Pass, a road turns off to the 8 000 hectare Royal Natal Park (named after the British Royal visit in 1947), some 15 km away. In front of you is one of the Drakensberg's best-known vistas, a magnificent range known as 'The Amphitheatre' **(geosite 2, map 40)**. Famous peaks such as Sentinel, Beacon Buttress, Devil's Tooth and Eastern Buttress look down on the Thukela (formerly Tugela) River valley, while on the high plateau lies Mont-aux-Sources at 3 282 m. The Thukela

ABOVE: *Cannibal Cave, located close to the Royal Natal National Park within the Clarens Sandstone, is one of many impressive cave-like overhangs in the Drakensberg. Water cascading off the sandstone above has weakened the rock formations below to form a natural arch-like structure.*
INSET: *In Cannibal Cave the extensive overhang of massive, pale yellowish Clarens Sandstone rests at a very slight angle on faintly layered, light brown mudstone of the underlying Elliot Formation.*

River has its source here, and then cascades 850 m down the shear basalt face into Thukela Gorge, one of the highest waterfalls in the world. Hikes up the valley to reach the Clarens sandstone caves are well worthwhile. As usual, the dark red soil indicates the presence of Karoo dolerite sills and sheets. Needless to say, the best place to see the Drakensberg lavas – and the mountain splendour – is from the top, and a climb to the basalt plateau is recommended. For those with less time this can be done by road via Phuthaditjhaba (formerly Witsieshoek) in eastern Free State, and ultimately by vertical chain ladder.

Cathedral Peak

Continue on the R74 to Bergville, passing the Woodstock Dam on the Thukela River. Water is pumped from this dam up to the Sterkfontein Dam near Oliviershoek Pass, from where it supplies, in part, the needs of thirsty Gauteng, as well as generating hydroelectric power. The peaks around here – the Inner and Outer Horn, and Cathedral and its Bell – are all about 3 000 m **(geosite 3, map 40)**. Near the Cathedral Peak Hotel, you will see shales and sandstones of the Molteno and Elliot Formations, the former rich in plant fossils, and the latter well known for its dinosaur fossils. For the more adventurous, a 4x4 drive up the Little Berg via Mike's Pass at 1 830 m will bring you right into the basalt lavas.

Champagne Valley and Injisuthi Camp

With Champagne Castle (3 377 m), Cathkin Peak (3 149 m) and rugged Sterkhorn and Dragon's Back ridge in the background, this is a delightful and well-conserved valley leading off the R74 from Winterton. The road to Monk's Cowl camp site gets you as near to the Berg as possible and is the gateway to several wilderness hiking trails **(geosite 4, map 40)**. The nearby Injisuthi area offers breathtaking hikes in pristine wilderness and some San rock art, notably the famous Battle Cave scenes. Injisuthi and Mafadi peaks on the Lesotho border, at 3 410 m and 3 446 m respectively, are now recognised as the highest points in South Africa.

Giant's Castle

This famous area, backed by Giant's Castle peak at 3 314 m, is reached from the N3 near Estcourt. It is a well-known self-catering resort, famous for its rock art attractions. The impressive open-air Bushman Cave Museum at the Main Caves depicts the daily life of the San people and their rock art **(geosite 5, map 40)**. Game is plentiful in the reserve, particularly the once-endangered eland, an animal of special importance to the San Bushmen.

Sani Pass

The southern Drakensberg is reached via the towns of Underberg and Himeville on the R612 from Ixopo, or on the R617 from Howick, and several resorts are to be found in this grand but less-travelled region. The exciting Sani Pass provides the only road access into Lesotho from KwaZulu-Natal, via a deeply incised valley that reveals the

TOP: *In the distance, peaks of the High Berg can be seen – Cathedral Peak, The Bell and the Inner and Outer Horns – all made of dark Drakensberg lavas; in the middle distance, yellowish Clarens sandstone forms the Little Berg.* CENTRE: *At Giant's Castle an impressive reconstruction at the Bushmen Cave Museum at Main Caves depicts the daily life of the San hunter-gatherer people.* ABOVE: *Across the provincial border, the colourful cliffs of the Clarens Formation, made of fine-grained sandstone, once wind-blown desert sand, are characteristic of the eastern Free State landscape. This shows Mushroom Rock in the Golden Gate National Park.*

full Drakensberg geological sequence, from the upper Beaufort shales at the base of the pass to the lavas at the top. The pass, a challenging 12 km and the only road to cross the High Berg, is steep and unsurfaced, with numerous hairpin bends that take you to a height of 2 865 m (**geosite 6, map 40**). Once the jealously guarded preserve of 4x4s, it is now accessible to any reasonably robust vehicle, though to go beyond the crest of the escarpment and enter Lesotho, you will need a passport. Close by is Hodgson's Peak that reaches 3 256 m, while just over 10 km north of the top of Sani Pass in Lesotho is Thabana Ntlenyana, at 3 482 m, the highest peak in southern Africa. The nearby Bushman's Nek Pass is open to pedestrians only.

The world's greatest rock art collection

South Africa's original people, the San (or Bushmen), inhabited this remote mountain stronghold for thousands of years, enjoying a traditional Stone-Age hunter-gatherer lifestyle. In the early 1800s, as both African tribes and colonial settlers moved into the San's hunting grounds and depleted the game, these people became the hunted, and by the late 1800s they had practically disappeared from the Drakensberg. They left a priceless but fragile legacy – the Drakensberg has the world's richest collection of Stone-Age rock art, and this was one of the prime reasons for proclaiming it a World Heritage Site. There are some 600 rock-art sites, collectively showing over 35 000 individual paintings on the walls of the caves and overhangs where they lived, depicting the traditional hunting life and religious ceremonies of the San. These are invariably located within the Clarens, or Cave, sandstone. The Game Pass Shelter in the Kamberg Nature Reserve, and the Main Cave at the

Giant's Castle Reserve are both well known for their spectacular paintings and are definitely worth a visit. Should you wish to travel to one of the more remote sites, local guides are available, and any of the hotels or parks offices can put you in touch with them.

The caves and overhangs of the Drakensberg provide the world's greatest collection of San rock art. This picture of the mystical eland is from the Kamberg Nature Reserve.

Golden Gate Highlands National Park (in the Free State)

To get to the Golden Gate Park in the Free State, take the R712 off the N5, either via Clarens or Phuthaditjhaba (formerly Witsieshoek), or the 'Maluti Route' from Ficksburg. Covering 12 000 hectares and set in the rolling and rugged hills of the Maluti Mountains, this highland park is a westward extension of the KwaZulu-Natal Drakensberg, known here by its local name, 'Maluti'. In the village of Clarens you find yourself surrounded by the colourful sandstone bluffs so typical of the eastern Free State landscape. This very prominent fine-grained sandstone formation, previously known as Cave Sandstone because of its numerous cave-like overhangs, is now called the Clarens Formation. From Clarens, the scenic road into Golden Gate (**geosite 7, map 40**) follows the course of the meandering Little Caledon River, which has its source on the high ground of the park.

The geological formations within the park are of the upper part of the Karoo Supergroup, and consist mainly of flat-lying sandstones and subsidiary siltstones and mudstones. The spectacular cliffs of cream-, yellow- and red-weathering Clarens sandstone make this the defining formation, and were deposited around 200 million years ago. The characteristic caves and overhangs have developed by selective weathering of softer strata, accelerated by regular winter freezing. Overlying the thick sandstone are dark basaltic lavas of the Drakensberg Group, which make up the highest peaks. The sandstone formations are cut by Karoo dolerite dykes and sills, which have in places baked and hardened the sandstone. A good example of this is where the often-photographed Brandwag buttress is 'backed' by a thick dolerite dyke.

The changing environment of sedimentary deposition and the evolution of animal and plant life make a fascinating story, a palaeontologist's delight. Deep below the Clarens sandstone, sediment of the Molteno Formation was deposited on tropical, well-vegetated, braided river flood plains and wetlands, as revealed by an enormous wealth of plant fossils. Over these and directly underlying the Clarens sandstone, red mudstones and sandstones of the Elliot Formation reflect drier conditions, with the earliest dinosaur fossils making their appearance. Fossils of small primitive mammals that sought refuge from the dragon-like predators in the undergrowth have been found. Eventually, most prey and predators were driven to more hospitable climes in Gondwana as the climate became increasingly arid and a vast desert of shifting sands formed. The Clarens sandstone speaks eloquently of this desert environment. Look closely at these beds: the kind of cross-bedding you see is found only in wind-blown sand dunes. It is as though the plains were being cleared of life in preparation for the devastating flood basalts soon to come.

The Brandwag buttress at Golden Gate, made of Clarens sandstone, is at the left of the photo. Centre and to the right of the Brandwag is a dark brown, dyke-like feature composed of Karoo dolerite. Heat from the intrusion of the dyke led to the hardening of the adjacent sandstone, resulting in its partial preservation. The high ground is of Drakensberg lavas.

18 The Little Karoo

GEOLOGICAL OVERVIEW

The Little Karoo, centred on Oudtshoorn, offers unquestionably unique scenery, thanks to its geology. To the north and south of the valley system it is hard quartzitic sandstone of the Table Mountain Group that makes the towering ridges of the Swartberg and the Outeniquas; between them, softer rocks of Precambrian formations and much younger late Jurassic formations have been weathered away to form broad valley floors. Formations both somewhat older and far younger than the rocks of the enveloping Cape Supergroup mountains are juxtaposed tightly against each other. It's an unusual geological sandwich: Table Mountain quartzite is the bread, with the filling made up of sediments of the Kango and Kansa Groups, which are both somewhat older, and the very much younger Uitenhage Group, including, most conspicuously, the Enon Formation.

This is because one of the most extensive fault systems in the country, running from 100 km west of Port Elizabeth all the way to Tulbagh, has some of its most extreme expression in these parts. This fault system is extensive, and it has shown all too dramatically that it is still active, not only by the movement beneath Ceres and Tulbagh in 1969 (see p. 20), but also in other ways along its length in recent geological times.

Both the faulting and the spectacular folding around Oudtshoorn were brought about by forces deep below the surface, causing dramatic compression of the crust, with the subterranean movement directed from the south. The horizontally deposited sediments of the Cape Supergroup and their basement became folded, pushed up along east-west elongate axes and dragged down along the adjacent belts. Folding could only accommodate the strain up to a point, then rupturing began. The whole of the southern mass became dislodged and thrust over the northern block in a series of steep faults and thrust faults, which are nearly horizontal.

Aeons later, the compressional regime long since forgotten, other forces were at work deep in the mantle below the mountains as Gondwana started its dismemberment. The faults of earlier times, remaining as zones of weakness, were rejuvenated by new forces, this time tensional, and steep-sided rift valleys were formed. Along the mountain slopes, vast amounts of sediment were washed by torrential storms into new basins: the Enon conglomerate and associated sediments were thus formed.

Viewed from the south, the Swartberg Pass road can be seen snaking up the highest slopes, shaped from resistant quartzites of the Table Mountain Group. In the foreground, the conspicuously planed darker slopes are of the underlying Kango Group.

Geology of the route

For purposes of route planning as you explore the passes, we are assuming that you arrive in Oudtshoorn on the N12, either via Beaufort West or via George. (See also ch. 14, Beaufort West to George, pp. 246–251.) We suggest you follow – as described below – a circular route over the Swartberg Pass to Prince Albert, and back to Oudtshoorn via Meiringspoort. Afterwards, and assuming you are heading for either the Cape Peninsula or Gauteng when you leave, we suggest you travel via Calitzdorp and the Seweweekspoort to join the N1 at Laingsburg.

In and around Oudtshoorn

If you find the town of Oudtshoorn charming, it's a fair bet that one of the reasons is the old stone buildings. The ostrich boom that made the town famous started in 1906 and, though Queen Victoria had died five years earlier, the gracious architecture her reign had inspired was to outlive her, as is evident in old Oudtshoorn. But it's not only the old architecture that will have attracted your attention; it is also the sandstone of which the houses, churches and museums are built. At the northern end of town, and visible from the road to the caves, are shallow quarries, mostly overgrown with grass and scrub now, where substantial quantities of material have been excavated. It is sandstone from the Kirkwood Formation, formed at the same time as – or slightly later than – the Enon conglomerate. You can see this sandstone in some of the road embankments on the northern side of town, cross-bedded in part and interbedded with mudstone and beds of pebbles.

Whichever way you proceed from Oudtshoorn, you will see bare slopes of red Enon conglomerate not far from the town. These should remind you that one of the main fault-bounded basins, formed when the break-up of Gondwana was still in its infancy, has left us the Little Karoo. The redness of the slopes is due to iron oxide minerals having been fed into the system as sediments were being

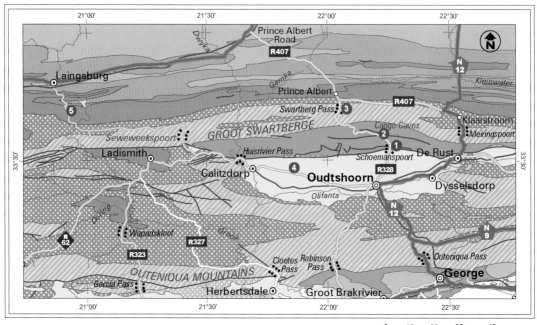

MAP 41   SEE KEY FOR MAP ON INSIDE BACK COVER FLAP

0   10   20   30   40   Kilometres

deposited. And, although only relatively small amounts of the oxide were involved, it takes very little iron to give a lot of colour. Being heavy, the grains of iron oxides, magnetite and/or haematite, which on oxidation would give rise to the pigmenting colour, would have been dumped with the coarser material, leaving the sandy material free of it, which is why the Kirkwood sand, deposited further from the source than the conglomerate, has none of the colour.

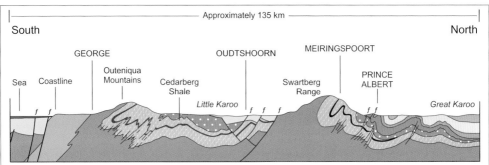

NORTH-SOUTH GEOLOGICAL SECTION THROUGH THE SOUTHERN CAPE FOLD BELT

(Note: The vertical scale is exaggerated for greater clarity)

There is a wealth of geology in this simplified profile, which provides a vivid illustration of how geology shapes our landscape. It reaches from the Karoo in the north just onto the edge of the complex of offshore basins that formed during the break-up of Gondwana, in the south. In the centre it crosses the arch of metamorphosed sediments that formed the floor of the Cape Fold Mountains and the Enon sediments around Oudtshoorn. After descending the Outeniqua range behind George, we see Basement sediments again, here intruded by granite. Offshore, though we don't see them, oil drilling has intersected more Cretaceous sediments.

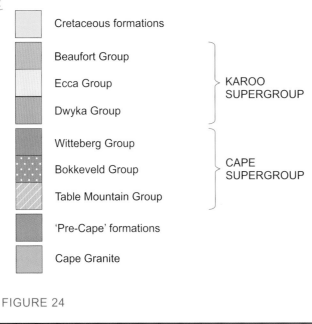

Cretaceous formations

Beaufort Group ⎫
Ecca Group   ⎬ KAROO SUPERGROUP
Dwyka Group   ⎭

Witteberg Group   ⎫
Bokkeveld Group   ⎬ CAPE SUPERGROUP
Table Mountain Group ⎭

'Pre-Cape' formations

Cape Granite

FIGURE 24

The contrast in shape between the older, prehardened clasts and the younger clasts, still quite malleable at the time of folding, and reshaped during it, provides vital clues for geologists assembling the bigger picture.

The Swartberg Pass and Cango Caves

The Swartberg Pass has been compared to the more famous Khyber Pass. Though not its equal in fame, perhaps for scenic splendour it almost rivals its Himalayan counterpart; for geology we would dare to suggest it outstrips it.

Heading north from Oudtshoorn on the R328 towards the Swartberg Pass, you go through Schoemanspoort, which gives you the best possible cross-section of Precambrian rocks of the Kango and Kansa Groups in the Little Karoo. They are marine sediments, including the limestones in which the Cango Caves are found, greywackes or turbidites, and thick conglomerates of the slightly younger Kansa Group – and about as different from the Enon conglomerates as you could imagine. They are well lithified and clearly old; they are grey and the bedding is almost vertical, though it is difficult to pick out; the cobbles and pebbles are separated from each other by a great deal of much finer material; and some of the pebbles have been stretched out during the folding, so that you have to look hard to believe they were once pebbles.

The best place to see this cross-section is about 18 km north of the Caves Motel towards the end of the poort **(geosite 1, map 41)**. The place is easy to find: stop where you see a thick and very obvious quartz vein in the cutting on the right-hand side of the road. This snow-white vein dips to the north at a shallow angle and there's nothing like it between Oudtshoorn and the caves. Retrace your steps a short distance back from the vein and you will get a good look at the conglomerate. See how some of the clasts are equidimensional, that is, not elongated, while others have been pulled out into the cleavage direction until they look like pencils. The explanation is this: the latter clasts

have been identified as coming from a formation not very much older than the conglomerates themselves, and it's apparent that they were still somewhat malleable when the deformation occurred. The much older clasts had been carried in by rivers from more distant sources and, having been lithified for many millions of years, could not be deformed.

North of Schoemanspoort, the Cango Caves, of course, are a supremely geological experience **(geosite 2, map 41)**. In the information sector at the mouth of the caves, there is a display showing every conceivable aspect of the geology and more recent prehistory of the caves. The whole story is vividly and clearly told, with a wealth of authentic illustrative material set out. A film is shown periodically of the caves in the complex that are not open to the public, and it's certainly worth seeing. The multicoloured lighting and music that made a visit to the caves a decade ago a jarringly unnatural experience are gone, and you can now enjoy one of the foremost natural wonders of South Africa with a minimum of contrivance. (To read about the origin of caves, see pp. 280–281.)

After viewing the caves, head on up the pass. On the way, along the winding gravel road to the top, the views of the valley to the south are breathtaking, but the spectacular geology is on

Cango Caves

Apart from providing a world-class tourist attraction, the Cango Caves' deepest recesses comprise a laboratory of inestimable value. Deep in the caves, more than 1 km from the mouth, and inaccessible to all but specially authorised scientists, the temperature is so stable that whether the peaks of the Swartberg are snow-clad or the ostriches drooping in the searing heat, the cave maintains a steady 17.5° C. But, as the average annual temperature outside changes, so the temperature within the cave slowly adjusts. Stalagmites in the cave faithfully preserve a detailed and continuous record of temperatures in South Africa over the last 30 000 years, pointing also to past climates and to palaeoenvironment and sea level changes. Study of a particular stalagmite has revealed that at the Last Glacial Maximum, 15 000 to 18 000 years ago, the mean annual cave temperature – and so the average annual termperature outside – was 5–7°C lower than today. It has shown, too, that temperature today varies less from year to year than it did 5 000 or 25 000 years ago, and that the seasonal change – from summer to winter – was more extreme.

A fine example of a cross-bedded unit in Table Mountain sandstone. This photograph was taken near the Teeberg viewpoint, not far from the crest of the pass, on the northern side.

the north side of the crest. The folding of the Cape Supergroup sediments that you're about to see happened in four distinct phases. The first started soon after the glacial Dwyka tillite – the first Karoo sediment – was deposited, and the fourth and last ended during middle Beaufort times, 48 million years later. As mentioned in the introductory section, the tectonism was in response to compression from the south. Throughout the folding process, there was much thrusting, in which large slices of rock were dislocated – an important part of the tectonism. The Cedarberg shale, sandwiched between layers of quartzites, because of its easily plasticised nature compared to the hard, brittle quartzites above and below it, offered an important plane of dislocation, in other words, sliding, with quite different styles of movement above and below it.

Because of the movement directed from south to north, most of the beds and fold structures dip to the south. In the deeply dissected northern slopes of the Swartberg you will see ample evidence of this predominantly southerly dip in the valley system that the road follows down towards the Great Karoo.

About 1.5 km after you've started your descent down the northern slope of the range, you'll see the first appearance of the Cedarberg shale. A stop at the Teeberg picnic site is worthwhile, to follow the outcrop of the shale band to the east, and generally to admire some magnificent scenery **(geosite 3, map 41)**. And as you head down, your eye will be caught by the beautiful folding to the west of the road. Although it's not as obvious as that you saw looking east from Teeberg, it occurs in the quartzites directly above the Cedarberg shale, but not in those higher up; these quartzites have tended to move en masse over the obviously deformed lower quartzites, and the shale, which although it has acted as the plane of dislocation, has accommodated the strain internally.

Microscopic examination of the shale here would show it to be unrecognisable from the undeformed rock. Being softer than the rocks above and below it, it offered Thomas Bain – who, following in the footsteps of his illustrious geologist and road-builder father Andrew Geddes Bain, built his magnum opus between 1883 and 1886 – a useful zone to cut into to get down the northern slope. The road follows the Cedarberg shale for several kilometres in the middle stage of its descent, with a small borrow-pit in the shale just north of the 'Blikstasie' (Tronk) signboard. As you reach the poort that leads out of the pass, at Tweede Waterval, you will see a beautiful north-opening syncline, with an axial plane that dips shallowly to the south. And by the time you can see the end of the tight poort ahead of you, the 700 m-high vertical beds of quartzite are an awe-inspiring sight you'll want to stop and look at. One kilometre north of this, you pass the vertical contact between the top of the Table Mountain Group and the base of the predominantly shaly Bokkeveld Group.

Then you go through a comparatively low range – the Oukloof Mountains – of intensely deformed Witteberg sediments, which are mainly quartzites, with some finer-grained sediments included. These, too, are almost vertical in a gross sense, and you are soon through them. Coming into picturesque Prince Albert, note the Dwyka tillite in the low cutting to the left of the road just after the cemetery. It's quite weathered for the most part and does not have the conspicuous big clasts that are generally so characteristic of this formation. It's noteworthy, though, because seeing it tells you that in the short distance since leaving the Swartberg Pass, you have crossed the entire Bokkeveld and Witteberg Groups.

Seven hundred-metre-high cliffs of vertical-standing quartzite of the upper Table Mountain Group can be seen near the northern end of the Swartberg Pass. These have been tilted through 90 degrees.

Prince Albert was once in the news for the alluvial gold rush that took place near here. It happened on a few farms, 40 km northeast of the village, in 1891. The first 65-gram nugget, found in 1875, was dismissed as a flash in the pan. But when another was found 16 years later, 300 m from the first, it was too much to dismiss and the rush was on. After only four months, interest was waning, but a few optimists hung on and it was only in 1895 that the last serious digger left the field. A total of 36 kg of gold was recovered in that time. For a gold field that's not much, but it's certainly more than a flash in the pan. Like the Millwood gold field further south (see ch. 6, p. 136), the gold in these rocks – here sandstones of the Beaufort Group – probably originates from hydrothermal quartz veins. Try and visit the museum to see its excellent display of mammal-like reptiles.

Meiringspoort

From Prince Albert, if you want to return to Oudtshoorn via another route that's quite as dramatic as the Swartberg Pass but stays at base level, travel eastwards to Klaarstroom along the R407 and continue southwards along the N12 through Meiringspoort (see p. 249). The road to Klaarstroom is in the uppermost part of the Bokkeveld Group, once you have first cut obliquely southwards from Prince Albert through the Witteberg rocks. You are mostly driving along the strike of the sediments and the best geology you see is to the south of you in the kloofs cutting into the Swartberg. Meiringspoort was immortalised by the writings of CJ Langenhoven.

Huisrivier Pass

Now in a new direction as you head westwards towards Calitzdorp, and about 15 km out of Oudtshoorn, you cross the Wynands River. As you come out of this valley, you see that the Little Karoo Basin is closing in on you, with the Outeniqua Mountains to the south and the Swartberge to the north. Looking to the south, on the flanks of the Outeniquas, note the red Enon conglomerate slopes, and in front of them the younger, more drab-coloured Kirkwood sandstones and mudstones. Closer still, at the foot of the slopes, see how beautifully planed the floor of the modern Olifants River valley is. About 30 km west of Oudtshoorn you start to see good terracing associated with old courses of the Olifants River and its tributaries on the south side of the road, and some of the bizarrely sculpted Enon conglomerate hills that characterise this formation in these parts ahead to the right (**geosite 4, map 41**). A visit to the spectacular outcrops at Red Hills (just 10 km off the route) is recommended. By this point you will have noticed the khaki-brown Kirkwood sandstones in the low road cuttings. Remember that these sediments are Cretaceous in age, while the terraces cut across them are younger, of various ages in the Tertiary, the terraces getting younger as they get lower and closer to the present river level.

West of Calitzdorp you cross the major Cango Fault and are back in the Precambrian Kansa Group sediments as you start up the Huisrivier Pass. The rocks are mainly appropriately coloured greywackes and shales, conspicuously veined, with quartz veins up to half a metre thick not uncommon, and pyritic in part, with the pyrite now oxidised and leaving rusty stains on the face of the road cuttings. You drive along the fault for a long way, with Cape Supergroup sediments generally not far to your left. Once you're out of the pass, you'll see some Kango conglomerate again, essentially the same as between Oudtshoorn and the caves, but these are not nearly as perfectly displayed, being quite weathered and in a state of decomposition.

Seweweekspoort

With the settlement of Amalienstein to the left of you and the village of Zoar in sight ahead, take the gravel road to the right. You'll cross Kansa sediments to start with, but entering the poort you're back in Cape Supergroup quartzites, with the magnificent folding that characterises these sediments in the fold mountains. The scale of the scenery – and the geology – is awe-inspiring.

Look at the height of the towering peaks around you compared to where you are – never very far, as you thread your way through the poort, from the little stream. And remember that this is the stream that cut this valley over many tens of millions, perhaps over a hundred million years, working its way back from the young coastline to the high plains behind the mountains. In the rainy season, it's wise to call the local authorities to check on the passability of this secondary (gravel) road.

Rooinek Pass

Once you're out of the Seweweekspoort, you find yourself at a T-junction where you should turn left. You're now in the foothills that make the transition from the low Karoo to the high summits, comprising the mixed sediments at the top of the Table Mountain Group and, further west, the shaly Bokkeveld. You drive through quite a tight valley with some of the highest peaks in the Cape to your south and hills of Witteberg sandstone to the north. You proceed on a gravel road for just over 40 km, but rest assured that what lies ahead makes it well worthwhile. After a few kilometres of tar you're on the broad flood plain of the Groot River with striking folding ahead of you, comprising sediments of the Witteberg Group.

To leave the Groot River valley, you turn north towards Laingsburg and proceed up the Rooinek Pass onto the Great Karoo plains. Here you will see some of the most memorable folding anywhere, on quite a different scale from that which you've seen in the other passes (**geosite 5, map 41**). These rocks are Witteberg siltstones and shales, commonly colour-banded, and the individual dragfolds are a matter of a few metres across, with the colour-banding emphasising the folding in a most pleasing way.

Once back on the plains, you're still in the folding and emerge from the Witteberg sediments into Dwyka tillite, here with clasts very conspicuous, up to about a third of a metre in their longest dimension. Then you pass through an anticline, with the massive tillite clearly draped over bedded Witteberg sediments, before re-entering the tillite and moving up through the Ecca Group sediments, passing briefly across a syncline of infolded Beaufort Group, and back into the Ecca. The sediments look quite similar but tell of quite strongly contrasting depositional environments (see summary of Karoo environments, ch. 9, p. 176, table 5).

That brings you to Laingsburg and onto the N1. We hope you enjoyed your time in one of the best exposed fold mountain chains anywhere in the world.

The folded shales and siltstones in the Rooinek Pass show there is no downward limit to the scale of folding.
They, too, show the almost horizontal axial plane seen in some of the megafolds.

For this stream to have carved its deep gorge through these ultrahard rocks in Seweweekspoort would have taken many millions of years. It is easier to imagine if we think that in times of higher rainfall in the geological past it may have been a wide, raging torrent.

Glossary

accretion: process by which rigid cratons expand over geological time, as orogenic (mobile) belts become 'welded' onto craton margins

acid: rocks – generally igneous – containing more than 67% silica (SiO_2)

Acid Phase: old term for that part of the Bushveld Complex comprising acid intrusives, mainly granite and granophyre

aeolianite: sandstone derived from windblown sand

African (Erosion) Surface: land surface formed after commencement of the split-up of Gondwana, ending approximately 18 million years ago

alkaline: applied to rocks relatively deficient in silica (SiO_2) and rich in sodium and/or potassium

alumina: aluminium oxide (Al_2O_3)

aluminosilicate: describes the common minerals in which alumina (Al_2O_3) and silica (SiO_2) are important components

amazonite: rare, green variety of microcline feldspar

amphibole: family of generally dark, common rock-forming (i.e. aluminosilicate) minerals, rich in magnesium, iron, calcium and/or sodium

amphibolite: metamorphic rock comprising mainly amphibole and feldspar, with little or no quartz

amygdale: small gas bubble in lava, filled with a secondary mineral such as quartz or calcite (*see* vesicle)

anastomose: tendency of a mature, low-energy, flat-gradient stream or river to form a netlike pattern

andalusite: metamorphic mineral with the composition Al_2SiO_5

andesite: *see* table 1, p. 14

anticline: *see* fig. 15, p. 121

anticlinorium: composite series of smaller synclinal and anticlinal folds that together form a larger downward-opening fold structure; (*see* anticline, synclinorium)

Archaean: the oldest rocks of the Precambrian, older than 2 500 million years

artesian: commonly applied to a spring that comes to the surface from an underground aquifer that lies topographically above it

augen: used when a mineral or collection of minerals in metamorphic rocks forms an eye-shaped unit that is conspicuously larger than the groundmass it is set in

axial plane: *see* fig. 15, p. 121

axis: *see* fig. 15, p. 121

bankenveld: describes terrace-like topography with large, flattish terraces and minor scarps

basalt: *see* table 1, p. 14

base metal: comprising mainly copper, lead, zinc and nickel

basement: applied to the floor onto which a sequence of rocks was deposited; commonly applied to Archaean formations

bauxite: weathered rock composed of hydrated alumina; the ore of alumina, from which aluminium is derived

bed: smallest unit in a sedimentary series, separated from units above and below by a clear bedding plane

bedding: characteristic given to a sequence of sediments by its beds

beryl: mineral with composition $Be_8Al_2Si_6O_{18}$; forms aquamarine and emerald

biotite: common, rock-forming mica, generally dark brown

boudinage: applied to units in a metamorphic rock where a formerly continuous sheet has been pulled open during tectonism

breccia: rock comprising angular fragments, most commonly created during faulting, occasionally by volcanism

calcite: common mineral form of $CaCO_3$, translucent in individual crystals; where finely crystalline, they appear white

calcrete: secondary rock consisting mainly of calcium carbonate, and formed over a long period of time at or near the ground surface by the movement through the soil of upward-moving ground water; also called 'surface limestone' (*see* silcrete)

carbonatite breccia: carbonatite is an unsual carbonate-rich rock of igneous origin, often associated with alkaline igneous rocks

chert: extremely fine-grained silica rock, commonly found with limestone or dolomite, but conspicuously harder than either of those rocks; commonly grey

chromite: mineral consisting mainly of the oxide of chromium, from which the chromium can be recovered, and forming an important part of the Bushveld Complex

clast: individual constituent of sedimentary, less commonly volcaniclastic, rocks

clastic: applied to a rock composed of clasts, commonly used synonymously with 'sedimentary'

cleavage: *see* fig. 15, p. 121

closed fold: *see* 'isoclinal'; *see* fig. 15, p. 121

competence: property of rocks that defines how they behave during tectonism, e.g. sandstone is more competent than shale or schist, and does not show the cleavage they do

complex: generally, an assemblage of rocks of any age or origin that has been folded or metamorphosed together

concretion: nodule formed by the concentration about a central nucleus of soluble constituents of sedimentary rocks

conglomerate: most commonly applied to a sedimentary rock containing rounded or semi-rounded clasts as large as or larger than pebbles; *see* table 2, p. 15

craton: fragment of the earliest part of the Earth's crust, comprising the most ancient sedimentary and volcanic rocks and the granites that intruded them

crocidolite: blue asbestos, a fibrous form of sodium-rich amphibole

cross-bedding: internal bedding within a single bed and oblique to the bedding planes that define it; formed by air or water currents active during deposition

cryptocrystalline: so finely crystalline that the crystals cannot be seen with a magnifying lens

diabase: shallow intrusive equivalent of basalt; in South Africa used of rocks older than the formation of the Karoo Supergroup, whose diabase-composition intrusives are called dolerite

diatreme: near-surface part of a volcanic pipe

differentiation: process whereby an originally homogenous magma separates into different fractions, as some minerals crystallise and settle, leaving magma of composition different from the original

dip: attitude of a tabular body of rock, usually a bed or assemblage of beds

dip slope: topographic feature formed when an inclined unit, usually a sedimentary bed, is hard enough to resist the weathering that has removed overlying material

dolomite: limestone that contains a substantial amount of magnesium carbonate in addition to calcium carbonate

dome: upward-convex roughly circular feature, often meaning basement over which younger formations were draped and have been partially removed

drag-fold: *see* fig. 15, p. 121

dune rock: *see* aeolianite

Dwyka: river in the southern Karoo where the tillite that resulted from the Gondwana glaciation, the lowermost formation of the Karoo Basin, was first described; the name of the Group that contains tillite and allied sediments; *see* fig. 16, p. 146; table 5, p. 176

dyke: near-vertical tabular intrusive body

Ecca: river and pass in the Eastern Cape, where the generally fine-grained sediments that form the second major sedimentary grouping in the Karoo Supergroup were first described; the name given to this extensive Group of sediments; *see* fig. 16, p. 146; table 5, p. 176

eon: the most fundamental division of geological time

exfoliation dome: dome formed when the weathered outer material of a usually igneous rock has been removed

fault: fracture where one block of the Earth's crust, of any size and in a brittle, i.e. non-fluid, state, has moved relative to adjacent crust

feldspar: one of the commonest rock-forming minerals in igneous and metamorphic rocks, consisting of aluminosilicate of sodium, potassium and/or calcium; also found in some sedimentary rocks

feldspathic: containing feldspar as a principal ingredient

ferruginous: iron-rich

float: detached rock material lying on the ground surface

fluvial: pertaining to rivers and river flow

fold belt: elongate zone of folding, typical of an orogeny

fold closure: part of the fold immediately around its axis, i.e. the hinge zone

fold plunge: dip of a fold structure; strictly the dip of the fold axis

foliation: structure resulting from the separation of minerals into different layers parallel to the schistosity

formation: assemblage of rocks that share broadly the same age and environment of origin

gabbro: *see* table 1, p. 14

garnet: any one of a complex group of rock-forming minerals usually rich in iron, calcium and manganese; mostly found in metamorphic rocks and in kimberlite

glacial till: sediment left behind when ice sheets or glaciers melt

gneiss: *see* table 3, p. 17

graben: generally elongate block of the Earth's crust dropped down between faults during extensional tectonics

granite: *see* table 1, p. 14

granitised: describing rocks subjected to such high temperatures and pressures that melting has occurred and the recrystallised rock has the appearance, texture and mineral composition of granite

greenstone: old term used to describe basic volcanic rocks, usually in Archaean 'greenstone belts', where low-grade metamorphism has converted the original mafic minerals mainly into the dark green metamorphic mineral chlorite, often with some greenish hornblende and grass-green epidote

greywacke: massive, poorly sorted, dark grey sandstone with angular grains, generally including rock fragments; usually formed during periods of crustal instability

group: major unit of stratigraphy comprising more than one formation, formed in a period and environment where crustal conditions were broadly constant

heap leach process: metallurgical extraction process not requiring fine crushing or costly extraction equipment

heavy minerals: minerals that are dense enough to be naturally concentrated by wind action

haematite: common iron oxide mineral (Fe_2O_3)

hornblende: most common member of the amphibole family of rock-forming minerals; generally blackish and found in granite, gneiss and amphibolite

hornfels: fine-grained contact metamorphic rock, hardened by the heat of a nearby intrusion

hydrocarbons: materials formed by decay of marine organisms that may accumulate to form commercially exploitable oil and gas

hydrothermal: relating to heated magmatic emanations rich in water

igneous contact: contact where an igneous rock (*see* table 1, p. 14) is intruded into an older rock; useful in dating rocks (*see* sedimentary contact)

inclusion: crystal, rock fragment or small bubble of liquid or gas, enclosed in a bigger crystal

inlier: 'window' of older rock completely enclosed by younger rocks, either a high-standing part of the floor of a sedimentary basin, or formed when a small area of the younger formation has been removed by erosion to expose the floor

inselberg: isolated hill or mountain dominating the surrounding plains

intermediate: grouping of igneous rocks between acid and mafic

intrusion: body of igneous rock that penetrates an older rock, or the process of such penetration; gives rise to intrusive and intruded

isoclinal: used to describe a fold whose limbs are parallel

isotope: one of two or more subtly differing forms of a chemical element

jasper: extremely finely crystalline quartz, coloured red by intermixed iron oxide

jaspilite: rock composed of fine alternating bands of red jasper and black iron oxide

joint: fracture plane separating adjacent blocks of rock between which there has been no movement

kaolinisation: process in which some rock-forming minerals, mainly feldspar, are converted – usually to the clay mineral kaolin, a hydrated aluminium silicate; also applied to the weathering of granite

kimberlite: ultramafic intrusive rock, dark when fresh and yellow when weathered; the primary ore of diamonds, though most kimberlites are effectively barren

kimberlite pipe: carrot-shaped intrusion in which kimberlite is commonly found

komatiite: group of ultramafic volcanic rocks, having a distinctive chemical composition, representing hot, magnesium-rich magmas that erupted on Earth's early crust; named after the type-area where they were originally found in the Komati valley, near Barberton

lapilli: small fragments blasted out of volcanoes

layering: phenomenon seen in sequences of beds or strata of contrasting appearance

Liesegang banding: colour-banding resulting from rhythmic precipitation of material from solutions passing through sedimentary rocks

limb: *see* fig. 15, p. 121

limestone: bedded sediment consisting chiefly of calcium carbonate ($CaCO_3$)

lithification: process of conversion – usually of long duration – of a newly deposited sediment into a rock

lunette dunes: crescent-shaped dunes along the downwind rim of pans, formed by dust and sand blown off the pans

mafic: applied to generally dark rocks and minerals relatively rich in magnesium and poor in silica

Mafic Phase: now-outdated term used for Layered Suite of the Bushveld Complex (*see* Acid Phase)

magma: molten or partly molten phase of

igneous rocks, which cools and solidifies to form such rocks

magmatic: rock or mineral deposit derived from a magma

magnetite: common blackish iron oxide mineral, Fe_3O_4, magnetic, giving rocks that contain it their magnetic property

Main Reef: the best known gold-bearing conglomerate found in the Witwatersrand Supergroup, originally discovered near Johannesburg in 1886

Main Reef Leader: another gold-bearing conglomerate in the Witwatersrand Supergroup, occurring a short distance above the Main Reef, and often containing more gold than the latter

marble: metamorphosed and recrystallised equivalent of a sedimentary carbonate rock, such as limestone or dolomite, often used as a decorative or monumental stone

marker: usually thin and easily recognised rock unit occurring at a more or less constant position within a larger formation, used to determine geological position

massif: mass of conspicuous hills or mountains not forming part of a range

massive: descriptive term for a rock unit having a homogeneous structure, without obvious bedding, layering or banding

megacryst: relatively large crystal or mineral grain in an igneous or metamorphic rock that is easily visible with the unaided eye

member: distinctive subdivision of a formation that merits separate description because of distinct character

mesa: isolated, steep-sided, flat-topped mountain

metamorphic: applies to minerals, processes and regions resulting from metamorphism (*see* table 3, p. 17)

metasediment(s): metamorphosed sediments

metavolcanics: metamorphosed lavas

microcline: whitish rock-forming mineral of the feldspar family, made up of silica (SiO_2), alumina (Al_2O_3) and potassium, and closely related to orthoclase

mobile belt: large linear geological region where rock formations are characterised by strong metamorphism and structural deformation, partly surrounding or between older stable craton(s)

monoclinal: sharp downward flexure or fold structure made of strata dipping in only one direction

moraine: material deposited by a glacier or large ice sheet

olifantsklip: rough pattern resembling elephant skin shown on weathered dolomite, the result of slow chemical weathering

olivine: silicate mineral composed of silica (SiO_2), and magnesium and iron oxides (MgO, Feo), common in ultramafic and some mafic rocks

open fold: fold structure in which the angle between the fold limbs is generally more than 70°

orbicular granite: unusually textured granitic rock made up of rounded, concentrically zoned mineral concentrations, or orbicules, in a usually finer matrix

orogenic zone: geologically deformed region reflecting large-scale folding and faulting, typical of a long-lived period of mountain building, or orogeny

orthogneiss: term applied to gneiss derived from rocks of igneous origin, in contrast to paragneiss which denotes gneiss of sedimentary origin

outlier: isolated occurrence of younger rocks entirely surrounded by outcrops of older rocks, or a detached remnant of younger rocks found on older rocks (*see* inlier)

pahoehoe: Hawaiian word for usually basaltic lava, or a flow of this lava, having a smooth, lobe-like or ropey, wrinkled surface indicating solidification from a very fluid lava stream

palaeo-surface: old surface that has subsequently become buried

paragneiss: term applied to gneiss derived from rocks of sedimentary origin (*see* orthogneiss)

pegmatite: vein-like intrusion of very coarse-grained, crystalline, typically granitic minerals, such as quartz, feldspar and mica, and occasionally small amounts of tourmaline, beryl, topaz and other rarer minerals, formed during the final stage of granite formation

peneplain: extensive land surface of flat to very gentle relief formed by the long-lived erosion of land to its base level

petroglyph: prehistoric rock engraving made by the San people on smooth rock surfaces

phyllite: low-grade metamorphic rock in which micaceous minerals have tended to form parallel to the foliation, but not to the extent seen in a schist

pillow structure: structure formed when some mafic lavas are erupted under water, resembling a mass of pillows

placer: alluvial deposit containing valuable minerals, usually gold or diamonds

plagioclase: group of common rock-forming minerals of the feldspar family, containing calcium and sodium oxides (Na_2O and CaO), silica (SiO_2) and alumina (Al_2O_3)

planation: the act of planing, or levelling

plastic: applied to deformation where the deformed material does not return to its pre-deformation state when the deforming pressure is released, as opposed to elastic deformation, which leaves no permanent effect

platinum group elements (PGE): naturally occurring mixture of chemically related elements comprising mainly platinum (Pt) and palladium (Pd), and lesser amounts of iridium (Ir), rhodium (Rd), ruthenium (Ru) and osmium (Os)

pluton: discrete, usually granite intrusions of generally rounded shape and of relatively limited size that form from a larger, deeper granitic magma

porphyry: hypabyssal or extrusive igneous rock in which relatively large conspicuous crystals (or phenocrysts) are set in a finer-grained or glassy matrix

Proterozoic: *see* table 4, p. 21

province: region showing broadly similar rock types, level of metamorphism, structural history and geological age

pseudotachylite: unusual rocks melted and shattered by the meteorite impact at Vredefort; characterised by widespread thin veinlets and breccias with dark, glassy matrix, representing rock shattered and melted by the catastrophic impact event

pumice: highly porous or vesicular volcanic rock that floats on water

pyrite(s): most common iron sulphide mineral (FeS_2), brassy-looking when fresh and commonly known as 'fool's gold'

pyroclastic: poorly bedded volcanic rock composed of angular fragments of erupted material of variable size, formed during volcanic explosions; also volcaniclastic

Pyroxene: family of common silicate minerals found in igneous rocks and rich in Mg, Fe and Ca

Pyroxenite: medium- to coarse-grained igneous rock consisting mainly of pyroxene

quartz: commonest form of silica (SiO_2) and one of the most abundant minerals in the Earth's crust

quartzite: common metamorphic rock composed essentially of quartz grains, formed by the complete recrystallisation of quartz-rich sandstone

recumbent isoclinal fold: *see* fig. 15, p. 121

reef: refers to a vein (usually gold-bearing quartz) of extractable minerals; in South Africa it is also used for the thin, gold-rich conglomerates of the Witwatersrand

regression: period of time during the life of a sedimentary basin when sea level recedes and newly formed sediments are exposed to the air (*see* transgression)

residual mountain: mountain that originates because all the surrounding high-standing material has been eroded and washed away

rheomorphism: process associated with deep burial and very high-grade metamorphism, whereby gneissic rocks and migmatites eventually begin to melt and flow

rhombohedral: minerals that crystallise or cleave in rhombohedrons; the latter term refers to crystals that show faces having the shape of a rhombus, or an oblique parallelogram, such as certain calcite crystals

roof pendant: remnants of the rock body that is intruded by igneous batholiths or plutons and which hangs down into the cooling magma

run: diamond-bearing alluvial channel

salt weathering: decomposition of rock or packed sand, accelerated by any of a variety of mineral salts present in the rock or sediment

sandstone: consolidated sedimentary rock made up of sand-sized grains (clearly visible), usually predominantly of quartz and lesser feldspar, cemented together by silica, clay minerals or carbonate

scarp: plateau edge, vertical or nearly so

schist: metamorphic rock in which platy or flaky minerals (micas in particular) lie parallel to each other, to give the rock conspicuous foliation, along which it may be easily broken

schistose: having the appearance and texture of a schist

sedimentary contact: position of the base of a package of sediments, where it lies on a rock surface that is usually much older than the sediments (*see* igneous contact)

seif dune: linear dune, commonly grouped in parallel ridges of considerable length

sericitic: very fine-grained aggregate of white mica (muscovite), invariably the alteration or weathering product of feldspar

series: term formerly applied to a unit of stratigraphy approximately equivalent to a formation in today's terminology, several of which made up a system

serpentinite: fairly soft rock composed largely of the serpentine group of minerals, and generally formed by the alteration of ultramafic rocks, rich in olivine

shale: fine-grained, layered, sedimentary rock made of deposits of clay-like sediment or fine silt and mud

sheet: in igneous geology, this refers to a shallow, more or less tabular intrusion that cuts through the intruded rock strata at a fairly shallow angle (*see* dyke); it may also refer to a layer of extrusive lava

silcrete: hard layer of secondary cherty rock formed by the upward movement of silica in solution and its deposition near-surface under dry conditions (also called 'surface quartzite') (*see* calcrete)

silicate: mineral with the SiO_2 radical forming a major part, including most of the rock-forming minerals

sill: shallow, tabular intrusion that intrudes parallel to the bedding of the intruded sedimentary rock strata (*see* sheet)

slimes: in metallurgical usage, the fine-grained, muddy residual material

that is left after the wet extraction from pulverised ore of valuable minerals, such as gold or platinum (*see* tailings)

stratigraphic column: idealised graphical section, or column, of geological strata or formations, youngest at the top and oldest at the bottom

stratum: layer of sedimentary rock that shows its own specific character and is distinct from the layers above and below it

stromatolites: finely layered, concentric, mound-like structures found in dolomite and formed by microscopic algal organisms

structure: arrangement of deformed rocks as seen today

subduction: process whereby one crustal plate moves beneath another, along a subduction zone, causing earthquakes and generating new magma

subhorizontal: nearly horizontal

subvertical: nearly vertical

suite: used in igneous intrusive and high-grade metamorphic geology as the collective grouping of related rocks; equivalent to 'group' in sedimentary classification

supergroup: largest grouping used in the classification of geological units, made up of more than one group

supracrustal: relatively younger sedimentary and volcanic rocks, and their metamorphic equivalents, that overlie rocks of the crystalline Basement, usually granitic gneisses

syncline: *see* fig. 15, p. 121

synclinorium: composite series of smaller synclinal and anticlinal folds that together form a larger upward-opening fold structure; *see* fig. 15, p. 121 (*see also* anticlinorium)

syntaxis zone: used to describe the zone around Cape Town where the western and southern branches of the Cape Fold Belt meet, and where folding is not conspicuous

system: term formerly used to describe a group or series (qv), where Group and Supergroup are used today

tailings: in metallurgical usage the usually fine-grained material that is discarded or rejected after the extraction of valuable minerals from ore, e.g. gold or diamonds (*see* slimes)

tantalite: ore of tantalum metal, valuable mineral found in some pegmatites

tectonism: deformation of the Earth's crust by means of folding, thrusting and faulting

terrane: geological setting or type of geology in a general sense; may also be spelled 'terrain'

thrust fault: fault produced by low-angle or near-horizontal compression in which the upper block is moved obliquely over the lower block

thrusting: process giving rise to thrust faults, with considerable lateral movement

relative to vertical displacement

tiger's eye: yellowish-brown ornamental stone formed by the replacement of blue asbestos by silica

tight fold: fold structure in which the angle between the fold limbs is generally less than 30°

tillite: accumulated glacial debris that has turned into rock, comprising a jumbled mix of boulders, pebbles, gravel and sand set in a matrix of glacial flour

tonalite: *see* table 1, p. 14

topaz: silicate mineral which may be used as a gem

tor: small, bouldery, granite hill, the remnant left after the erosion of the surrounding granite

transgression: period of time during the life of a sedimentary basin when sea level rises and deposition spreads over older sediments and extends further inland, creating an unconformity (*see* regression)

trough cross-bedding: bedding seen in fluvial sandstone where discrete troughs of bedded sandstone overlie and overlap one another

tuff: fine-grained pyroclastic rock formed from the deposition, usually in water, of volcanic ash, the result of faraway explosive volcanic activity

turbidite: sedimentary rock made of coarse sediment of shallow-water origin that was redeposited under deeper-water conditions down-slope by a denser current called a turbidity current

ultramafic: igneous rock containing an exceptionally low silica (SiO_2) content, and consisting almost entirely of magnesium- and iron-rich minerals, comprising rocks such as peridotite and kimberlite

unconformity: contact in a sedimentary assemblage that reflects a break during sedimentation, of some considerable duration, during which erosion and possibly tilting of the older sediments may have occurred

uplift: elevation of the land surface relative to sea level

vesicle: small cavity within a volcanic rock formed by the expansion of a bubble of gas or steam during its solidification, giving rocks that are vesicular (when filled with many cavities), and forming amygdales when filled with secondary mineral

wad: common name for dull black or dark brownish-black manganese oxides, usually of earthy appearance, and of variable composition

xenocryst: foreign crystal or crystal fragment that was picked up by a magmatic body as it ascended, e.g. diamonds in kimberlite

xenolith: foreign rock fragment within an igneous rock, generally unrelated to the magma; comparable to but larger than a xenocryst

Bibliography

Antrobus, ESA (ed.). 1986. *Witwatersrand Gold – 100 Years*. The Geological Society of South Africa.

Bulpin, TV. 1985. *Scenic Wonders of Southern Africa*. Books of Africa (Pty) Ltd.

Cairncross, Bruce & Dixon, Roger. 1995. *Minerals of South Africa*. The Geological Society of South Africa.

Cluver, MA. 1978. *Fossil Reptiles of the South African Karoo*. South African Museum.

Cowey, Antony (compiler). 1994. *Mining and Metallurgy in South Africa: A Pictorial History*. Mintek.

Curror, WD. 2002. *Golden Memories of Barberton*. Revised and enlarged by Hans Bornman. African Pioneer Mining (Pty) Ltd.

Dingle, RV, Siesser, WG & Newton, R. 1980. *Mesozoic and Tertiary Geology of Southern Africa*. AA Balkema.

Directorate: Mineral Economics. *South Africa's Mineral Industry 2002/2003*. Department of Minerals and Energy, Republic of South Africa.

Eales, Hugh V. 2001. *A First Introduction to the Geology of the Bushveld Complex*. The Council for Geoscience as Popular Geoscience Series #2.

Hartzer, FJ, Johnson, MR & Eglington, BM. 1998. *Stratigraphic Table of South Africa*. The Council for Geoscience.

Haughton, SH. 1969. *Geological History of Southern Africa*. The Geological Society of South Africa.

Hendey, QB. 1982. *Langebaanweg: A Record of Past Life*. South African Museum.

Hilton-Barber, Brett & Berger, Lee. 2nd ed., 2004. *Field Guide to the Cradle of Humankind. Sterkfontein, Swartkrans, Kromdraai & Environs World Heritage Site*. Struik Publishers, Cape Town.

Joubert, P & Johnson, MR. South African Committee for Stratigraphy. 1998. *Abridged Lexicon of South African Stratigraphy*. The Council for Geoscience.

King, LC. 1951. *South African Scenery: A Textbook of Geomorphology*. 2nd ed. revised. Published by Oliver and Boyd.

MacRae, Colin. 1999. *Life Etched in Stone: Fossils of South Africa*. The Geological Society of South Africa.

McCarthy, T & Rubidge, B (eds). 2005. *The Story of Earth & Life: A southern African perspective on a 4.6-billion-year journey*. Struik Publishers, Cape Town.

Mendelsohn, F & Potgieter, CT (eds). 1986. *Guidebook to Sites of Geological and Mining Interest on The Central Rand*. The Geological Society of South Africa. *Reader's Digest Illustrated Guide to Southern Africa*. 1978. The Reader's Digest Association, South Africa (Pty) Ltd.

Reimold, WU & Gibson, RL. 2005. *Meteorite Impact! The danger from space and South Africa's mega-impact, the Vredefort Structure*. Chris van Rensburg Publications (Pty) Ltd.

Simkin, Tom & Fiske, Richard S (eds). 1983. *Krakatau 1883: The Volcanic Eruption and its Effects*. Smithsonian Institute Press.

South African Committee for Stratigraphy. Kent, LE (compiler). 1980. *Stratigraphy of South Africa*. Handbook 8, Part 1. Geological Survey of South Africa.

Tankard, AJ, Jackson, MPA, Erikson, KA, Hobday, DK, Hunter, DR & Minter, WEL. 1982. *Crustal Evolution of Southern Africa: 3.8 Billion Years of Earth History*. Springer-Verlag.

The Automobile Association of South Africa. 1987. *Off The Beaten Track – Selected Day Drives in Southern Africa*. The Motorist Publications (Pty) Ltd.

Viljoen, MJ & Reimold, WU. 1999. *An Introduction to South Africa's Geological and Mining Heritage*. Mintek in association with The Geological Society of South Africa.

Wagner, PA. 1914. *The Diamond Fields of Southern Africa*. 1st ed. The Transvaal Leader, Johannesburg; 2nd impression (1971) Struik Publishers, Cape Town.

Wannenburgh, Alf & Dickson, JR. 1987. *The Natural Wonder of Southern Africa*. Struik Publishers, Cape Town.

Wilson, MGC & Anhaeusser, CR (eds). 6th ed., 1999. *The Mineral Resources of South Africa*. Handbook 16. The Council for Geoscience.

Winchester, Simon. 2003. *Krakatoa: The Day the World Exploded*. Viking.

Index

A

Accretion 27, 312
Acid rocks 66, 86, 88-9, 90, 132, 189, 192, 195-6, 312
Aeolianite 16, 70, 72, 81, 141, 145-6, 162, 312
African (Erosion) Surface 111-2, 126, 129, 131, 143, 147, 149-151, 158, 169, 250
'African Eve' 70
Agglomerate 15, 167, 229, 255
Alberton Formation 39
Algae 26, 56, 92, 93, 282, 283
Algoa Group 146
Alkaline rocks 21, 86, 186, 189, 312
Allanridge Formation 257
Alumina 157, 312
Aluminium 97, 156-7, 164, 190, 197
    ore 155
    oxide 157, 312
Amazonite 267, 312
Ammonites 164
Amphibole 17, 98, 203, 264, 312
Amphibolite 17, 98, 252, 264-5, 269-270, 312
Anastomosing 110, 312
Andalusite 17, 185, 189-190, 312
Andesite 14, 45, 86, 222-3, 235, 256, 261, 312
Anorthosite 89
Anticlines 120-1, 149, 212, 246-7, 254, 310, 312
Anticlinoria 120, 312
Apatite 96
Archaean
    Basement 39-40, 277
Asbestos 41, 260
    chrysotile 203
Augrabies 269
    Falls 252-3, 268
    Gneiss 268
    Granite 252-3, 268-9
Avens 280-1

B

Balmoral Granite 195
Bankenveld 50, 312
Barberton 94, 202
    Belt 21
    Mountain Land 193, 201, 202-3
    Supergroup 203-4
Basalt 13-4, 21, 26-7, 39-41, 45, 62, 87, 95, 100-1, 116, 164-5, 167, 169, 172, 176-8, 182, 204, 235, 257-8, 261, 290, 293, 296, 299, 312
    amygdaloidal 167, 257-8, 290, 293-4, 312
    floats 103, 313
    flood 227, 256, 294, 299
Base metals 215, 252, 272, 312
Basement 38, 42-5, 55, 57, 59-60, 76, 78, 80, 84, 98-101, 106, 143, 158-160, 163, 166, 169, 173, 180-3, 201, 205, 215, 227, 239, 244, 251, 255, 258-9, 263-4, 267, 275, 277, 279, 288, 300, 304, 312
Bauxite 155, 157, 312
Baviaanskloof Gneiss 99
Beaufort Group 84, 112, 114-6,

118, 122, 146, 150, 152-3, 156, 166, 169, 176-180, 182, 244, 293, 295, 298, 304, 307, 310
    biozones 180
Bedding 17, 32, 39-40, 43-5, 57, 96, 102, 112, 122, 125, 147, 180, 187, 194, 200, 204, 229, 246, 256-7, 270, 305, 312
Beit Bridge Complex 101, 103-4
Berea Formation/Red Sand 80, 159, 162-3
Beryl 222, 267, 312
Biotite 76, 99, 103, 158-9, 169-170, 183, 217, 252, 264-5, 269, 312
Bird Reefs 39
Black Reef Formation 34, 38, 49-50, 55, 57, 96, 174, 200-1, 254-5, 258, 274-5, 277-9, 284-9
Bokkeveld Group 32, 72, 124, 126, 129-131, 138, 146, 210, 212, 248, 304, 308-310
Boudinage 263, 312
Breccia 15, 51, 54, 59, 61, 92, 138, 166, 189-190, 204, 229, 261, 280-281, 312
Bredasdorp Group 72
Breede River Valley 125
Brixton Quartzite 39
Bushveld Complex 21, 27, 34, 51, 53-6, 84, 86, 88-9, 95, 98, 114, 184, 187-8, 190, 192, 194-5, 198-200, 275, 286

C

Calcification 81, 162, 280
Calcite 96, 103, 281, 294, 312
Calcium 17, 26, 86, 97, 265, 283
    carbonate 15-16, 81-2, 117, 132, 211, 236, 283
    sulphate 211, 214
Calcrete 15, 117, 214-5, 236, 238, 240, 258, 262, 265, 312
Cambrian Basin 78
Campbell Rand Dolomite 258-9, 280, 283
Cango
    Caves 305-6
    Fault 309
Cape
    Basin 148, 209
    Fold Belt 25, 27, 62, 107, 118, 126, 128, 146-9, 176, 206, 233, 244, 246, 248, 304
        cross-section 304
    Suite 62, 65, 136
    Supergroup 3, 16, 21, 27, 32, 62, 65, 67-8, 107, 123-5, 128, 136, 142, 146, 156, 206, 209-210, 213, 223, 244, 246-7, 300, 304, 307, 309
    Thrust Belt 248
Capping 15, 78, 80, 94, 100, 111-2, 116, 134, 147, 169, 172, 177-8, 244, 284, 288
Carbon 130, 242
    dating 30, 31
    dioxide 26, 90, 242, 283
    isotopes 31
Carbonate 15, 282, 286
    minerals 289
    rock 280, 283
    Sequence 283
Carbonatite 14, 51, 312

Carletonville gold field 38, 43, 256
Cave Sandstone 298
Caves 34-5, 56-7, 72, 92-3, 250, 279-281, 289, 293, 296-7, 299, 306
Cedarberg Formation 32, 125, 210, 212, 249, 307
Cement 82, 197, 211, 214-5
Cenozoic Era 21
Central Rand
    gold field 38
    Group 39-40, 44-5, 174
Chalcedony 15
Chert 15, 21, 43, 95, 123, 260, 282, 312
Chlorite 17, 203
Chrome 89, 95, 184, 188, 197, 199
Chromite 88-9, 188, 199, 312
Chromium 97, 188
Chromitite 89
Chuniespoort Group 95, 201, 254
Clarens Formation 101, 103, 173, 176-8, 204, 244, 290, 293-9
Clastic rocks 15, 17, 81, 312
Clasts 61, 80, 122, 143, 147-8, 156-7, 250-1, 287, 304-6, 308, 310, 312
Clay 16-7, 44, 82, 211
Cleavage 17, 120-1, 136, 247-9, 305, 312
Climate 24, 153, 157, 237, 294, 299
Clinker 211
Coal 10, 15, 69, 77, 102-3, 106, 109, 122, 161, 171-2, 176, 192, 195-7, 229, 231
    mines 171, 197, 198, 230
Coastal lakes 137
Cobalt 97
Complexes 32, 312
Concordia Granite 206-207, 217
Conglomerate 15, 38-9, 40, 44-5, 47, 49, 80-1, 90, 100, 127, 131, 136, 138-9, 169, 174-5, 212, 226-7, 234, 249-251, 255-7, 263, 286, 300, 302, 305-6, 309, 312
Contact 45, 66-8, 80, 85, 151, 189-190, 250, 313
Continental Drift 10, 29, 77, 122, 125, 294
Copper 88, 104-5, 154-5, 188, 217, 220, 223, 272
    mining 105, 206, 219, 252
Cordierite 17
Coronation Reef 39
Corundum 96, 97
Cradle of Humankind 12, 34-5, 49, 56-57, 59, 280
Cratons 25-6, 105, 252, 312
Cretaceous Period 66, 111, 116, 133-5, 142, 145, 164, 304, 309
Crocidolite 260, 312
Cross-bedding 66, 70, 72, 74, 76-7, 79-82, 103, 110, 128-9, 145-6, 212, 257, 299, 307, 312
Cross-cutting 32, 103, 212, 286
Crown Lava 39, 44, 45
Crustal plates 13, 17-9, 22, 79, 126, 163, 264
Cullinan 52, 53, 192, 194
    Diamond 34, 52
    mine 34, 51-53
Curries Camp Gneiss 265

D

Dacite 14
Damara Province 25
Darling pluton 209
Daspoort Formation 50-1, 199
Decollement 248
Decomposition 76, 309
Deformation 32, 45, 61, 103, 104-5, 128, 163, 223, 248, 252, 263-4, 267, 306-8
De Kaap Valley 278-9
Diabase 14, 50, 85, 95, 101-2, 186, 189, 194, 198, 199-200, 252, 259, 284, 312
Diamictite 210
Diamonds 52-3, 96, 105, 114-5, 232, 235-6, 238-9, 240-4
    mines 51, 240-242
Diatremes 242, 312
Differentiation 88, 89, 312
Dinosaurs 21, 116, 164, 176, 245, 279, 293, 296, 299
Diorite 14, 86
Dipping 35, 38, 57, 59, 95, 120, 124-5, 128, 167, 183-4, 199, 212, 227, 252, 254, 261-2, 278, 284, 286, 289, 307, 312
Dolerite 14, 16-7, 21, 30, 62, 66, 106, 112-3, 115, 117, 142, 146, 150-2, 154-8, 164, 169, 171, 173, 176-180, 182, 189, 236, 238-9 244-5, 252, 293-6, 299
Dolomite 15, 21, 26, 34-5, 38, 50-1, 55-7, 85, 92, 95-6, 171-2, 174, 186, 200-1, 254-5, 258-9, 277-286, 288-9, 312
Dongas 142, 152, 153
Drakensberg 14, 22, 87, 111, 116, 172, 290-299
    cross-section 293
    escarpment 12, 179, 182, 292
    Formation 290, 294
    Group 21, 27, 62, 115, 165, 167, 176-7, 181-2, 244, 293-4, 297, 299
    to Durban
        cross-section 182
Dune Rock 70, 72, 74, 79, 81, 132, 141, 313
Dunes 70, 80, 126, 137, 141, 144-6, 161, 164, 173, 176, 182-3, 209, 237, 262-5, 270-1, 273, 299
Dunite 14
Dwaalheuwel Formation 187
Dwyka Group 27-8, 75, 122-3, 143, 146-9, 156, 159, 162-3, 171-2, 176, 180, 182-3, 195, 229, 231, 237, 243-4, 246-7, 258, 304, 307, 308, 310, 313
Dykes 14, 62, 66, 85, 103, 106, 112, 150-1, 169, 176, 189, 222, 242, 259, 294, 299, 313

E

Earth
    core 13, 26
    crust 13, 16, 18, 25-6, 62, 89, 300
    magnetic field 13
    mantle 13, 26-7, 105, 242, 255, 264, 300
Earthquakes 18, 20

Ceres 20, 125, 300
Tulbagh 20, 300
East Rand gold field 38, 175, 224, 227
Eastern Cape Fold Belt 146
Ecca Group 10, 74, 77, 79-80, 87, 103, 120, 122-3, 146-7, 149-150, 152, 156, 158-9, 162, 166, 169, 171, 176-180, 182, 192, 195, 198, 229, 231, 237, 244, 246-7, 304, 310, 312
Eclogites 242
Elliot Formation 176, 244, 293, 295-6, 299
Elsberg Formation 226
Enon Formation 127, 131, 136, 138, 249- 251, 257, 300, 302, 304, 309
Eon 21, 25-6, 34, 104-5, 227, 264, 312
Ermelo coal field 161, 171
Erosion 15, 22-3, 32, 44-5, 60, 62, 70, 72, 76, 79, 100, 111, 122, 125-7, 131, 143, 147, 149, 155, 158, 181, 209, 237, 250, 257, 270, 274-5, 287, 291, 294
Escarpment
Great 111, 118, 178, 193, 198-201, 215, 245, 274-289, 291
cross-section 277
Evander gold reef 38, 161, 171

F

Faulting 19-20, 32, 42, 44-5, 50, 55, 59, 65-7, 76, 79, 87, 98, 100-2, 125, 129, 134, 143, 158, 162, 168-9, 175, 182-3, 190, 250, 256, 263-4, 300, 313
Feldspar 15, 17, 66, 76, 81, 87-8, 96, 103, 157-9, 206, 215, 217, 222, 264-5, 267-9, 300, 313
Felsic rocks 14, 17, 86, 166, 167
Felsite 14, 86, 193, 195-6, 198
Floodplains 23, 176, 180, 231, 299
Fluorite 96, 189
Fluorspar 96, 189
Folding 16-7, 19, 26, 32, 43, 62, 65, 78-9, 98, 118, 120-1, 123, 125, 128-9, 134, 136, 138, 142, 146-8, 150, 152, 163, 206, 209, 214, 246-50, 262, 264, 270, 300, 304, 307, 310
terminology 120, 121
Folds 122, 183
types 120, 121, 251, 310, 312-4
Formations 32, 252, 313-4
Fossils 10-11, 28, 30, 56-7, 70-2, 82, 92, 106, 115-6, 142, 150, 164, 176, 180, 231, 233, 244-5, 280, 293, 296, 299, 209
Foyaite 189
Friersdale Charnockite 265
Fuchsite 203

G

Gabbro 14, 86, 95, 114, 154, 169, 205, 313
Gariep
Province 25
Supergroup 27, 206, 213-4
Garnets 103, 313
Gas fields 127, 133, 134
Geological formations 33
naming 32
groups 32, 33
maps 33
Geomorphology 33, 153
Geyser Granite 98
Ghaap Plateau 258

Glacial
'flour' 77
scratches 77, 79
striae 79, 243
till 124, 313
Gneiss 16-7, 35, 76, 85, 97-9, 100-1, 103-4, 143, 158-160, 163, 169, 173, 182-3, 201-2, 206, 217-20, 222, 252, 265, 267-270, 277, 313
augen 270, 312
Godwan Formation 201, 278, 279
Goedehoop Formation 267
Gold 37, 45-6, 48, 69, 100, 106, 169, 175, 197, 228, 255-6, 277-8
alluvial 49, 58, 136, 201, 286, 287, 308
fields 34, 38, 45, 49, 224, mines & mining 47, 49, 57, 69, 94, 100, 112, 136, 171, 202-3, 224, 232, 234, 256
ore 57-8
reefs 38, 39, 40
rushes 49, 136, 275, 278, 285, 308
Gondwana 10, 12, 27-8, 62, 72, 76-7, 116, 126, 148, 177, 180, 195, 293
break-up 29, 35, 79-82, 111, 127, 131, 158, 181, 291, 294, 304
Goudplaats Gneiss 99, 101
Government
Reef 39
Subgroup 39, 40, 44
Graafwater Formation 32, 65, 67
Graben 40, 256, 257, 313
Grahamstown Formation 129, 131, 147, 250, 251
Granite 3, 13-7, 21, 26-7, 30, 34-5, 38-9, 42-5, 50, 54-5, 59- 62, 65-8, 70, 76, 85-7, 94, 98-9, 100, 107, 110, 125, 127-8, 136, 143, 158, 160, 163-4, 169-170, 180, 182-3, 186, 189, 193-6, 198, 201-2, 204, 206, 209, 213, 215, 217, 227, 239, 252, 254-5, 258-9, 264, 266, 269, 277, 279, 304, 313-4
plutons 100, 202, 264, 314
Granite-gneiss 25, 38, 42, 60, 78, 98, 100, 106, 181, 201-2, 205, 269, 273, 275, 277, 288
foliated 43, 313
Granodiorite 14, 40
Granophyre 14
Greenstone 35, 38-42, 44-5, 58-9, 85, 94, 193, 198, 202, 205, 254, 279, 313
belts 21, 25, 34, 97-8, 100, 104, 203-4
Greywacke 210, 246, 305, 309, 313
Griqualand West Basin 258
Groundwater 90, 130, 147, 251
Gypsum 96, 211, 214, 215

H

Haib Formation 223
Hartley Formation 261
Hekpoort Lava 38, 187
Hematite 15, 187, 303, 313
Hominids 12, 21, 57, 70, 92
Hornblende 98-9, 158, 217, 313
Hornfels 17, 313
Hospital Hill Subgroup 39-40, 44, 110
Houtrivier Gneiss 101
Hypabyssal rocks 14

I

Ice
ages 21, 23, 28, 82, 124, 137, 148, 231
cover 28, 111
sheets 27, 35, 75-7, 195-6, 231, 246
Igneous rocks 14, 16-7, 21, 28, 30, 86, 98, 151, 189, 217, 266, 294
classification 14
Ignimbrites 166, 196
Ilmenite 83, 161, 164
Inselbergs 22-3, 90, 262, 270, 313
Insizwa Dolerite 155
Intermediate rocks 86
Intrusion 16-7, 21, 26-7, 41-3, 51, 62, 66, 98, 100, 102, 107, 136, 146, 169, 177, 180, 182, 186, 188, 200, 202, 205, 209-10, 217, 220, 222, 241-2, 252, 265
Intrusive rocks 14, 17, 30, 151, 269
Iron 17, 21, 26, 43, 81, 86, 88-91, 97, 106, 111, 130, 162, 169, 209, 211, 214, 217, 257, 260, 271, 283
Age 54, 92
hydroxides 90
ore 100, 192, 215, 252, 260-1
oxide 15, 26-7, 81, 130, 162, 211, 250, 260, 302-3
pigmentation 90, 162
Iron-nickel 13
Ironstone 51, 9
banded 15, 26, 43, 45, 100, 190, 256
Isotopes 28, 30-1, 313

J

Jasper 15, 260, 313
Jaspilite 43, 313
Jeppestown Subgroup 39-40, 44
Johannesburg 40, 47, 49, 52, 61
Dome 35, 50, 55-56, 59, 186, 254
cross-section 38
Subgroup 39, 44
Johnstone Reef 39
Jozini Formation 165-7, 193, 204-5
Jurassic Period 125, 131, 135-6, 138, 140, 145, 250, 300

K

Kaaimans Group 136
Kaap Valley
Granite 201
pluton 278
Kaapsehoop 201, 274-5, 277, 279
Kaapvaal Craton 25-7, 51, 78, 85, 105, 160, 163, 193, 217, 234-235, 242, 252, 256, 262, 264, 283
Kango Group 27, 250, 300-1, 305, 309
Kansa Group 249-50, 300, 305, 309
Kaolin 66-7, 147, 212, 214-5, 217, 313
Karoo 21, 103, 106, 112, 115, 118, 148, 180, 232, 304
Basin 27, 42, 62, 84, 95, 106, 150, 176
cross-section 244
formations 103, 166, 263
Great 118, 307
Igneous Province 294
Little 300-311
rocks 100, 162

Sea 77, 148, 150, 225, 231
Sequence 27-8, 116, 172-3, 231
Succession 103
Supergroup 14, 21, 27, 35, 60, 76-79, 84, 87, 100-1, 110, 112-3, 117, 122, 124, 134, 142-3, 146, 148, 154-6, 160, 163, 165, 169, 171-3, 175-9, 181-2, 193, 195, 199, 204-5, 227, 229, 237-9, 244, 246-7, 258, 264, 293-6, 299, 304, 307
volcanism 78-9, 87, 100
Kheis Metamorphic Province 25
Kimberley 240-242
'big hole' 232-3, 239, 241
reefs 39-40, 44-5, 47, 69
Kimberlite 13, 51, 105, 115, 189, 232, 239, 241-2, 313
pipes 53, 238-9, 313
Kirkwood Formation 302, 309
Klerksdorp gold field 38, 234, 256
Klerkskraal Anticline 254
Klipriviersberg Group 174
Koeberg Nuclear Power Station 68-9, 209
Kolobeng Norite 188
Komatiite 14, 41, 313
Koperberg Suite 220
Koras Group 263
Kromdraai gold mine 56
Kruger National Park
eco-zones 205
geology 205
Kuruman Eye 259
KwaZulu-Natal Basin 78
Kwetta Granite 169

L

Landscape
creation 23, 148
evolution 111, 126
lowering 111
Lapilli 196, 313
Lava 14, 26-7, 34, 38-41, 44-5, 50, 87, 89- 90, 115-6, 163, 165-7, 169, 174-6, 181-2, 186, 189, 192, 196, 202, 204, 226, 228-9, 235, 239, 243-4, 252, 255-6, 258, 284, 290-1, 293-4, 296-9
flood 21, 176
frothing 73
pillow structures 252, 314
Leaching 143, 216, 251
Lead 217, 272
isotope '206' 31
Lebombo
axis 168
Group 27, 165, 204-5
Monocline 79, 165, 168, 183
range 160, 167, 193, 204
cross-section 166
Lebowa
Granite Suite 88
Granophyre Suite 88
Letaba Formation 101, 165, 167, 204
Liesegang banding 72, 130, 143, 147, 206, 209, 212, 313
Lime 132, 200, 210-1, 238, 381
Limestone 15-7, 26, 56, 72, 92-3, 200, 206, 210-1, 214, 222, 254, 258, 265, 280, 305, 313
Limpopo Mobile Belt 25-7, 85, 105
Lithification 15, 70, 146, 151, 305-6, 313
Livingstone Reef 39
Loskop Formation 229

M

Maalgaten pluton 136
Mafic rocks 14, 17, 51, 66, 86,

88-9, 114, 156, 188-9, 203, 220, 222, 252, 265, 270, 313
Magaliesberg 37, 55-56
  Formation 50-1, 54-5, 86, 95, 184, 186-7, 194, 198-9
  range 50, 184, 187-8
Magma 13-4, 16, 27, 30, 43, 62, 65, 88-9, 100, 154, 189, 196, 242, 268, 294, 314
Magnesite 203-4
Magnesium 17, 56, 86, 254
  carbonate 203-4, 283
  silicate 97
Magnetite 15, 43, 45, 88, 100, 104, 114, 130, 192, 195, 303, 314
Main Reefs 39-40, 44, 46-7, 49, 227, 314
Makwassie Porphyry 235
Malmani Subgroup 34, 38, 50-1, 55-7, 92, 95-6, 171-2, 174, 186, 200-1, 254-5, 277-80, 282-6, 288-9
Malmesbury Group 27, 62, 65, 68, 97, 107, 125, 136, 206, 208-12, 214
Manganese 67, 90-1, 130, 181, 190-1, 206, 213, 252, 254
  oxide 130, 191, 213-4, 254, 255
Maputaland Group 164
Marabastad gold field 94
Marble 17, 103, 206, 214, 314
Matoks Granite 100
Matopos Granite 98
Merensky Reef 89, 188
Mesas 122, 127, 149, 163, 180, 222, 270, 273, 314
Mesozoic Era 21, 115, 180
Metamorphic rocks 14, 16, 32, 62, 78, 85, 97, 100, 103, 125, 136, 163, 182, 189-190, 215, 217, 220, 222-3, 231, 252, 263-4, 267, 304, 314
  classification 17
Metamorphism 26, 30, 54, 97, 105, 146, 187, 206, 209, 214, 231, 252, 260, 262, 265
Metavolcanics 97, 314
Meteorites 54, 61, 106, 109-10
  impact 53, 60, 61
Mica 15, 17, 43, 169, 222, 265, 267-8
Microclines 43, 314
Middelburg coal mine 196
Migmatite 17, 104
Millwood gold field 136, 309
Mine dumps 48, 87, 95, 104, 184, 227, 230, 234, 236, 238-9, 255
  reclamation 48, 174
Mineral hardness scale 96-7
Mining 33-4, 37, 40, 188, 220, 272-3, 286
  opencast 163, 198, 204, 229, 261
Miocene Period 72, 111, 136
Molteno Formation 295-6, 299
Mondeor
  Conglomerate 39-40, 44-5, 225
  Formation 226-7
Moraine 77, 148, 176, 314
Mountains 22, 42
  formation 22, 150, 163, 264
  residual 22, 24, 65
Mozaan Group 169
Mpageni Granite 202
Msikaba Formation 143, 158, 159
Mudstone 15, 17, 67, 76, 112, 150, 152, 176-8, 180, 182, 212-4, 293, 295-6, 299, 309
Muldersdrift Complex 254
Muscovite 222
Musekwa Formation 101

N
Nababeep Gneiss 215
Nama
  Group 27, 206, 222-3
  Succession 223
Namaqua Metamorphic Province 27, 163, 206, 217, 252, 262-4, 269-70
Nanaga Formation 145
Nardouw Formation 32
Natal
  Arch 165, 168, 182
  Basin 76
  Group 76-9, 82, 143, 159, 163, 173, 180-3
  Metamorphic Province 25, 27, 76, 78, 143, 158-60, 163, 173, 181-3, 263
  Monocline 79, 168, 183
Nebo Granite 86
Nelspruit Suite 201-2, 286
Nickel 88, 154-5, 188
Norite 14, 86, 95, 188
Nsuze Group 169
Nzhelele Formation 101

O
Oil 109, 127, 134, 197, 304
Okiep copper mines 217, 221
Olifantshoek Supergroup 27, 261-2
  red beds 21
Olivine 88, 97, 154, 314
Onverwacht Group 203
Orange Grove Quartzite 39-40, 44-5, 58-9, 227, 254
Orange River Group 222
Ordovician
  Basin 78
  Period 78, 82
Orogenies 25, 26, 314
Oxide minerals 27, 88, 130
Oxygen 26-7, 92, 283

P
Paardeberg pluton 209
Pahoehoe 294, 314
Pakhuis Formation 32
Palaeozoic Era 21, 115, 180
Palladium 89, 154, 188
Pans 198, 236, 237, 258, 259
Parktown Shale 39, 43, 59
Parys Granite 61
Pavements 77
  glaciated 74, 77, 79, 243
  scratched 79
Peat 15, 195, 231
Pegmatite 14, 43, 100, 103, 202, 217, 222, 252, 264, 267, 269-70, 314
Peneplains 23, 111, 150-1, 251, 264, 270, 273, 291, 314
Peninsula Formation 32, 64-6
Peridot 97
Peridotite 14, 242
Permian Period 115, 231, 245
Permian-Triassic extinction 21, 176
Permo-Carboniferous Period 21
Petroglyps 243, 314
Phosphate 71-2
Phanerozoic Eon 21, 27
Phyllite 17, 212, 214, 314
Piekenierskloof Formation 32, 212
Pietersburg Group 94, 97-8
Pilanesberg Complex 189
Pilgrim's Rest mine 285
Plagioclase 43, 76, 103, 215
Platberg Group 257

Plate tectonics 18-9
Platforms
  wave-cut 80, 137, 141
Platinum 34, 53, 89, 114, 154, 184-5, 188, 197
  Group Elements (PGE) 88-9, 188, 314
Pleistocene Period 72, 82
Pliocene Period 111
Plutonic rocks 14
Pongola Supergroup 160, 169
Potassium 86
Power stations 68-9, 171-2, 177, 192, 196-7, 209, 229, 296
Precambrian
  Basin 84
  Formations 84, 87, 95, 300
  Period 21, 78, 85, 143, 159, 183, 192, 208, 214, 216, 252, 282, 300, 305, 309
Premier mine 51
Pressure 97-8, 129
Pretoria Group 35, 38, 50, 55, 57, 89, 184, 186, 189-90, 192, 194, 198-200, 254, 277, 279, 284, 286, 289
Promise Reef 39
Proterozoic Eon 21, 25, 26, 314
Provinces
  geological 32, 314
Pseudotachylite 61, 314
Psilomelane 254
Pumice 72-3, 314
Pyrite 45-6, 49, 136, 309, 314
Pyroclastic rocks 90-1, 166, 204, 256, 314
Pyroxene 88, 266
Pyroxenite 14, 86

Q
Quartz 14-5, 17, 45, 76, 86, 88, 96, 103, 159, 169, 209, 214, 217, 225, 227, 250, 267, 269-70, 286, 314
  glassy 43, 265, 268
  Porphyry 14
  recrystallised 54
  reefs 49, 58
  rose 267, 270-1
  sand 70, 78, 81
  veins 37, 49, 85, 103, 136, 209-10, 212, 305, 309
Quartzite 17, 35, 38-40, 44, 50-1, 54-5, 58-9, 61, 64-7, 86-7, 94-5, 100-02, 104, 110-1, 126, 128-9, 131-2, 136, 138-9, 141, 146, 158, 169, 175, 184, 186-90, 194, 198-201, 206, 209, 212, 217, 226-8, 234, 247, 249, 251, 255-6, 258, 261-4, 267, 271, 274-5, 277-9, 284-9, 300-01, 307-9, 314
  sericitic 267, 315
Quaternary Period 145, 159

R
Rayton Formation 194
Rehabilitation 68, 161, 164, 227
Rhodium 188
Rhyolite 14, 165-7, 196, 204-5
Riemvasmaak Gneiss 269
Rietfontein Fault 40
Rift valleys 18, 27, 100-1, 163, 168, 291, 300
Ripple marks 51, 96, 122
Rivers 24, 141, 148, 176, 180, 270, 280
  action 32, 81
  alluvium 23, 45-6, 159, 164, 176, 210, 277, 289
  braided 45, 110, 176, 257, 299

deltas 62, 66, 77, 81, 231
  gradients 42
  terraces 23-4, 131, 215-6, 265, 309
  transport 15, 22, 24, 42, 44, 46, 62, 77
  valleys 23
Robberg Formation 138, 139
Robinson Deep 40
Rock
  art 297, 298
  tools 54, 92, 289
Rocks
  age 28, 30
  categories 14
  dating 28, 30
  uranium-lead 31
  floor 89
  roof 89
  strata 32
  unlayered 77
Rooiberg Group 87, 89-90, 192, 195-6, 198, 230
Rubies 97
Rustenburg Layered Suite 88-9
Rutile 161, 164

S
Salt 54, 237, 258, 259
Sand 16, 67, 82, 145, 162, 164-5, 173, 181, 209, 211, 214
  flats 70
  red 74, 80, 262, 264-5, 270-1
Sandstone 9, 15-7, 26, 30, 35, 39, 44, 62, 64-7, 70, 72, 74-82, 87, 90, 96, 101-3, 110, 112, 116, 122, 124, 127, 135-6, 138-9, 143, 146-7, 149-52, 158-9, 163-4, 171, 173, 176-9, 181-3, 189, 195, 204, 206, 209-10, 212, 214, 222-3, 229, 231, 247-8, 257, 263, 278, 290, 293-300, 302-3, 307, 309-10, 315
  basal 66
  carbonaceous 103
  cliffs 78
  feldspathic 212, 313
  pavements 79
Sapphires 97
  star 97
Sasol 109, 134, 171, 197, 229
Scarps 24, 45, 50, 79
  retreat
  parallel 111
Schist 17, 59, 68, 97, 169, 202-3, 210, 214-7, 263, 267, 315
Sea levels 65-6, 72, 81-2, 111, 133, 135, 137, 159, 306
Sediment 17, 28, 42, 44-5, 60, 62, 66-8, 75, 77-80, 82, 87, 89-90, 95, 97, 100-02, 104, 106-7, 112, 118, 122, 124-5, 127-9, 131, 134, 136, 138, 140, 142-5, 147-50, 152-4, 159, 163-4, 169, 171-2, 175-6, 180-2, 186-7, 190, 192, 195, 198-9, 202, 206-7, 209-10, 213, 215, 217, 222-3, 227, 229, 237, 244-7, 249-50, 252, 254, 256-7, 260, 263-4, 286, 299-300, 304-5, 307-10
  colours 130, 150
  lacustrine 130
  submerging 42
Sedimentary
  bands 123
  basins 42
  rocks 13-6, 26, 28, 30, 34, 60, 62, 87, 97, 151, 163, 267, 275
  classification 15
  structures 79
Sedimentation 24, 27, 32, 43-5,

89, 148, 255, 282, 288, 294
Serpentine 203
Serpentinite 41, 204, 315
Sezela Suite 159
Shale 15-7, 26, 35, 38-40, 43-5,
50-1, 55, 57-9, 61, 65, 72, 79,
80, 87, 95, 97, 112, 114, 120,
122, 125-6, 129-31, 138, 146-
7, 149, 152, 158-9, 169, 171,
176-80, 182, 186, 191, 194,
199-200, 208, 210, 212, 222,
229, 231, 234, 237, 239, 246-9,
256, 260, 262, 274, 279, 284,
286-7, 289, 293, 296, 298,
307-10, 315
Shearing 37, 105, 202, 251, 264,
266-7
Sheets 112, 150, 154-7, 171, 178-
9, 296, 315
Shell fragments 70, 82, 132
Shorelines 62
movement 44
Sibasa Formation 101
Silcrete 15, 111, 126, 129, 131,
147, 149-51, 315
Silica 15, 95, 97, 111, 117, 196,
211, 235, 251, 257, 260, 294
cement 78
content 14
Silicate 315
minerals 14, 159
rocks 13
Silicification 131
Sills 14, 101-2, 106, 112, 150-1,
169, 171, 173, 177, 179, 189,
194, 198-9, 239, 275, 284, 294,
296, 299, 315
Silt 44, 82, 209
Siltstone 15, 122, 164, 176,
180, 187, 189, 223, 247,
293, 299, 310
Silver 217, 272
Sinkholes 280, 281
Skurweberg Formation 212
Slate 17, 65, 189, 190-1
Slimes 315
dams 48, 219, 227, 234, 273
Slurry 48
Soapstone 97
Sodium 86, 97, 260
carbonate 54
chloride 54, 237
sulphate 237
South Africa
crust 25
geology
framework 25
history 26-27
landscape 22
mountains 22
tectonic domains 25
South Rand
coal field 177
gold field 38, 175
South Reef 49
Southern Cape Fold Belt
cross-section 304
Soutpansberg 100, 101
cross-section 101
Group 100-102, 205
red beds 27
Springfield
Fault 79
mine 177
Stalagmites 279, 280, 306
Stalagtites 279, 280

Steel 197
Sterkfontein Caves 34, 56-57, 280
Stone Age 54, 289, 298
man 92
sites 43
Stormberg Group 116, 182, 295
Stratigraphy 32
Stratum 120, 315
Stresses 20, 98, 260
Strikes 95, 100
Stromatolites 15, 21, 92-3, 279,
282-3, 289, 315
Subduction 18, 73, 78, 118, 315
Subsidence 62
Sudwala Caves 279, 280
Sugarbush Fault 175
Suites 32, 315
Sulphide 272, 286
minerals 88, 156, 272, 286
Supergroups
geological 32, 315
Syenite 14, 86, 189, 205
Synclines 107, 120-2, 124-5, 175,
212, 246-7, 308, 310, 315
Synclinoria 120, 247, 315
Syntaxis zones 125, 315

T

Table Mountain 22, 27, 64-65,
69, 125
Group 9, 32, 62, 65, 67, 72,
124-5, 128-9, 132, 136, 138-9,
141, 146, 206, 209-10, 212-4,
249-51, 300-1, 304, 307-8, 310
Tailings 48, 104, 163, 188, 224,
227, 254, 315
Talc 17, 59, 96-7, 203
Talus cones 281
Tantalite 222, 315
Tarkastad Formation 293
Tectonic
domains 25
provinces 25
Tectonism 65, 98, 214, 217,
307, 315
Temperature 97-8, 111, 217, 242,
260, 306
Terraces 23, 24, 141
Tertiary Period 72, 111, 131-2,
146-7, 162, 164, 183, 309
Thrusting 98, 150, 248, 300,
307, 315
Tiger's eye 252, 260, 315
Tillite 28, 75, 77, 116, 122-3, 143,
147-9, 156-7, 159, 163, 171-2,
176, 180, 182-3, 195, 246-7,
258, 307-8, 310, 315
Tilting 32, 308
Time scales
geological 20-21
Timeball Hill Formation 50, 58,
95, 189-90, 286
Titanium 82-3, 97, 114, 161, 197
Tonalite 14, 40, 315
Topaz 96, 267, 315
Torbanite 109
Trachyte 14, 86
Transvaal
Basin 26, 42, 89, 188
proto-basin 288
Sea 51
Sequence 229, 277, 286
Supergroup 21, 27, 34, 38, 50,
85-7, 89, 92, 94-6, 172, 174, 184,
186, 192, 195, 229, 252, 254,

256, 258, 260-1, 275, 277, 283
Transvaal-Griqualand West
Basin 26
Triassic Period 116
Trompsburg
Anomaly 114-5
Complex 114
Trona 54
Tsunamis 18, 73
Tswaing Meteorite crater 34,
53-54
Tufa 289
Tuff 15, 167, 196, 209, 229, 315
Turbidite 123, 305, 315
Turffontein Subgroup 39, 40, 44

U

Uitenhage Group 131, 135-6,
145-6, 300
Ultramafic rocks 14, 41, 86, 88,
114, 203-4, 254, 265, 270, 315
Unconformity 32, 39, 67, 80,
206, 215-6, 315
Uplift 22, 27, 111, 168, 291, 315
Upper Group 2 (UG2) Layer
89, 188
Uranium 45-6, 69, 112, 114-5
isotope '238' 31
mineralization 113
oxide 45
Uranium-lead dating 31
Usushwana Complex 169
Usuthu coal mine 171

V

Vaal Reef 234
Vaalkoppies Group 264
Vaalputs Granite 265
Valley of a Thousand Hills 78,
181, 183
Valleys 139, 270
floors 102, 111
formation 23-4, 137
Vanadium 89, 114, 192, 195, 197
pentoxide 195
Vanrhynsdorp Group 27, 206,
214-6
Venetia mine 104-5
Ventersdorp
Basin 26, 42, 256
Contact Reef 45, 256
Supergroup 21, 34, 38-40, 44-5,
60, 174, 176, 226, 228, 232,
234, 239, 243, 252, 255-8
Verdite 203
Volcanic
eruptions 14, 26, 44, 72-3, 103,
176, 242, 256
froth 72
rocks 14, 17, 32, 90-1, 160,
166-7, 172, 174, 189, 192, 195-
6, 198, 203-4, 206, 209, 222-3,
229, 255, 257, 261, 264, 267
Volcaniclastic rocks 15
Volcanoes 20
Vredefort
Dome 34, 60-61, 106, 110
Meteorite 21, 35
Vryburg Formation 258

W

Waenhuiskrans Formation 72
Walter Sisulu National Botanical
Garden 58-9
Rock garden 58-9

Water 42, 109, 242, 280-1
flow 16, 81
vapour 26
Waterberg
Basin 42
Group 87, 90, 194
red beds 27
Waterfalls 58, 180, 182, 200, 249,
269, 284-6
Watersheds 38
Weathering 43, 49, 66-7, 79,
86-7, 95, 103, 111, 143, 157-8,
166, 169-70, 175, 177, 183,
186, 201, 213, 215-6, 227, 237,
265, 270, 284, 287, 294, 309
elephant-skin 96, 186, 258,
289, 314
spheroidal 150, 152, 245
tombstone 122-3
woolsack 217
Welkom gold field 38, 43, 112
West Coast Fossil Park 71
West Rand
gold field 38, 254
Group 39-40, 43-5, 59, 175, 257
Western Cape Fold Belt
cross-section 210
'White band' 123
Whitehill Formation 123, 176
Wilgenhoutsdrif Group 263
Witbank coal field 171, 195-6,
225, 229, 230
Witteberg Group 32, 124, 146-9,
210, 247, 304, 308, 310
Witwatersrand 48, 69, 241, 256
Basin 26, 38-9, 42, 45, 47,
61, 110, 112, 171-2, 175,
228, 235, 256
cross-section 40
stratigraphy 39
gold reefs 21, 26, 40, 53
alluvial theory 46
formation 44-6, 61
hydrothermal
theory 46, 313
placer theory 46, 314
Nigel mine 175
Sea 45, 227
Sequence 232
Series 38
Supergroup 34, 38-40, 44, 57,
60-1, 90, 106, 110, 174, 224,
226-8, 252, 254-7
System 38
Wolkberg Group 94, 274, 277,
286-9
Wonderboompoort 50-1
Wyllies Poort Formation 101-2

X

Xenocrysts 242, 315
Xenoliths 65, 242, 315

Y

Ysterberg Fault 94-5

Z

Zebediela Fault 95
'Zebra ore' 204
Zeolite 294
Zimbabwe Craton 25-6, 105
Zinc 217, 252, 272-3
Zircon 30, 82, 161, 164
Zirconium 161
Zululand Group 164-5, 182

AL" LUCANIA

WildBluePress.com

THE

WILDBLUE *
P.O. Box 10244*
Denver, Colorad*

WILDBLUE PRESS is registere*
Trademark Offices.

ISBN 978-1-948239-27-1   Trade Pa*
ISBN 978-1-948239-26-4   eBook

Editing by Cynthia Kellogg

Interior Formatting/Book Cover Desig*
www.totencreative.com